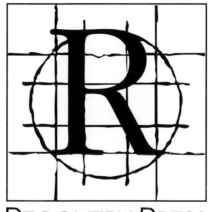

RECOVERY PRESS

COPING WITH THE STIGMA OF MENTAL ILLNESS

Patrick Corrigan ◆ Robert Lundin

Recovery Press
The University of Chicago
Center for Psychiatric Rehabilitation
7230 Arbor Drive
Tinley Park, IL 60477

First Recovery Press Edition 2001

ISBN 0-9674794-1-X

Book Design: Mark Morenz

Printed in USA by Abana Press,
Champaign, Illinois

Table of Contents

Hand me not this madman's fate
Cried I each sorrowful day.
Poltergeists find in me of late
Fertile ground for their deceitful play.

Woe to the life of a promising man
With a promising act to follow.
Lend him thy aid, be compassionate men!
And dig not his grave too shallow.

RKL

Foreword

Recently I had the honor of being interviewed for short segment on schizophrenia that was later aired on the *ABC Evening News with Peter Jennings*. In order to capture four minutes of airtime the television crews worked almost three very full days recording my daily activities and those of my family. While I was being interviewed for the segment, the producer asked me about my experiences and opinions concerning the use of pejorative terms in everyday parlance which refer to the mentally ill. I explained that I had some time ago put together a list of well over 100 such terms. She asked me which term I considered to be most offensive. Without much hesitation, I stated that I thought the term, "nuts," or perhaps "nut-case," was particularly off-putting. In that she had used this very term just shortly before asking this question, I could see that she was somewhat taken aback by my response. She asked that I explain why I, and presumably, other persons in recovery from mental illness, find this term particularly offensive.

My response at the time was not particularly well thought out, and was most inadequate, but in the ensuing months I have often thought back on my response to the television interviewer concerning my revulsion the "n-word."

Upon being asked to write a forward for a book with the title, Don't Call Me Nuts*!*, I initially dismissed the overture. My immediate reaction was that any authors who openly used the "n-word" in the title of their book, obviously had insufficient sensitivity concerning the extreme offensiveness of this term for persons with mental illnesses.

Upon further reflection, however, I have come to realize that it might be difficult for many readers to know what the "n" in the "n-word" stood for if it were not made explicit.

This being as it may concerning the title of the book, Don't Call Me Nuts! does in fact present a very valuable service to the millions of us in recovery from schizophrenia, bipolar disorder, and other forms of serious mental illness. It has frequently been said by various consumer-advocates that the stigma we face is in many ways more disabling than the illnesses themselves. For many of us this is certainly true.

Although there have been books published in the recent past which have addressed the topic of stigma in the media and elsewhere, to my knowledge, this is one of the first books on this important topic to be authored or co-authored by a consumer. This is also one of the first to not only describe the examples of stigmatizing activity, but to also put forth specific recommendations concerning how we can go about attacking the problem of stigma and diminishing its pernicious effects.

During the past generation there have been tremendous improvements in society's ability to treat persons with serious mental illnesses. Most of us with these conditions now can expect to recover to a good degree. Unfortunately, society's perception and attitudes toward the mentally ill have not changed much since the days when having a diagnosis of schizophrenia or another serious mental illness marked one to be thought of as being chronically confused, bizarre-acting, and, all too often, dangerous.

This volume that Patrick Corrigan and Bob Lundin have produced does an outstanding job of weaving the views of one who has personally experienced the effects of stigma with the expertise of a psychologist whose specialty-area is assisting such persons in their recovery. Working together, these authors present a virtual manual for addressing how recovering persons can go about being accepted as respected, participating members of society.

The time has clearly come for recovering persons, their families, advocates, and particularly mental health professionals, to seriously take up the challenges posed by stigma in society. The publication of this fine book serves as a rallying cry and marks a significant step forward in this critical area.

Frederick J. Frese III, Ph.D.
Assistant Professor of Psychology in Clinical Psychiatry Northeastern Ohio Universities College of Medicine, and First Vice President, National Alliance for the Mentally Ill (NAMI)

Preface

Consider the injustice of schizophrenia, manic depression, and similar mental illnesses. It is hard enough to deal with the symptoms and disabilities these disorders bring. But, in addition, persons must endure the prejudice and discrimination of a society that does not understand them. Many of us know about the ignorance that robs a capable person with mental illness from a good job or a safe home. We have friends and clients who have lost life chances, not because they failed to meet the challenge posed by their mental illness, but because they were labeled *mentally ill* by an unforgiving landlord or an ignorant employer. We know the shame that forces people to hide depression and anxieties from others. We know the embarrassment which causes persons to sneak in and out of mental health clinics. This book is written to provide those persons with the tools necessary to deal with stigma. With them, we pray they need to hide no more.

There are many victims of prejudice and discrimination. Perhaps the most apparent are the persons with mental illness themselves. They must withstand disapproving looks and loss of opportunities from the community. "It feels like a dirty secret," reported one person with schizophrenia. "I have to hide whole segments of my life from most everybody." Another person's comments were equally profound, "It's who I am. I'm tired of hiding it." Family members too are injured by stigma. Parents, brothers, and sisters frequently report feeling distanced from neighbors, co-workers, and friends as they share in the struggle with the family member challenged by mental illness.

"They were my golf buddies for years. But
when my son, John, got hospitalized the
first time, they started to fall away. We
stopped sharing stories about our kids.
And it made me angry. What was there to
be ashamed of?"

The list of victims also includes the public.
Citizens who believe the stereotypes and who discriminate against persons with mental illness deprive themselves of opportunities to get to know these people.
They also feed the ghosts that might potentially haunt
them about their own sanity. "If persons who have nervous breakdowns are weak and bad, then what am I
when I suffer anxiety and depression?" Finally, mental
health professionals can fall victim to the misconceptions and stereotypes of mental illness. Surveys show
that students and practitioners alike endorse many of
the misconceptions about mental illness that lead to
inappropriate treatment decisions. The irony here is
tragic. The psychiatrists, psychologists, social workers,
and nurses who are supposed to counsel persons about
mental illness may be as misguided about it as the general public. We should not assume that the title
"Doctor" absolves the holder of ignorance about mental
illness.

A Time of Change

No longer must we wait until researchers discover effective medicines and therapies to deal with the
symptoms and disabilities of schizophrenia, the mood
disorders, and other severe psychiatric disabilities. The

last 20 years have seen significant leaps in new psychiatric medications that affect many of the symptoms of mental illness. In addition, psychosocial rehabilitation helps persons adjust to the disabilities brought on by these disorders. Persons with mental illness are now viewed as active agents in selecting interventions that best serve their needs.

In like manner, significant leaps have been made in dealing with prejudice and discrimination. Empirical research and the experiences of advocates have led to a variety of strategies that help the victims of mental illness stigma. *DON'T CALL ME NUTS!* provides a comprehensive guide to these strategies. *DON'T CALL ME NUTS!* is written for persons with mental illness who no longer want to wait for society to accept psychiatric disability; these persons want to know to whom and how to disclose their experiences with depression, anxiety, and psychosis. This book was written for families who seek ways to join their son or daughter, brother or sister, in learning to quiet the shame of mental illness.

It is written for the consumer and family advocate who decide that one of the best ways to quiet this shame is to address the villainous society that fosters stigma and discrimination. Towards this end, *DON'T CALL ME NUTS!* summarizes social change strategies for helping one's community better understand and accept citizens with mental illness. This book is written for the public: for the citizen who questions whether persons with mental illness are treated justly and for individuals who recognize the undiagnosed illness in themselves and do not like the way they have disrespected others.

We combined a variety of materials and styles to produce this volume. *DON'T CALL ME NUTS!* reviews key studies to help the reader understand why people stigmatize and effective ways to impact prejudice. The book illustrates this research through poignant vignettes which are sometimes fictional but always representative. We include worksheets and scripts which persons might use to deal with their own shame or to facilitate community change. This material is divided into six parts.

Part I introduces stigma in terms of the human experience of Franklin Goodman. It then tries to make sense of this experience by examining the complex ways in which mental illness stigma appears. It also tackles an equally complex, but often overlooked question relevant to stigma: Who, exactly, comprises the group of persons with mental illness? Who might we lump into the category of persons who are stigmatized versus those who are not? Most readers can no doubt tell that just asking the question suggests how arbitrary is the injustice of stigma.

We believe that real change can only occur through action. Hence, Parts II, III, and IV review specific strategies to facilitate this action. Part II summarizes individual strategies which persons with psychiatric disability and their families might use to deal with being in the closet about mental illness. We review ways to deal with the pain of self-stigma as well as how to make the tough decision about whether to disclose one's mental illness.

Empowered persons are the polar opposite of stigmatized persons with mental illness. Part III provides a discussion of empowerment and a review of strategies that foster empowerment. Part IV discusses protest, education, and consumer contact strategies that change society's reaction to stigma. It also discusses the legal protections which citizens might use to deal with discrimination that results from mental illness stigma.

In Part V, we revisit the experiences of our fictional Franklin Goodman. In particular, we consider what might have happened to him had the strategies in this book been availed. Finally, we hope this is just the beginning of the reader's interest in battling mental illness stigma. We end the book with resources where persons can learn more about stigma-busting. This list not only includes other books, it also provides the addresses and contact information for advocacy groups that have been fighting stigma for the past decade and more.

In some ways, *DON'T CALL ME NUTS!* differs from other self-help books. Attitude change to offset the loss of self-esteem common to the stigmatized is a familiar target of self-help books. Helping people consider the costs and benefits of specific decisions provides another way to cope. Setting up therapy programs that empower participants is also consistent with self-help. Perhaps the odd bedfellow in this approach is trying to change *public attitudes* about mental illness. We recognize that changing the impact of stigma does not rest in the person's hands alone. Social change is also needed.

What business does a self-help book have promoting societal change? But that is the irony of societal change. Persons are better able to deal with the shame of psychiatric stigma when they can face the source of this stigma head-on and challenge it.

About the Authors

Patrick Corrigan is Associate Professor of Psychiatry at the University of Chicago where he directs the Center for Psychiatric Rehabilitation. Corrigan is a prolific researcher into the psychosocial experiences of severe mental illness; he has published more than 100 articles and book chapters. He is editor of *Psychiatric Rehabilitation Skills*, a journal for persons with severe mental illness, their families, and providers of service. Corrigan is also principal investigator of the University of Chicago Stigma Research Center which is funded by NIMH. Corrigan recently received the Dr. Martin Luther King, Jr. Humanitarian Award for his work in this area.

Robert Lundin, is publications director at the University of Chicago Center for Psychiatric Rehabilitation. Among his many duties, he works with Corrigan as managing editor of *Psychiatric Rehabilitation Skills*. A graduate of Kenyon College, in 1979 Lundin become severely mentally ill with a schizoaffective disorder while attending graduate school. He was not effectively treated until 1991 after which he was able to begin a career as a freelance reporter for the *Chicago Tribune* and other Chicago area newspapers. Lundin also has a keen interest in fine arts and mental health which led to his founding the Awakenings Project. For this work, Lundin was awarded "Advocate of the Year" by the National Alliance for the Mentally Ill of Illinois.

Acknowledgments

Although this book took the past two years to complete, it actually represents many years of work on stigma. Several people have supported this work. Many thanks to Amy Green, Kyle Uphoff-Wasowski, Phil River, David Rowan, Mary Ann Kubiak, Tony Peterson, Jim Mathisen, Molly McCoy, Kurt White, Princess Williams, Fadwa Rashid, John Campion, Maria Bergman, Christine Gagnon, and Hillel Goldstein for their help on our research projects. Our research also benefitted from the intellectual stimulation of three significant peers: David Penn, Paul Holmes, and Sarah Diwan. We also appreciate the helpful comments by Howard Goldman on earlier drafts of this manuscript. Special thanks to Lisa Morehead for her editing skills and determination to see this project through.

The University of Chicago Center for Psychiatric Rehabilitation is counseled by a Consumer Advisory Board. Made up of consumers and family members, this group has provoked us into further consideration of our views about stigma. We learned equally much from joining in on stigma-busting efforts. We also appreciate the wisdom of NAMI-Illinois and their stigma busters as well as the Illinois Mental Health Association. One of us (RKL) started the Awakenings Project, a traveling exhibit of art and literature by persons with mental illness. My interactions through that effort has re-energized my confidence in the human spirit. Several persons have helped me with the Awakenings Project including the late Trish Evers.

Much of our work on stigma-busting has been conducted in Illinois. Many readers might think the

State Office of Mental Health would be the cause of stigma. We have, on the contrary, found the opposite and have admired the State's leadership in anti-stigma and pro-empowerment efforts. We appreciate the leadership of Leigh Steiner, Associate Director of the Office of Mental Health as well as colleagues from her office: Dan Giffort, Richard Barton, and Joe Mehr. We also wish to acknowledge Andrea Schmook, Randy Starr, and Ted Washington of the State's Office on Consumer Affairs.

Finally, appreciation goes to our families, who have supported us through our respective journeys with mental illness and stigma. This book represents your influence. To Georgeen, Abraham, and Elizabeth, many thanks (PWC). And to my parents, Robert and Margaret (RKL).

PWC and RKL

to persons with mental illness
and those who have been the victims of stigma:
our clients, our friends, our family...
us

Chapter 1

Stigma and the Experience of Franklin Goodman

"And I always feel this with straight people, that whenever they're being nice to me, pleasant to me, all the time really, underneath they're assessing me as a criminal and nothing else. It's too late for me to be any different to what I am, but I still feel this keenly, that that's their only approach, and they're quite incapable of accepting me as anything else."

From Parker & Allerton (1962)

Serious mental illnesses strike with a two-edged sword. On one side, the various symptoms of the diseases directly interfere with independent living and quality of life. People with severe mental illness may be unable to accomplish their life goals because they are haunted by hallucinations, delusions, and emotional agitation. On the other hand, society's misconceptions about schizophrenia and other disorders lead to stigma. Ironically, the discrimination that results from this can be as disabling as the illness itself. It's an undisputed fact that many people with mental illness are unable to get fulfilling jobs and find comfortable housing *not* just because of the symptoms of their mental illness, but because of the discrimination that results from misconceptions about their illness.

Take the case of Franklin Goodman.[1] He had been released from a state hospital in Illinois after a recent flare up of his psychotic symptoms. At the time of admission, Franklin was highly agitated, telling a social worker that the police were going to capture him and torture him because he was the Son of Sam. After some coaxing Franklin told the on-call psychiatrist in the emergency room he was hearing the voice of the devil telling him he had murdered several little children. Staff on the unit found it hard to understand Franklin because he was not speaking rationally.

This was Franklin Goodman's third hospitalization since schizophrenia was first diagnosed eight years earlier at age 19. He made an excellent recovery from previous hospital stays. Franklin visited a psychiatrist about once a month at the community mental health center where he also met with a counselor to discuss strategies to cope with his mental illness. He was now fully employed at a local hardware store stocking shelves and working the cash register. Franklin had several friends in the area and was fond of playing softball with them in park district leagues. He was also very active in a local Baptist church, being especially proud of Bible classes he co-led with the pastor. Clearly, the reappearance of his symptoms had derailed his job, apartment, and social life. A new medication regime, counseling, and support were needed to get him back on track.

---

[1] Franklin Goodman is a fictional person who represents the experiences of authors' friends and clients with severe mental illness.

Unfortunately, recuperating from this episode was not solely a matter of recovering from symptoms. The reactions of friends, family members, and professionals affected what happened to him. The owner of the hardware store, Gene Simpson, was unnerved by Franklin's psychiatric hospitalization. He believed that mentally ill people could become violent and worried that the stress of the job might lead to a dangerous outburst in the shop. Franklin's mother had other concerns. She worried that the demands of living on his own were excessive:

> *"He's pushing himself much too hard trying to earn a living, keep his apartment clean, and do all his own cooking."*

She feared Franklin might abandon his apartment and move to the streets just like other mentally ill people she had seen down by the beach.

Franklin's doctors were genuinely concerned that this hospitalization signaled a more serious lack of stability than they had first thought. Like many psychiatrists, his doctors believed that schizophrenia was a progressively degenerative disease; psychiatric hospitalizations were milestones that the disease was worsening. The doctors concluded that Franklin's ability to live independently would soon wane. It's better to prepare for this failure now rather than wait for the inevitable loss of independent functioning. So the doctor, with the help of Franklin's mother and friends, talked him into leaving his job, giving up his apartment, and moving back home. Franklin's mother lived across town so he stopped attending church on Sundays. Franklin was also unable to meet with his other friends and dropped out of other league sports soon after. In one month's time, he lost his job, apartment, and friends.

Figure 1

Does one of these persons look like a raving maniac? How about an incompetent diabetic? The amazing lesson about stigma is that persons with mental illness look like, and are, just like the rest of us.

Where's the Stigma in Diabetes?

Contrast this experience to that of Harriet Ogglesby. Harriet was a 34-year-old clerk-typist for a small insurance broker in Omaha. Like Franklin Goodman, Harriet had been diagnosed with a chronic disease: in her case, diabetes. She had to carefully monitor her sugar intake and self-administer insulin each day. She watched her lifestyle closely for situations that might worsen her condition. Harriet also met regularly with a physician and dietician to discuss issues like blood sugar, nutrition, and exercise. Even though she had to be careful, Harriet had an active social life. She belonged to a folk dancing club that she attended at a nearby community college.

Despite carefully watching her illness, diabetes was taking its toll. Harriet was frequently exhausted after a day's work. She also suffered a few significant setbacks, the last occurring about a month ago when she required a three day hospitalization to adjust her medication. The doctor recommended a short break from work after discharge and referred her to the dietician to discuss appropriate changes in lifestyle. Believing family support was important, the doctor also discussed this sudden turn of events with Harriet's parents.

Even though diabetes is a life-threatening disease—in her most recent episode, Harriet Ogglesby was near coma when wheeled into the hospital—no one suggested she consider some kind of institutional care where professionals could monitor her blood sugar and intervene appropriately when needed. No one recommended Harriet give up her job to avoid work-related stressors which might throw off her blood sugar. No one said she should move home with her folks so they could watch her diet.

What is the difference? How could Franklin lose his job, apartment, and friends, while Harriet's situation remained relatively unchanged? It was not the course of their illnesses; both persons had been living successfully with their afflictions for several years. Nor their resilience to relapse; both had weathered previous setbacks. The difference seems to lie with the reactions of health professionals, friends, and family to each illness. Harriet's support system realized that recovery required a holistic understanding of the disease; work and social activities were vital to her recovery. Franklin's family and doctors missed the importance of work, recreation, and friendship, instead basing their decisions on misconceptions about schizophrenia.

But wait. There are surely other differences that distinguish Franklin and Harriet. The behavior of a person with mental illness is disturbing and fearful to people. Franklin was likely to be dangerous and unpredictable. Might we naively think that Harriet and her diabetes do not show these alarming signs?

The problem here is separating perception from reality. Family members who escorted Harriet to the ER were equally alarmed by her diabetic coma. They were probably fearful and paralyzed by the unpredictability of her relapse. Mental illness has not cornered the market on disturbing or unpredictable behavior.

The Impact of Stigma

Stigma and discrimination are no small matter. In Franklin's case it robbed him of his livelihood and independence. It took a man who was successfully coping with a difficult disorder and took away much of his responsibility and independence. Perhaps the equally menacing aspect of this picture is that there are no clear villains in the story. Franklin's mother was reacting out of what she thought was her son's best interest, an interest that was forged out of more than 25 years of day-to-day concern for Franklin. His psychiatrist was intervening based on what his medical judgement said was appropriate. Franklin himself fell victim to the stereotype about severe mental illness. He believed that persons with mental illness, like himself, were unable to overcome their disability and reach life goals on their own.

Recently, there has been a resounding call for medical treatments to cure these biological disorders called mental illness. The decade of the brain has witnessed some impressive interventions for the physical causes of schizophrenia, manic depression, and similar disorders. But, that will never be enough. There is now a similar call to challenge the causes of lost opportunity, to change society's reactions and stop stigma.

Differing Views about Stopping Stigma

Concerns about the pain of stigma and the injustice of discrimination are by no means new. Two psychiatrists, Thomas Szasz and R.D. Laing, independently wrote about the myth of mental illness in the 1960's. They believed that mental illness was a mirage created by society to repress groups of people who choose to act differently from the rest of the world. According to Szasz and Laing, people with schizophrenia do not differ from society because of biological illness and psychiatric symptoms. Rather, these people make lifestyle choices that challenge fundamental values of society. The person *chooses* to believe he is an international spy or chooses to speak metaphorically rather than in clear sentences. Mental illness, therefore, is an artificial construct created by society as a way to understand alternative lifestyles. People who do not want to settle down and have a family must be crazy. The mental health system was created by society to manage these persons.

If Szasz and Laing are right, diminishing the impact of mental illnesses such as schizophrenia is accomplished by correcting myths about mental illness rather than by treating the symptoms of the disease. The solution therefore lies in changing society and learning to accept divergent ways of behaving, not in psychiatry and its fancy treatments. This goal is accomplished by educating the public about the diversity of behavior.

Figure 2

Two prominent figures that improved attitudes about mental illness: Thomas S. Szasz and Clifford Beers.

Individuals and organizations with equally powerful views about mental illness and stigma have emerged from the grass roots. Ex-patient Clifford Beers, for example, wrote about his experiences in hospitals in *A Mind that Found Itself* (1905). Beers' efforts led to the founding of the National Mental Health Association, a group of community advocates seeking to improve the quality of services for persons with mental illness. In the 1950s, persons released from state hospitals in New York City gathered together on the steps of the Public Library to provide support and counsel. They complained that good community services were not being provided by the state. At about the same time, GROW began in Australia when Con Keogh and other consumers sought a group of peers in a sharing and caring community. They felt alienated from a community that could not understand their different experiences and chose to view these differences as weird or wrong. In the 1970's, survivor groups like the Insane Liberation Front in Portland and the Mental Patients Liberation Project in New York City appeared. Efforts of survivor groups were described in Judy Chamberlin's 1978 book, *On Our Own: Patient Controlled Alternatives to the Mental Health System.* "Survivor" has an interesting meaning here: not surviving mental illness, oh no! "Survivor" means having withstood the dehumanizing and disrespectful reactions of society and its agents charged with treating mental illness.

Viewing Mental Illness as Disease AND Discrimination

Insights of people like Szasz and Laing, Beers, Keogh, and Chamberlin are important in their historical significance. Stigma is viewed as a social injustice that needs to be erased for persons with mental illness to obtain a quality life. The illness aspect to mental illness seems almost incidental. More contemporary concerns about stigma and discrimination are not as radical. For example, the National Alliance for the Mentally Ill—a group started by parents of persons with severe mental illness—is in the midst of a ten-year campaign to identify and correct misconceptions about severe mental illness. In no way does this group believe that the biological vulnerability of schizophrenia is a myth and that psychiatry perpetuates this falsehood. The National

Alliance for the Mentally Ill is a major benefactor of research that seeks to identify and cure the biological causes of severe mental illness. Nevertheless, members of the group recognize the insidious effects of stigma and misconception.

Views like these are now echoed by many state mental health systems, traditional guardians of biological interventions for mental illness. They have, for example, developed offices of consumer affairs to promote interactions between persons with mental illness and the citizenry as a whole. These consumer advocates present themselves and peers as examples of recovery and successful living. For example, the State of Connecticut Department of Mental Health and Addiction Services is promoting a program called "Disclosure" to further this cause. They believe disclosing the breadth of psychiatric disability in Connecticut and revealing recovery stories will significantly reduce stigma and discrimination. The Federal Government echoes this priority. Its Center for Mental Health Services has an intramural office on consumer empowerment and funds extramural projects that attempt to discount stigma. They are vocal proponents of participatory action research, research efforts that include persons with mental illness as partners, thereby assuring that this information gathering enterprise does not become encumbered by societal misconceptions about mental illness. Even service groups made up of private citizens have shown their concern about stigma. Rotary International, for example, has inaugurated "Erase the Stigma," a campaign to educate business leaders from across the United States about the truths and misconceptions of severe mental illness.

Regardless of its roots—survivorism, medical care, or civic concern—there is a ground swell of agreement that stigma and discrimination breeds inequity that can no longer be tolerated. A variety of tools have been proposed to deal with this injustice at several levels. The purpose of *Don't Call Me Nuts!* is to provide a resource that summarizes these tools. Strategies like these will help persons with serious mental illness and other interested parties to stomp out stigma and discrimination, replacing it with the breadth of opportunities which persons with mental illness are entitled to as citizens and members of our community.

Language as a Beginning to Stigma-Busting

Advocacy groups must win battles on several fronts to de-stigmatize mental illness. Perhaps the most fundamental is to identify a label for discussing and writing about persons with schizophrenia and other severe mental illness. Hence, this is where we choose to begin our discussion of ways to challenge stigma. Just as we would no longer consider using the various epithets and "euphemisms" that refer to African Americans, so we need to be sensitized to language issues that undermine persons with mental illness adding to their stigma. Or, wording the question more affirmatively, "What is respectful language for discussing mental illness and its impact?"

Pejorative expressions like *insane, deranged, crazy, wacko, psycho, demented,* and *daft* clearly disrespect persons with mental illness. Similarly, the professional literature has its own vocabulary with problems: *schizophrenics, manics, depressives, patients, subjects, residents, recipients, participants, members, students, workers, clients, consumers*, and *survivors.* Although these words are seemingly more respectful than slang, they have problems of their own. Some of these terms reduce the person to a diagnostic category: schizophrenic, manic, and depressive. Others refer to persons only in terms of their role in treatment. All of them distinguish the person as mentally ill, and therefore, different from the normal population.

The Research and Training Center on Independent Living at the University of Kansas issued a report, endorsed by more than 35 organizations, about meaningful and respectful labels. They concluded that *persons with severe mental illness* is the least pejorative reference. This title recognizes the person as a person, thereby acknowledging his or her membership in humankind. It reminds the world that the person is first a person, an individual like everyone else with a unique history who also happens to have a mental illness. The addition of "with severe mental illness" distinguishes the kind of disability the person is struggling with: mental illness versus, for example, developmental disability, hearing loss, blindness, head injury, or speech disorder. The complete title recognizes persons with severe mental illness as full human beings whom deserve respect and all the rights of citizenship.

Chapter 2

The Insults Wrought by the Stigma of Mental Illness

"Why should there not be a patient confidence in the ultimate justice of the people?"

Abraham Lincoln

All to often, stigma is viewed as an obvious problem and the solution simple: We must stop this intolerance now! In reality, stigma poses a vast and complex predicament for society. To beat it, we need to understand the scope of the problem posed by stigma. We must comprehend the obvious as well as the subtle ways it raises its ugly head. We must grasp the breadth of its impact and determine the insidious ways it infects public opinion against those with psychiatric disability. Fortunately, mental health advocates and social science researchers have been studying stigma and ways to change it for the past several decades. In this chapter, we review what is known about stigma: how widespread is its venom and what kind of impact it has on people. Only with this kind of information are we able to handle its challenges.

The Scope of the Problem

Stigmas about mental illness are widely endorsed by the general public. Studies suggest that the majority of people in the United States and most Western nations endorse stigmatizing attitudes about mental illness. Although there is mixed evidence about stigma in Asian and African countries—perhaps the communal nature of these societies decreases stigma—most researchers remain concerned about negative attitudes towards persons with mental illness across the world. Nor do stigmatizing views about mental illness seem to be limited to uninformed members of the general public. Members of the media, government officials, and high-placed businessmen have all been known to harbor stigmatizing attitudes. Consider the comments made by journalist Don Feder in the October 19, 1999 edition of the Boston Herald.

> *"Here is an interest group in the making. Give me your schizophrenics, your paranoids, your manic depressives, yearning for what? Just what the public needs, another minority to which politicians can pander. Gov. George W. Bush will want to address their next convention and assure that compassionate conservatives care about their issues, too."*

True, there is a place for irony and satire in our culture. But this kind of mean-spirited message undermines any open-minded approach towards understanding mental illness.

Many well-trained professionals from most mental health disciplines also subscribe to stigmas about mental illness. Psychiatrists, psychologists, social workers, psychiatric nurses, among others, have all been known to paint a bleak picture of severe mental illness, silently inferring that "patients" are unable to care for themselves and should learn to view most work and interpersonal goals as unattainable. These views, while more subtle than disrespectful images in the news and film media, are nevertheless based on misconceptions and stigma. Families and persons with mental illnesses themselves also fall victim to stigma, damning the potentials of future life. Read Chapter 4 for a fuller discussion of this issue.

Granted, stigmatizing attitudes are not limited to mental illness. Persons with other physical illnesses and disabilities are also the object of disparaging opinion. However, the general public seems to disapprove of persons with severe mental illness significantly more than persons with other physical disabilities such as Alzheimer's disease, blindness, or paraplegia. Research suggests severe mental illness has been viewed as similar to drug addiction, prostitution, and criminality rather than to a physical disability. Unlike other physical disabilities, persons with mental illness are perceived to be in control of their illness and hence, responsible for causing it. The general public is less likely to pity persons with mental illness, instead reacting to psychiatric disability with anger and believing that help is not deserved.

Stigmatizing attitudes like these have a significant impact on mental illness. First person accounts in *Schizophrenia Bulletin*, a professional journal published by the National Institute of Mental Health, repeatedly describe the pain of stigma and discrimination. Consider these excerpts:

- *"At age 14, I was misdiagnosed with schizo-phrenia. Much like the metaphor of the struggling fish, I felt caught by diagnostic hooks, trapped in a wave of short-sighted treatment plans, and misunderstood by everyone around me. Although this diagno-sis ultimately proved inaccurate, I struggled with the stigma that had stripped away my identity. For the next 2 tumultuous years, I would be continually referred to as a 'schizophrenic,' with a barrage of mental health professionals reinforcing the label."* (Robert Bjorklund, 1998, p. 653.)

- *"There is much discrimination against peo-ple who seek or have obtained psychiatric treatment. No matter how productive and functioning they are, the stigma is still there. It not only exists in employment. I am considering graduate school and there too, questions about past and present psy-chiatric treatment confront me."* (Anonymous, 1981, p. 736.)

- *"When I was in the hospital, I was in sear-ing psychic pain. It did not help when the director of the hospital said, "Roberta, you may have a master's degree, but you are not master of yourself."* (Roberta L. Payne, 1992, p. 725.)

Out of the hearts of those who experienced stigma do we learn much.

Using careful sampling methods, survey research supports these accounts: one study found that 75% of family members participating in a nationwide survey said that relatives with mental illness had been affected adversely by stigma. Family members in this sample believed that stigma decreased self-esteem, hindered ability to make friends, and undermined success in obtaining employment. Persons with severe mental illness living in New York City viewed stigma with similar concern. They believed the public would exclude them from close friendships or competitive jobs because of their mental illness. The impact of stigma is not limited to the individual diagnosed with mental illness. One in five respondents in the family survey reported lowered self-esteem and strained relationships with others because of stigma.

Sensitizing Persons to Mental Illness Stigma

Regardless of these data, most people remain unaware of how common mental illness stigma is. Jot down on a piece of paper, or use Table 2.1 for this exercise that sensitizes persons to what might seem to be relatively minor statements about mental illness. It includes two steps. First, individuals filling out the worksheet are to list various statements about persons with mental illness heard on AM radio, seen on network television, or read in the daily newspaper. Rather than asking the individual to listen for *stigma*, they are encour-

aged to identify "over-generalizations and misattribu-
tions about mental illness." Most participants are quickly amazed at the frequency with which mental illness is
disrespected in the media.

Table 2.1

An Exercise that Sensitizes Persons to Mental Illness Stigma

Make a list of over-generalizations and mis-attributions about mental illness that you
hear on the radio or see on television.

For example: ➤

> "That person acts that way because he's crazy."
> "All psychos are violent."
> "Crazy people can't take care of themselves."
> "Psychotics should all be locked up."

_____

_____

_____

_____

_____

Replace terms like crazy and psycho with the name of an ethnic minority group.

For example: ➤

> "That person acts that way because he's Black."
> "All Latinos are violent."
> "Irish people can't take care of themselves."
> "Jews should all be locked up."

_____

_____

_____

_____

_____

Most people, who might have thought these were harmless statements about
mental illness, quickly become horrified at the similarity between disrespecting persons
with mental illness and persons of color. In fact, some advocates for disability have
equated the experience of mental health stigma with the injustice of disrespecting
ethnic and religious minorities.

Second, individuals are asked to replace key words in these statements that represent mental illness (e.g., crazy, wacko, mental case, psychotics) with a term that describes an ethnic (Latino or Black) or religious minority (Jews). Most Americans have become sensitized to inappropriate language used against these groups. Hence, they are frequently dismayed to see the same kind of injustice that has been perpetrated against people of color still continues when such language is used to describe mental illness. This kind of exercise works effectively in schools with youngsters as well as at church gatherings and adult service club meetings. Participants soon become sensitized to the disrespectful language that permeates our culture.

Concepts for Understanding Stigma

Now that we know stigma is widespread, how do we understand it? There are a variety of terms all related to understanding this idea of stigma; the terms used on the next several pages and throughout the book are summarized in Table 2.2. One way to understand stigma is as negative attitudes about persons with mental illness. Attitudes combine seemingly *factual statements* that represent real world observations (Those dogs are black.) with *values* or *emotional reactions* to the fact (I hate black dogs!). Emotional reactions can be either positive (I think all black dogs are cute!) or negative (I think black dogs are mangy looking).

Stereotypes are especially efficient types of attitude about social groups. They are "social" because they represent collectively agreed upon notions of groups of persons. For example, the collective of people called American citizens "know" that the social group called Irish American is prone to drink. Stereotypes are "efficient" because people can quickly generate impressions and expectations of individuals who belong to a stereotyped group; for example, that man in the uniform is a police officer so he will likely be a good person to seek out when I need help.

Stereotypes do not necessarily represent a group in a negative light. The police example is evidence of this. *Stigmas are stereotypes that reflect a group negatively.* Research by British and American researchers have uncovered three sets of stigmatizing attitudes (or negative stereotypes) about mental illness that are commonly endorsed by the average citizen.

1. *Fear and exclusion*: persons with severe mental illness are dangerous, should be feared, and therefore, be kept out of most communities.

2. *Authoritarianism*: persons with severe mental illness are irresponsible; their life decisions should be made by others.

3. *Benevolence*: persons with severe mental illness are childlike and need to be cared for.

Large scale research like this has failed to identify any attitudes that reflect persons with mental illness in a positive light.

Table 2.2
Definitions of the Various Terms Used to Describe Aspects of Stigma. (Examples especially relevant to mental illness are also provided.)

Term	Definition	Examples
Attitudes	The combination of seemingly factual views of the world and our values or emotional reactions to these facts. Attitudes can either be positive (representing something as valuable or reacted to with pleasant emotions) or negative (viewing something as lacking value or yielding unpleasant emotions).	Desserts are sweets which provide a wonderful end to a meal **(positive attitude)**. Desserts make me fat; I hate them at the end of a meal **(negative attitude)**.
Stereotypes	Stereotypes are attitudes about groups of people. They help us to think efficiently because we are able to understand persons quickly based on their group membership. Like attitudes, stereotypes are both positive and negative. Stigmas are negative stereotypes.	That man at the front of the room writing on the chalk board is a teacher; he'll know the answer **(positive attitude)**. That women on the park bench is talking to herself; she must be crazy **(negative attitude)**.
Prejudice	Just because persons are aware of a stereotype does not mean they agree with them. Prejudice occurs when a person endorses a negative stereotype about a group.	That's right, all men are insensitive clods. Ain't it the truth? All mentally ill are dangerous.
Discrimination	Discrimination is the behavioral action that results from prejudice. It represents the unfortunate ways people act when they believe and agree with a negative stereotype.	That guy's mentally ill. He can't pull his own weight. I'm not going to hire him. She just got out of the psych hospital. Those people are all dangerous. I'm not renting an apartment to her.

Perceptions (or How We View Mental Illness)

Note how we said that attitudes *seem* to represent factual information. In reality, attitudes represent our impressions of fact—how we perceive the world but not necessarily how it really is. Humans rely on careful observation of their world to understand it; the sights and sounds of interactions with others teach us who is useful and should be enjoyed versus who is dangerous and should be avoided. Unfortunately, cognitive researchers have shown that our ability to perceive and understand the world is often fooled rather than driven by fact.

Stereotypes influence ways in which we comprehend stigmatized groups and frequently lead to misperceptions about group members. More specific to the concerns of this book, stigma affects the public's view of persons with mental illness. The same person is viewed differently depending on the perceiver's expectations about that person. These expectations or *labels* actually influence what we see or hear. Consider the short vignette below as a statement by a person with mental illness recently released from a hospital.

> *"Sometimes I'm just not sure. I have these visions about what to do. But they disturb me greatly and I just don't know how to act. I get so pent up inside I could scream. I want to run into the street, grab someone, and say, 'Hey, do you know what this all means?'"*

Given stereotypes about mental illness, a citizen might perceive this as evidence that the person is psychotic ("I have these visions about what to do."), unable to control her emotions ("they disturb me greatly and I just don't know how to act."), and likely to be dangerous ("I get so pent up inside I could scream. I want to run into the street and grab someone."). Note, however, how perceptions change when we label the person as a frustrated community advocate who wants to stop gang violence in his neighborhood. He has a vision about how to change things. He is overwhelmed by the emotional experiences related to his dreams. This frustration and desire makes him want to shake up his neighbors. The same dialogue produces very different interpretations of the meaning behind the statement.

The impact of stigma is not limited to how we currently see and experience people around us. It also affects our recollections of persons in the future. Stigma can actually bias our memory so that persons with mental illness are recalled in a more negative light. Take, for example, Sam, a college student who relays 10 facts about himself during a job interview. Five of these facts are appropriate to an aspiring student ("I have ambitions of becoming a successful engineer."), and five represent "weird" experiences of a young adult ("Sometimes things are so stressful that I feel like I am living outside my body.") How would Sam be remembered if, during the interview, he was labeled a "psychiatric patient?" When the job interviewer sits down to write up her report about Sam a week later, she is likely to remember more "weird" things. Sam has out of body experiences; he may be a mental case. Few positives would be listed. If, on the other hand, Sam were labeled

a hard working dorm counselor, then the job interviewer would be likely to remember more appropriate facts:
"Let's see; that guy was taking a bunch of classes to
become an engineer." The effects of stigma and stereotype are so broad they affect our memory of interactions with others.

These conclusions suggest the general public per-
ceives and remembers persons with severe mental illness in a biased manner. Think of the problems this may
pose for changing society's stigma. Any information
which is presented to the public about mental illness,
even material that challenges psychiatric stigma, may be
perceived inaccurately. Hence, stereotypes seem to be
resilient to evidence that challenge them.

> *Advocate*: Did you know that most per-
> sons with severe mental illness are not
> dangerous even in stressful situations?

> *Average person:* So you're saying they are
> so socially inept that they can't be
> assertive even when faced with tough situ-
> ations.

The advocate is trying to challenge attitudes about pairing mental illness with violence. The average person
cannot hear this new information because she believes
that most persons with mental illness are incapable of
caring for themselves. Unlearning stereotypes is a bit
more difficult when information that contradicts these
stereotypes is perceived incorrectly.

Prejudice—What We Really Feel About Mental Illness

Most everybody is aware of stereotypes. We all have heard such nasty statements as Irish Americans are drunks, Catholics are beholden to the Pope, and the mentally ill are dangerous. You cannot live in a culture like ours without having learned statements like these in the past. However, being aware of these stereotypes does NOT mean that a person agrees with them. Just because I have heard that all persons with mental illness are incapable of making decisions does not mean I concede that assertion.

Agreeing with stereotypes is the definition of *prejudice*. Saying "That's right, all Micks are drunks." is prejudicial to Irish Americans. Admitting that all persons with mental illness are incompetent is prejudice. Prejudice can be public; for example, openly stating that all persons with mental illness are homicidal maniacs. Alternatively, it can be private. It might take the form of haphazard agreement with stigma:

> *"I suppose that news story about all mentally ill being homeless is right."*

Alternatively, it may appear as a person who fully endorses negative stereotypes about mental illness but chooses not to let others know.

> *I'm sure psych patients are dangerous but I'm not going out on a limb and say anything at the school board meeting.*

Behaviors (How We Respond) Towards Mental Illness

Perhaps the worst part of stereotypes and prejudice is its behavioral consequence, *discrimination*. Citizens react to prejudice with discrimination:

- *Harry is mentally ill and unstable. I'm not going to hire him.*
- *I heard this guy Phil has been in a psych hospital. No way I'm going to rent an apartment to him.*
- *Adrianne has spells of depression. I'm not letting her daughter Laura come to our play group.*

Although being viewed negatively by the majority may generate anger or self-reproach, it is loss of jobs, unfair housing, diminished income and the countless other kinds of discrimination that cause the greater misery. Hence, strategies that seek to change society's reaction to mental illness must not only replace stigmatizing attitudes with more informed opinion, it must change the way members of the public act towards persons with mental illness.

Behavioral discrimination occurs most obviously when a person in a powerful role withholds an opportunity. Landlords do not rent an apartment to someone because he or she was in a psychiatric hospital. Employers fail to offer a job interview because the person with mental illness has not worked recently. A store clerk will not accept a credit card from a person because she seems depressed. Neighbors fight against a proposal for opening a halfway home in the area.

Behavioral discrimination also takes more subtle forms. Train passengers move their seats when a person with facial tics sits next to them. Volunteers refuse to work homeless shelters because, "You know they are all cast offs from the psych hospital." Mothers do not permit their children to play with a classmate who's father is known to suffer from mental illness. This kind of pulling back is equally hurtful to persons with mental illness who are trying to fit into their community.

Stopping discriminatory behavior is not enough. Affirmative actions are also needed. Affirmative action begins with the kind of legal efforts that require hiring a person or leasing them property based on membership into a stigmatized group. Affirmative action also includes efforts to reach out to persons with mental illness and include them as *full* members of the community. Churches, synagogues, and mosques need to actively encourage persons with mental illness to join them. Social clubs and civic groups need to pursue these folks. Politicians running for elective office need to seek their grassroots support. In addition, the general public needs to join the stigma-busting agenda. Just as racial injustice is the problem of the entire population (not just persons of color), so stigma against mental illness needs to become the concern of all members of the community, not just of people vested with personal interests.

What is the Relationship Between Attitudes and Behaviors?

How do we change discriminatory behaviors and promote affirmative actions? One of the prominent questions of research psychology is whether behavior change first requires improvement in attitudes. Does the average person change the way she acts towards a group (e.g., a wealthy executive stops talking down to blue collar workers) when her attitude towards that group improves ("I now realize blue collar employees are hard working like me")? This assumption is mapped out in the flow chart in Figure 2.1.

Figure 2.1
The relationship between perceptions, attitudes, and behaviors.

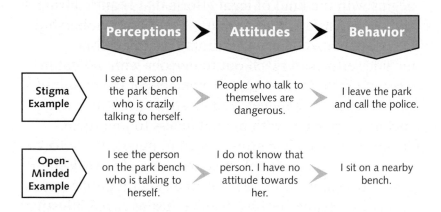

According to this diagram, people behave based on their perceptions of the world. First a person sees or hears someone to whom they must react. Obviously, reactions would differ depending on who they saw and what that person was doing; we would respond differently to a mugger versus our grandfather. The example in Figure 2.1 has a person sitting on a bench talking to herself.

Perceptions by themselves are not enough to come to conclusions about someone. Attitudes and other knowledge structures add interpretation to perceptions. They help make sense out of perceptual experience. Based on personal history, the public may have developed attitudes which lead them to believe the person on the bench is rehearsing lines for a play, talking aloud a problem with her boss, or grossly psychotic. Citizens then decide how to respond to a stimulus based on their interpretation. The person passing by may be intrigued by the young actress and sit down to talk. In the stigmatizing example of Figure 2.1, the pedestrian is frightened by the "dangerous" psychotic and runs away.

This chain of events suggests behaviors can be improved by starting with the first links in the chain. Hence, one way to stop discriminatory behaviors is to change attitudes from "that person is crazy" to "that's a person about whom I need to know more." Perceptions and attitudes are the place to begin in changing discrimination. Education programs target attitudes and perceptions (see Chapter 8).

Despite this carefully-tested model, there is evidence that change in attitude frequently does not affect behavior. We all know people who resolve to change their health habits ("I need to eat better; I am going on a diet.") but who in fact continue the same old ways ("Despite my intentions, I'm going to eat those greasy potato chips."). Changing discrimination may require two attacks. Efforts need to target attitudes and perceptions. However, when these efforts are too slow, stigmabusters need to be more demanding. In these cases, discriminatory behaviors should be challenged directly. Protest and boycotts (also discussed in Chapter 8) are effective tools for this goal.

Where Do We Learn Stigma?

Given how immoral prejudice and stigma are, from where do we learn them? Two answers to this question are summarized in Table 2.3. Stereotypes that are *constructed by experience* are acquired through regular contact with members of a particular group. The public learns stereotypes about mental illness by directly interacting with persons who have a psychiatric disability. This kind of approach assumes the public acts as a statistical scientist. If I meet ten people with mental illness, all who are homeless and poorly dressed, I learn that mental illness results in an inability to care for self and ending up on the streets. If I meet no persons with mental illness who work, I infer that persons with mental illness are incapable of obtaining and keeping a regular job. Unfortunately, as any good statistician can tell us, numbers are wrong. What might be concluded about Irish Americans if they were only encountered in bars? Hence, stereotypes based on limited experience can be full of errors. Moreover, they are typically overridden by the second way in which stigmas are learned.

Table 2.3
Two Ways in Which Stigma Is Learned

Constructed by Experience	Socially-Given Stigma
We develop attitudes about groups based on the sum of our interactions with them. Persons with limited experiences of a group will develop limited attitudes.	Attitudes are learned about groups based on our lore, myths, and other representations of them. In America, television, films, and other media are the biggest source of this kind of stereotype.

Socially given stereotypes represent cultural lore about a group handed down by community elders and other authorities. They come from our myths and legends. Many centuries ago, these myths may have been learned around the campfire. Mass media serve this role in modern times. Movies, newspapers, radio programs, the Internet, and television shows are common sources of information about severe mental illness. Unfortunately, much of this information is inaccurate and leads to stigma.

Media analysis of ways in which film and print represent mental illness have identified two common misconceptions spread by these sources: people with mental illness are homicidal maniacs who need to be feared, and they are childlike and should be protected by parental figures. Each of these images have been circulated by the media groups that dominate our culture. It's no wonder that the average person, and from a very young age, learns that persons with mental illness are dangerous and cannot care for themselves. Otto Wahl wrote an excellent book (called *Media Madness: Public Images of Mental Illness*) that provides many examples of disrespectful images of persons with mental illness (check the *Learn More About It* section of this book for more information about Wahl's text).

They're All Homicidal Maniacs

Headlines scream this message all the time: "Psycho-Killer on the Loose," "Maniac Terrorizes Neighborhood," "Mental Patient has Escaped." The majority of the time that mental illness is discussed in the news media, it is represented as dangerous. Consider how unfair this is. Clearly, most everyone with psychiatric disability is living lives free of violence. Yet, all the news media focuses on are criminal acts. This problem is not unique to mental illness; newspapers always tend to focus on gore and mayhem. But what impressions of mental illness are left the public if all we hear is about the violence?

Equating mental illness with crime is not limited to the news. One survey discussed in Wahl's book found about 3 out of 4 sitcoms and drama series that include persons with mental illness cast that person in a dangerous role. Consider these plots lifted from the Washington TV guide:

- *Vegas*: Dan teams up with two police-women to find the psychotic killer who is murdering officers.

- *Hill Street Blues*: Bates goes undercover to find a psychopath who's killing prostitutes.

- *Remington Steele*: An amnesiac targeted for death surprises Laura and Remington by having multiple identities and several wives.

Otto Wahl provides more than 150 examples of shows with similar plots in his book.

Teen horror films are perhaps the biggest purveyor of the notion of homicidal maniacs. The Texas Chainsaw Murderer, Freddie Kruger, Norman Bates from *Psycho*, Jason from *Friday the 13th*, and *Halloween*'s Michael Meyers have been haunting American theaters for two decades and more. Not just once, by the way, these movies have returned for three, five, and even nine sequels. The escaped and psychotic villain is hatcheting up small town teens.

This kind of image is even shared with young children. Consider a page from *Uncle Shelby's ABZ Book* by Shel Silverstein. "There are crazy murderers ready to break into the house and kill your family while you sleep." Granted it's tongue-in-cheek, but children are taught early to fear persons with mental illness.

Representing mental illness as dangerous and to be avoided is an insidious habit that occurs on respected news programs too. Consider the September 1997 presentation of 60 Minutes titled *Secrets and Lies*. Should adoption agencies reveal whether their children have mentally ill parents? The implied message is that children with mental illness are losing packages; they'll grow up damaged and dangerous. Adoptive parents have a right to know. Perhaps an irony in this show was the announcer, Mike Wallace. Wallace has publicly discussed his bouts of major mental illness and is a national advocate against stigma. Despite this agenda, he promoted a stigmatizing image of mental illness. Would CBS run a show questioning whether it was legal to hide an adopted child's ethnic background?

Equally subtle images are found in the advertising world. Readers are supposed to laugh about Crazy Eddie's record asylum, "sales worth being committed for," and prices set by maniacs out of control. An ad showing a jar of peanuts in a straight jacket, with the tag line "Certifiably Nuts," actually won a CLIO award for innovative retail packaging. This marketing firm made light of an instrument used to restrain people as a means to sell a product. Nor can the messages in these ads be discounted as harmless fun. Consider an ad where the writers are saying that persons with mental illness need to be "weeded out" from the work force!

Persons with Mental Illness Can't Care for Themselves

Alternatively, persons with mental illness are represented as childlike, almost cute, beings. Christopher Lloyd and Michael Keaton played such characters in a 1989 film, *The Dream Team*. In this film, four mental hospital patients wander through Manhattan where their carefree day was derailed by zany problems. This kind of movie confuses the disabilities of mental illness with the problems of childhood or the humor of slapstick. Moreover, it suggests that the problems of mental illness are best handled by all-knowing parental figures. Doctors know better than their patients; they should decide, for example, whether it's time for a person to return to work. This kind of subtle message serves to undermine persons' power over their lives.

The media broadcasts a related message: people with mental illness are reckless free spirits to be tolerated. Several movies have promoted this image. Barbara Streisand's *Nuts*, for example, portrayed this; rather than being dangerous, persons with mental illness are eccentric, perhaps Bohemian in tastes. The ironic part of this message that portrays persons with mental illness as Bohemian is frequently incorporated into anti-stigma programs. Streisand believed she was attacking prejudice against mental illness. Instead, she was saying persons with mental illness should be stomached like any kind of annoying group in society: flower children, Libertarians, and Hari Krishnas.

Mental Illness, Humor, and Stigma

Comics in newspapers often run story lines that disrespect the experiences of mental illness. In one widely distributed cartoon, Gary Larson, a very talented humorist of the 80s and 90s, unfortunately spoofs the relationship between therapist and client. In the process, Larson greatly disrespects the person with mental illness by having the therapist label him "Just plain nuts!" Doug Marlette continues the theme in his strip Kudzu. In this group, praise from an admirer is belittled because the person is receiving care for psychiatric problems. Nor, once again, do we see this medium limited to adults. Saturday cartoons are frequently permeated by maniacal villains or silly loons. This is the subtle message given by the cartoon "Animaniacs."

Television shows have similar plots. Consider these programs from the 1996 season.

- On a *Home Improvement* episode, Jill plans to return to school to study psychology. Her husband replies, "If your dream is to work with nuts, you should go back to Macadamia."

- Football coach Hayden Fox on the series named *Coach* describes the new president of the University: "That woman is nuts! The Loon of the Blue Lagoon."

35

● On the *Drew Carey Show*, the star is told
  this story. "We had a crazy guy at Drug-
  Ko. Turned out he accidentally took a
  drug that turned him into a psychopathic
  ax murderer. It's not on the market yet.
  Apparently it gives you headaches."

Many thanks to a column from Karen Rivedal in the
Northwest Herald where this trend in TV was noted. In
her column, Rivedal bemoans this kind of simple-minded humor at the expense of persons with mental illness.

Is There a Place for Sarcasm?

This is America; lampooning groups is a right in
our culture. Isn't it reasonable for critics to respond that
mental health advocates should back off? We wouldn't
be surprised if some readers of this book quietly chuck-
led at the punch lines in these jokes. Do mental health
advocates need to lighten up a bit? Sarcasm serves an
important goal in our society. It provides a chance for
the common man to poke fun at those in power. When
an editorial cartoonist helps us to laugh at government
officials, we remind politicians and ourselves that we are
all from the same stock. Especially in America, no
humans can view themselves as higher caste. Satire
brings the high and mighty to common levels.

Unfortunately, it does not help those who suffer
prejudice and discrimination rise to similar levels.
Instead, it further reminds those, who are one step
down, that below the threshold is where they remain.
Recall that the 'step-n-fetchit' humor of previous gener-
ations had this purpose for African Americans. This

humor represented Blacks as less intelligent, less hard-working, or more brutish; it was trying to keep this group down. We would be horrified if ethnic humor continued today. In like fashion, humor against persons with psychiatric disability keeps them under the thumb. It dehumanizes their troubles and allows a frequently hostile community to continue in its disrespectful and discriminatory actions against them.

Signals that Lead to Stigma

How does the public know who to hurt with mental illness stigma and to whom it does not apply? What are the "signals" that a particular person has a mental illness? How does the average citizen recognize *that* person as wacky and should be avoided while *another* is "normal" The famous sociologist, Irving Goffman, suggested that cues which signal the stigma of mental illness may not be readily apparent; he illustrated this point by distinguishing easily hidden from readily obvious kinds of stigma. Examples of each group are summarized in Table 2.4. The group with relatively obvious characteristics that lead to stigma include persons from a cultural minority with an apparent physical trait which leads them to believe that their different-ness is obvious to the public; (e.g., Africans have dark skin.) Persons with easily hidden stigma, on the other hand, can conceal their condition; they have no readily manifest mark that identifies them as part of a stigmatized group. Citizens do not know whether a person is gay unless he or she reports it. The public cannot determine whether persons are mentally ill by looking at them.

Table 2.4

Examples of Stigmatized Groups that are Easily Hidden versus Readily Obvious.

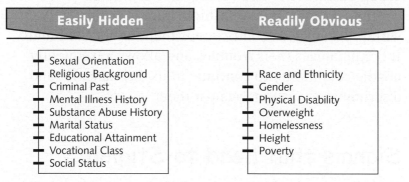

Easily Hidden	Readily Obvious
Sexual Orientation	Race and Ethnicity
Religious Background	Gender
Criminal Past	Physical Disability
Mental Illness History	Overweight
Substance Abuse History	Homelessness
Marital Status	Height
Educational Attainment	Poverty
Vocational Class	
Social Status	

Some readers might argue that even these distinctions are guilty of perpetuating stereotypes. For example, we might think the Black, White, Asian distinction of racial groups is obvious until someone tries to classify people like golfer Tiger Woods. Mr. Woods views himself as a member of several groups including African and Asian American.

The general public must infer mental illness from four signals: labels, psychiatric symptoms, social skills deficits, and physical appearance. According to labeling theory, persons who are called "mentally ill" (that guy at the front of church is "mentally ill") or are otherwise known to have such a label (like being observed coming out of a psychiatrist's office), are the object of stigma and discrimination. Results of one study showed, for example, that persons who were publicly labeled "mentally ill" had less income and were more likely to be underemployed compared to a similarly impaired, but unlabeled, group.

Critics have countered labeling theory by arguing that bizarre behavior, and not the label per se, is the source of negative responses from the public. They concluded that labels are not really a problem. Bruce Link from Columbia University tested this opposing view in an experiment where label and odd behavior were manipulated; results showed citizens were likely to stigmatize a person labeled mentally ill even in the absence of any behavior consistent with psychosis. Hence, Professor Link posed a modified labeling theory where he concluded that although a psychiatric label does not lead to mental illness, it certainly is associated with negative societal reactions which, in turn, worsen the course of the person's disorder.

As suggested by Link's research, another set of signals which may lead to stigma result from the way persons with mental illness behave. Many of the symptoms of severe mental illness—inappropriate affect, bizarre behavior, language irregularities, and talking to self aloud—may be obvious to the public. Symptoms like these tend to produce more stigmatizing reactions than those associated with labels alone.

> *Look, that guy is just babbling to himself.*
> *There's a wacko for ya."*

Moreover, poor social skills that are a function of psychiatric illness also lead to stigmatizing reactions. Deficits in eye contact, body language, and choice of discussion topics potentially mark a person as mentally ill and lead to stigmatizing attitudes.

Finally, research suggests personal appearance may signal stigmatizing attitudes. In particular, physical attractiveness and personal hygiene may indicate mental illness and lead to stereotyped responses; (e.g., "that unkempt person in the hamburger stand must be a mental patient.") Note, however, the potential for misidentifying as mentally ill based on appearance. For example, many street people with slovenly appearance are believed to be "mentally ill" when, in actuality, they are poor and homeless.

Putting It All Together

Stigma seems to be understood through a mish-mash of terms: signals, stereotypes, emotions, and behaviors. Bernard Weiner is a psychologist who has developed a model on how we normally think and act that brings all these ideas together into one model. Called *Attribution Theory*, this model is summarized in Figure 2.2. According to Weiner, attribution theory is a model of human motivation and emotion based on the assumption that individuals search for causal understanding of everyday events.

● *"Why did I get a pay raise?"*

● *"How come Republicans were voted out of congress?"*

● *"Why did Harry (a person labeled as mentally ill) hit his friend, Sarah?"*

The answer to these questions lead to decisions and actions.

● *"I got a pay raise because I was on time for work. I'm going to keep being punctual."*

● *"Republicans were voted out of Congress because the economy is sluggish."*

● *"Harry hits people because he's mentally ill and those people are morally inferior. I'm going to tell the landlord not to let him move into the apartment next to me!"*

When encountering successful or unsuccessful *outcomes*, people ask themselves why this outcome and not another. Encountering success or failure leads to emotional and behavioral responses.

Figure 2.2
One model that sums up how we think about and act on stigma. Citizens naturally try to explain everyday events in terms of their causes or attributions. These attributions lead to emotional responses. Citizens who believe a person is in control of a bad event are angry with that person. A person who is not in control of a bad event is believed to be a victim and is pitied. Anger leads to punitive behavior, seeking retribution for one's errors. Pity leads to helping behavior.

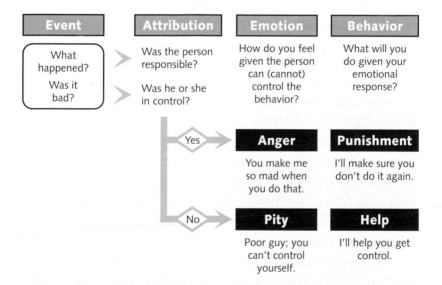

Research by our group at the University of Chicago has shown this model to have significant value for understanding stigma and discrimination in mental illness. According to our studies, meeting a person with mental illness is an outcome that leads to a search for causal attributions. How does the average citizen understand the labels or behaviors of the person with psychiatric disability? What kind of emotions and behaviors do these attributions yield? The focus of research in this area is to identify thoughts and actions that affect causal attributions like these.

Controllability of Causes

Controllability refers to the amount of self-control an individual exerts over a behavior.

> *"Let me ask you this. Does a mentally ill person have any control over his or her temper, or is it the illness alone that makes them dangerous?"*

People are likely to blame others when they are viewed as personally in control. For example, a trial court is likely to judge more harshly the driver who was drunk when he struck a pedestrian than the driver who lost control because of poor brakes. Neighbors are likely to place greater responsibility on the person with mental illness who caused her symptoms by several years of illegal drug use versus the results of a head injury that occurred after a car accident.

Weiner's theory suggests that controllability and responsibility attributions are associated with emotional responses. Persons who are viewed to be in control of a negative event (e.g., showing psychotic symptoms) are more likely to be held responsible and reacted to angrily.

> *"Annette could have stopped her hallucinations and didn't have to hit Sarah. Boy, I'm mad at her."*

Alternatively individuals who are not believed to be in control of a negative event are pitied by others.

> *"Poor Annette. She tries to control her
> anger but just can't handle her illness."*

Reaction to the same situation (Annette getting angry) leads to different emotional reactions based on how a citizen interprets Annette's responsibility for that behavior.

Additional research has shown that uncontrollability attributions about an event lead to pity and helping behavior. For example, persons whose mental illnesses are attributed to a head injury sustained in a car accident are more likely to receive sympathy from others. This sympathy may lead to helping behavior;

- *"I'd be willing to give him a ride to work."*

- *"Annette has seizures and can't control her anger. I think we should all be more patient with her. In fact, I'm going to let her move into my spare bedroom until she is over this hump in her life."*

There are four kinds of helping behavior that may result from sympathy: *instrumental* support (e.g., solving a problem), *tangible* support (e.g., the donation of goods), *informational* support (e.g., providing advice), and *emotional* support (e.g., reassurance). This distinction parallels the various support roles which the mental health system and peers provide persons with mental illness. Assertive community treatment involves instrumental and tangible support. Skills training and psychoeducation serve the goals of informational support.

43

Individual and group psychotherapies facilitate emotional support.

As outlined in Figure 2.2, research shows that viewing bad events as under a person's control ("Annette hit Sarah on purpose.") leads to anger from others and punishing behaviors. Persons who believe that a mental illness is under an individual's control (e.g., because they lack character), are likely to angrily respond to that individual and act towards him or her in a punishing manner. Two kinds of punishment might result: *retribution* (i.e., wrongdoing justly merits punishment) and *utilitarian punishment* (i.e., punishment serves to help persons fit back into society). There still seem to be some examples of retribution in the mental health system. Some mental health professionals may blame persons for the problems that result from mental illness and believe they should be disciplined for their misbehavior. Utilitarian notions of punishment, however, are more obvious in current psychiatric practice. Utilitarian notions include reform or rehabilitation of the guilty, protection of society, and deterrence. The reform function of punishment is apparent; all states in the union provide laws that mandate inpatient and/or outpatient treatment to rehabilitate persons who are not fully capable of deciding about and participating in these treatments. The deterrence function is also evident; most states permit civil commitment to protect society from persons who are considered dangerous to others.

A third, punitive response to controllability attributions may involve avoiding that person.

> *"I'm going to stay away from that guy
> 'cause he's nuts!"*

Citizens might take away opportunities from an individual because of perceived control over psychiatric symptoms. These response costs might include withholding opportunities for competitive jobs and good housing.

> *"I'm not going to give Harry a job. He's hitting people on purpose."*

There have actually been laws that prevent a group from dating, marrying, and having children. As outlined above, persons with mental illness are frequently deprived of opportunities like these.

The relationship between events, attributions, emotions, and behavior suggest how complex stigmatizing reactions are. They also suggest targets for improving attitudes and behaviors towards persons with mental illness. This book describes many ways to target these disrespectful images to yield better opportunities for persons with mental illness. We briefly review these strategies here.

Suggestions for Challenging Mental Health Stigma

As outlined thus far in this chapter, stigma appears in different forms and causes a variety of problems for persons with mental illness. The media including newspapers, movies, and television disperse stigmatizing images and slogans about severe mental illness throughout our community. Messages from parents and other authorities teach children that persons with mental illness are dangerous or cannot care for themselves. Observations of labeled "patients" like the homeless lead to biased attributions about mental illness. We have grouped these various problems into three areas as outlined in Table 2.5. Each area corresponds with the next three parts of this book:

- Individual Strategies for Dealing with Stigma

- Personal Empowerment and Stigma

- Changing Society's Reaction to Mental Illness.

We review these three parts briefly here.

Table 2.5
Three Specific Problems With Stigma and Ways to Remediate it.

Problems Caused by Stigma	Ways to Remedy The Problems
Personalize shame. Lower self-esteem. Doubtful about future.	Learn to challenge self-stigmatizing thoughts. Decide whether to disclose.
Loss of personal control over one's life. The pain of labels.	Strategies that foster personal empowerment.
Society is misinformed. They have unnecessary worries. They respond unjustly.	Education about the myths of mental illness. Protest against disrespectful images. Facilitate contact between the public and persons with mental illness. Consider legal and political remedies.

(1) Challenging The Private Shame of Stigma through Attitude Change

Some people experience stigma and prejudice as a private shame that diminishes their self-esteem. This kind of shame leads to self-doubt about whether he or she is able to live independently, hold a job, earn a livelihood, or find a life mate. Even though they may have mastered their symptoms and disabilities, persons with mental illness must overcome stigmatizing reminders that they fail to recover or do not become useful members of society.

"Struggling with going in and out of the hospital and the depression and craziness was bad enough. But all the disapproval hurt much more: My sisters thinking I was lazy, especially because my brother, Ed, was a doctor. My uncles no longer asking me to go fishing with them because 'I needed my rest.' But what really hurt was when my parents gave up... I think it was after my hospitalization in 1990. They stopped believing I would beat it. They stopped pushing me to get a job. They talked about me living in a halfway house. They thought I was a mental patient and not their son. Mom and Dad had bought into all the societal stuff about mentally ill patients.

The loss of faith was much harder than my time in the hospital. I began to believe it too. I'm not going to be able to work. I'll never find someone to marry. I'll always live in homes."

Persons who are depressed learn to reframe unhappy thoughts about themselves *("I'll never be successful.")* and the world *("Everybody else is able to cope. Why can't I?")* in a more positive light. A variety of cognitive strategies help people challenge depressing thoughts and develop beliefs that counter the sadness. In a similar manner, persons can learn to challenge stigmatizing views of themselves and negative expectations about their future using cognitive strategies. For example, persons struggling with the stigma of mental illness *("I'm mentally ill. I can't make it on my own.")* might learn to collect evidence that disputes the stigma *("Many people with worse disabilities have made it.")* and construct counters for subsequent times when bothered by the public *("If others can do it, so can I!")*. Chapter 4 more fully reviews how persons might deal with the stigmatizing thoughts and beliefs that unjustly lead to a sense of personal shame.

Some people may choose to deal with stigma by selectively disclosing their history with mental illness. They may decide to avoid public disapproval by not sharing their difficulties with everyone. Instead, they seek out a small number of persons who are likely to empathize with their challenges and support efforts in pursuit of their goals.

"I felt like I was going to explode at work when I couldn't tell someone. Co-workers would be talking about their college years, or their stretch in the Army, or

*that time they got their first job... years
when I was in and out of the hospital.
They'd turn to me and ask what I was up
to and I'd have to excuse myself or make
something up. I felt ashamed that I couldn't
be honest. But, I also felt angry that no one
would understand. It's not my fault I have
this gap.*

*"Then I met Beverly. It took several
months, but eventually I figured she would
be someone who could handle my disclosure. Beverly never seemed to get nervous
when I failed to discuss my past. Instead,
she had a charming way of teasing me
about my life, just like a good friend. And
she always responded with an open mind
when I tested her views about mental illness. We saw this movie once where they
presented a depressed person as a moral
degenerate. Over coffee afterwards, Beverly
actually got mad about it.*

*Beverly has known about my men-
tal illness for about a year now. I thought
she might pull away, you know, be scared
of the crazy. But now, I can go to her desk
and bitch about things and I feel she
knows."*

Persons are better able to consider whether to
disclose when they weigh the costs and benefits of disclosure; this issue is more fully discussed in Chapter 5.
Persons with disabilities need to weigh the benefits, for
example, of letting their employer know (*"My supervisor will be more patient with me."*) versus the cost of dis-

closing (*"The boss might think I can't handle my job."*). Persons can also learn the signs of a peer to whom it is safe to disclose. Is a person like Beverly likely to respond and be supportive?

We must, however, be aware of the paradox in trying to help people decide whether to disclose. An unintended message is made; namely, that mental illness is indeed something that should be hidden. This kind of message could reinforce attitudes of shame.

(2) Challenging The Pain of Public Labels through Empowerment

People who have been labeled as mentally ill experience additional harm from stigma. Labels frequently come from public knowledge that the person was hospitalized.

> *"I know my family tried to keep it to themselves. But these things just get out. I went away for two weeks and it seemed that everyone knew I had been in a psych hospital. Whether it was genuine concern or the object of gossip, people at church—at the store, at the local park—all seemed to know and look at me differently."*

Persons who are labeled mentally ill are unable to hide from public disapproval. As a result, they are more likely to experience societal hostility and discrimination.

Empowerment has been defined as the *opposite* of the distancing experienced by persons who are stigmatized (this point is thoroughly developed in Chapter

6). The impact of empowerment is significant; despite societal stigma, empowered consumers endorse positive attitudes about themselves. They have good self-esteem, believe themselves to be competent, and are optimistic about the future. The impact of empowerment is manifested by the person's desire to affect his or her stigmatizing community. Persons believe they have some power within society, are interested in affecting change, and wish to promote action.

In Chapter 6, we review strategies that foster empowerment. Empowerment includes any strategy that provides the person control over his or her treatment. For example, treatment providers have turned the entire clinical enterprise over to "consumers" in the spirit of empowerment. George Fairweather developed a residential program run by program participants as far back as the 1960s. He believed that the symptoms and deficits of institutionalized persons would greatly diminish if these individuals were empowered to care for themselves in a lodge setting. In such a setting, persons with mental illness benefit from the consensus-building process needed to design and maintain effective residential and vocational programs. Moreover, their sense of self efficacy and esteem is enhanced by living and working with peers.

An interesting paradox arises out of the empowerment movement. Rather than choosing to hide one's mental illness, many persons fight stigma by coming out of the closet and grabbing public control of their life. This is shown by the number of consumer advocacy and mutual-help groups that have been founded *for* persons with mental illness *by* persons with mental illness. These groups provide support for the person to fight the shame and discrimination that accompanies stigma.

(3) Challenging Societal Ignorance through Public Action

Society also suffers from stigma about severe mental illness. Citizens are misinformed about members of their community with psychiatric disabilities. This misinformation leads to unnecessary fears and worries. It also leads to misperceptions about the actions of fellow citizens. Fear and misinformation result in hostility and anger. Members act on this fear by robbing persons with mental illness of rightful opportunities. Employers fail to hire and landlords do not lease to persons with severe mental illness. Entire communities express outrage at the thought that a mental health residence might move into their neighborhood.

Advocates since the turn of the century have developed a variety of strategies for trying to change attitudes about racial minorities. Chapters 7 and 8 discuss the relevance of these strategies for changing the public's view of mental illness. These strategies include protest, education, and contact. Groups protest inaccurate and hostile representations of mental illness as a way to challenge the stigmas they represent. These efforts send two messages. To the media: STOP reporting inaccurate representations of mental illness. To the public: STOP believing negative views about mental illness. Protest is a reactive strategy; it diminishes negative attitudes about mental illness, but in many cases fails to promote more positive beliefs that are supported by facts. Education provides information so that citizens make more informed decisions about mental illness. Education also corrects the myths and misconceptions that underlie mental illness stigma. Education strategies are augmented by face-to-face contact. Stigma is diminished when members of the general public meet persons with schizophrenia who are able to hold down jobs or live as good neighbors in the community.

Community action to change public attitudes and behavior is not enough; sometimes, legal action is needed. Chapter 9 reviews the legal protections afforded Americans with mental illness. We discuss the American with Disabilities Act and how it helps persons deal with discrimination in the work world. We review the Fair Housing Act and its implication for stigma and discrimination in the residential world. We also provide pointers about political advocacy; ways for persons with mental illness to affect the government agenda in their community, in their state, or at the federal level.

Summary

Only by understanding stigma can we hope to beat it. As shown in this chapter, stigma and its impact are described by a complex picture. In part, stigmas are thoughts or attitudes we have about persons with mental illness. While these thoughts might be positive, stigmas are largely negative beliefs. These beliefs cloud our perceptions of mental illness. They lead to negative emotions towards persons who are mentally ill. Negative beliefs (or prejudice) yield discriminatory behavior. Believing that persons with mental illness are *responsible* for their problems—(i.e., they choose to be psychotic)—especially seems to be a source of stigma and discrimination.

This complex description of stigma leads to three ways to fix it. (1) Persons with mental illness learn how to reframe self-stigmatizing beliefs about themselves into more reasonable (and less hurtful) self statements. In addition, persons with mental illness consider the various ways in which they might disclose their experiences with mental illness to others. (2) People can undermine the impact of stigma by gaining personal power over their lives. A range of strategies that foster personal empowerment are reviewed in this book. (3) Society must stop promoting disrespectful and stigmatizing images of mental illness. This goal may be accomplished through public education and protest. It may also be achieved by facilitating person-to-person contact among persons with mental illness and the general public. There are also laws which protect persons with mental illness against discrimination.

Chapter 3

Who is the Person with Mental Illness?

"Success is to be measured not so much by the position that one has reached in life as by the obstacles which he has overcome while trying to succeed."

Booker T. Washington

Marie was first diagnosed with schizophrenia at the age of 19. She was grossly psychotic, hearing voices, and believing she was the wife of the devil. She was hospitalized ten times before she was 21. Eventually, she received one of the new antipsychotic drugs which had excellent results. She then earned a nursing assistant degree from the community college and went to work for a local senior citizens program. She got married to Mark last year and now lives in a two bedroom apartment in Parkland.

Bennett has a terrible fear of elevators. He panics and runs out of them before the

door closes. It has become a major prob-
lem since his company moved to the 35th
floor of a downtown building. He had to
quit his job and is unable to find further
work because of this phobia. Bennett's
income is falling quickly and he had to file
bankruptcy to handle delinquent bills.
None of his classmates from Harvard
thought he would end up with such prob-
lems.

Nobody at work ever knew that Emil had
manic depression. About once a year, he
would have a manic episode followed by a
severe depression. He wasn't able to go out
for about three weeks after. Fortunately,
Emil had a close set of friends who would
help him through the episode. They'd sleep
over, cook, and otherwise keep him compa-
ny. With appropriate help from his psychia-
trist, Emil was eventually able to get back
to work.

Betsy suffered from terrible test anxiety.
Before she learned relaxation strategies, she
could barely get into a classroom to take
exams. However, after a few audiotapes, she
learned breathing exercises and became a
whiz at tests!

Which one of these people has a mental illness?
And who's psychiatric disorder is the most severe? In
some ways, Marie represents the prototype of mental illness; she has a diagnosis of schizophrenia which started

in young adulthood and led to severe symptoms. Bennett has what is usually considered to be a milder psychiatric diagnosis, a phobia or irrational fear of something in his environment. But, consider the impact of the two illnesses. Marie, despite having schizophrenia, has learned how to manage the illness, has obtained a respectable job, and has settled down with her husband. Unable to work, Bennett's world is tumbling down around him.

Emil's experience with mental illness is like the tree falling in the empty forest; is it a mental illness if no one knows? He escapes the label and all the harm which stigma creates. Betsy suffered what professionals might consider the minor headache of mental illness, test anxiety. Most readers might dismiss this altogether from the category of major psychiatric disorders. But, while in college, tests for Betsy were as painful as someone else's experience with major depression or psychosis. Moreover, the impact of test anxiety remaining untreated could have had major repercussions; failing classes, dropping out of school, and not attaining the career for which she aspired.

This book is about the stigma of persons with severe mental illness. What we have taken for granted, up to this chapter, is a definition of what exactly is mental illness and who lives with mental illness. Sorting out who does and does not have a mental illness seems like such an easy task.

● *Psychotics to the left; neurotics to the right.*

● *You're mentally ill; you're normal.*

● *Insane people are obvious!*

However, when we take a closer look at these assumptions, we find that simple definitions distinguishing those with mental illness from those without allude us.

Seeking a Definition of Mental Illness

Although there are agreed upon "dictionaries" that define mental illness (in the United States this dictionary is the Fourth Edition of the *Diagnostic and Statistical Manual of Mental Disorders*, also known as the DSM-IV), there is no single manual that allows the psychiatrist to clearly divide a group into those with mental illness and those without. This is not meant to say we should throw out books like the DSM-IV. Rather, there is no clear resource that would help us answer the question posed at the beginning of this chapter:

> *"Who among Marie, Bennett, Emil, and Betsy has a mental illness?"*

In part, that's because in this chapter we are using the term "mentally ill" as a social label that differs from the very specific diagnoses that are included in the DSM-IV. As a social label, mental illness suggests a cohesive group of people that differs from the "norm." Like Black and White, or Male and Female, we often assume that Mentally Ill and Normal are clearly identifiable groups.

Researchers in cultural psychology, who study minority groups, have struggled with this problem—identifying ways to distinguish members of ethnic groups from the majority. They have focused on questions like "What is the best method to distinguish among members of white, black, and other ethnic groups?" Some insights from this area may be relevant for distinguishing among people who have a mental illness and those who do not. Borrowing strategies from cultural psychology is especially fitting given that many proponents of empowerment for persons with mental illness view their disability as the result of prejudicial forces that are similar to those experienced by ethnic minorities.

Research Strategies from Cultural Psychology

One of the assumptions underlying any kind of classification is that the human population comprising everyone is heterogeneous; namely, it is made up of a vast number of diverse groups. Some sense can be made out of this heterogeneity by dividing the population into meaningful subgroups. For example, the American population might be divided into ethnic subgroups that include African Americans, Anglo Americans, Asian Americans, Latinos, and Native Americans. Such subdivisions are thought to represent theoretically meaningful distinctions. In other words, African Americans and Latinos are *really* different from each other; this difference is not based on erroneous perceptions of some biased researcher. The division between subgroups is defined by objective criteria which describe mutually exclusive groups. Such criteria that have been used to distinguish cultural subgroups include *genealogy* (what was the ethnic background of your blood relatives), physical features (for example, skin color), and endorsement of various cultural practices (preferences in music or literature). Using these data, a person is clearly assigned to one ethnic group (Simon is African American because his parents were African, he has black skin, and he prefers music and literature that is labeled African) to the exclusion of another (he's not Asian).

In like manner, perhaps the population could be divided into groups of persons with and without mental illness based on some criterion that applies to the former group but not the latter. One criterion frequently used to differentiate people with mental illness from those without is a *history of mental health care*. But how do we define "mental health care?" At its narrowest, persons with mental illness might be described as individuals who have had repeated hospitalizations and a long course of medication to ameliorate psychiatric symptoms. Marie is an example. Broader classifications might include individuals who need relatively short hospital stays and brief medication regimens to address transient mental illnesses. Emil requires medications but is able to avoid hospitalization; does he have a mental illness?

At what point would "an experience with mental health providers" not be included in the definition of persons with mental illness? Are visits to a psychiatrist for psychotropic medication sufficient? And what about psychotherapy; are individuals who have participated in some kind of therapy considered persons with mental illness? Given that the vast majority of the American population will eventually see a mental health professional for treatment of some kind, defining person with mental illness based on *any* experience with professionals would include everyone in what was assumed to be the relatively rare group of persons with mental illness.

Self identification   Cultural psychologists have realized that the assumption about classification systems and mutually exclusive groups may be wrong, at least when using objective data to verify different groups. We suspect that many persons were dissatisfied with our prior assumptions about Simon, namely, if he is African American, he cannot also be Asian. Some people have objective attributes and lineage which qualify them for more than one ethnic group. Famed golfer Tiger Woods, for example, views himself as both African and Asian American. Moreover, assigning people to groups based on objective data ignores the importance of self-identification. It is probably more meaningful for an individual to call him or herself African American than to show objective attributes and ancestral lines believed to be consistent with that group. Therefore, at its simplest definition, members of a specific ethnic group are individuals who *identify themselves* as part of that group. Similarly, persons with mental illness may be those who identify themselves as such.

Self-identification assumes that cultural groupings are described by common values and beliefs such that individual members can reliably decide whether these characteristics describe them. These can be distinguished into positive values and beliefs that represent one's group and negative experiences that may result from hostile interactions with majority cultures. For example, Table 3.1 lists several positive and negative attributes that have commonly been used to describe the African American experience. Lists such as this one are developed by focus groups comprising individuals from the specific culture who are asked to list fundamental characteristics of their heritage. Persons might then use these values and beliefs to rate themselves regarding their cultural identity.

Table 3.1

Some Positive and Negative Experiences and Beliefs Endorsed by African Americans and Persons with Mental Illness as Characteristic of Their Groups.

AFRICAN AMERICAN	PERSONS WITH MENTAL ILLNESS
POSITIVE EXPERIENCES AND BELIEFS	
Strong work and achievement ethic	
Highly supportive extended family	
Strong religious orientation	
Greater acceptance of gender equality	
Sensitive to interpersonal matters	
NEGATIVE EXPERIENCES AND BELIEFS	
Less acceptance by majority group	The need for treatment conveys a sense of powerlessness
Fewer cultural role models in high-ranking government and business positions	Difficulties in "qualifying" for housing
	Lack of work opportunities
Negative stereotypes including beliefs about danger, ambition, and intelligence	Social isolation
	Exploited for entitlements
	Treatment resistance due to previous bad experiences gets reframed as "noncompliance"

To our knowledge, a list of positive beliefs and negative experiences that are characteristic of persons with mental illness has not been developed. However, a survey of the literature written by mental health advocates has yielded some frequently discussed experiences with which persons identify; these are also listed in Table 3.1. Interestingly, the characteristics of persons with mental illness seem to be dominated by negative experiences; mostly experiences that result from stigma and an overly-restrictive mental health system. Unlike identification with ethnic groups, it is not some positive experience that leads to identifying oneself as having a mental illness. Persons with mental illness do not have the well-developed culture that distinguishes minority groups, nor do they share a heritage marked by a unique lore or life view. Rather, it seems to be negative experiences with the majority culture, including mental health providers, that led to personal identification. Hence, the analogy of persons with mental illness being like ethnic minorities may be limited. Only the person's sense of displeasure with the majority is shared with other cultural groups.

Do You Identify Yourself as Mentally Ill?

According to the previous discussion, one answer to "Who is a person with mental illness?" is *people who say they have a mental illness*. Let us consider two different ways in which this formula may play out.

Remember Marie? She is now 32 years old and has had more than a dozen years of struggling with schizophrenia. Despite this disability, things are working out well: no hospitalizations in five years, working a good job, keeping a nice home, and living with a supportive husband. By many persons' standards, she has beat her mental illness and recovered. Still, Marie frequents mutual help groups where she provides support to peers who are struggling with more acute problems related to their illness. She is also an outspoken advocate against stigma. She testifies at government hearings where she identifies herself as a person with mental illness who is outraged by the disrespectful images of mental illness that are rampant in our society. *Marie is a person who identifies herself as having a mental illness.*

John Henry has a very similar history to Marie. He has struggled with schizophrenia since he was 19. He is now 32, married, and working a great job in a law office. He has not been hospitalized in five years and almost no one at work or in his social circle knows about his illness. John Henry wants it that way. Not only does he choose not to let others know about his past, he does not view himself as a person with mental illness. "I'm a complex being with only a very small piece of me having to do with mental illness." *John Henry is a person who does not identify himself as having a mental illness.*

The focus of the question here is not whether persons with mental illness *should* publicly label themselves as having mental illnesses. Openly disclosing one's experiences with mental illness is a complex decision that each person needs to make for him or herself. (Some strategies that help persons make the decision about disclosure are discussed in Chapter 5.) The point for discussion here is how the person responds to the question of self-identification; yes or no, do I view myself as having a mental illness? In the above example, two persons with the same experiences view themselves and their mental illness differently. Marie thinks it is a significant part of herself. John Henry denies that mental illness is central to his core. Let's take a closer look at each of these responses.

I'm Not a Person with Mental Illness!

As we concluded above, some people argue that mental illness is a significantly different kind of group from other stigmatized peoples such as African Americans. African Americans have an honorable heritage; black leaders encourage their children to actively embrace it. One way to challenge racial stereotype is for people to openly wear their history and ancestry, to shout out their membership in a stigmatized group. "I'm black and I'm proud of it!" The more persons who identify themselves as black, and let the rest of the world know of their honorable background, the faster the walls of prejudice will come tumbling down.

Perhaps, so some people believe, membership in the group of persons with mental illness is different in this regard. Rather than embracing and declaring one's membership in the club of mental illness, it seems that the purpose of the entire mental health care system is to move people OUT of this group. Treatment, rehabilitation, and support programs are designed to help people overcome their mental illness. According to some definitions, recovery means "I'm not mentally ill any more!" Persons influenced by this perspective do not choose to identify themselves as having a mental illness.

Let's consider this point another way. Identity is the way someone speaks about him or her self. Identity reflects answers to the "Who am I?" question. In response to this question, John Henry said, "I am male, African American, working in a law office, a college grad, married, and enjoying life." Nowhere in this definition does he respond with an "I am" statement that includes mental illness.

Psychologists recognize that a person's identity is drawn from all of his or her life experiences. Some of these experiences are viewed as central to the "Who I am" questions: work status ("I'm a legal assistant."), educational accomplishments ("I'm college educated."), marital status ("I'm happily married.") and recreational pursuits ("I love golf!"). People often ignore negative experiences as part of the "Who am I?" question. They may ignore such statements as "I'm a high school drop out" or "I couldn't make it in the Army." Persons who do not choose to identify themselves as having a mental illness are not recognizing their experiences with psychiatric disability as central to questions regarding self identity.

Isn't this denial?   There is evidence that suggests significant numbers of persons with schizophrenia and other severe mental illnesses lack insight into their illness. They are unable to understand their diagnosis or report how psychotic symptoms are abnormal.

*"Even though I hear voices, I don't halluci-
nate."*

*"There is nothing wrong in believing I am
the son of God."*

Moreover, these persons frequently are unaware how
their psychiatric illness and psychotic symptoms undermine life goals and cause significant disabilities. They
are unable to make the connection between an inability
to keep a job, build meaningful relationships, and keep a
home with one's psychotic symptoms or mood disorder.
Research suggests that lack of awareness in their disease is not due to poor motivation alone. It is an incorrect assumption to believe that people with mental illness just don't want to admit they have a mental illness.
Rather, this lack of insight may be related to a primary
biological deficit of the illness (some researchers believe
under functioning of the frontal lobes of the cerebrum).

Many mental health professionals conclude that
persons need to have insight into their illness. Without
this insight, they cannot participate fully in their illness
or make informed decisions about their future. Hence,
some clinicians might say that not including mental illness in one's identity is a sign of the illness and likely to
worsen outcome.

*"Persons with mental illness should admit
they have one!"*

In fact, a key purpose of therapy is to confront persons
with mental illness with their disease and the limitations
it imposes.

We need to keep in mind, however, that awareness of one's symptoms—insight into one's disease—is
not the same as identifying with that disease. Consider
this parallel example. Almost everyone has had an experience with an illness that has laid them up in bed for a
week or more. Days later, they are aware how the illness made them weak, interfered with work and family
obligations, and dominated their life. They are also
aware that they better heed these warning signs if they
are going to avoid a relapse. "I am going to watch my
diet, get more sleep, and avoid stress." Just because they
have this awareness does NOT mean they are an
invalid. "I'm a sick person." This kind of illness does not
lead to changing one's self-image.

In a similar vein, just because someone is or is
not aware of their psychiatric symptoms does not mean
they should say, "I am a person with mental illness!"
There is no evidence of which we are aware that shows
persons with mental illness need to identify with mental
illness to have a successful outcome. Let us reiterate an
earlier point however. While there is not research that
suggests persons with mental illness must identify with
their disability, there is research that suggests people
who are aware of the extent of their symptoms and disabilities are likely to be more successful in the pursuit
of their life goals.

Is this semantics or does this distinction really
matter? Health care advocates for the past two decades
have been encouraging persons to distinguish between
their symptoms and their identity. They have been making this assertion for all sorts of disabilities (blindness,
hearing impairments, paraplegia), not just mental illness.
Two key reasons support this distinction. First, persons

are better able to address problems related to distinct symptoms than difficulties with who the person essentially is. Medical and psychological science has had immense success in changing symptoms and improving behaviors. Who we essentially are seems to defy this kind of change! Second, this kind of distinction leads to greater hope. Persons who are optimistic about their future can better manage their disease and are more likely to overcome their disabilities.

I'm a Person with Mental Illness!

The above discussion may lead the reader to think that excluding mental illness from one's identity is the best course. Hence, John Henry is adopting a better view of his psychiatric experience than Marie. Marie is hanging on to her past and needs to give it up, to move on in life. Others would argue that it is not wise for persons to ignore an important part of who they are, be that experience positive or negative. Being in touch with one's personal heritage is essential for understanding the history of his or her life that, in turn, is necessary for making changes en route to life goals.

Consider if the widely accepted goal was to not identify with a minority group; for example, to support self-identification in race relations. About 30 years ago, "color blindness" was circulated as a way to deal with racial diversity. According to this view, the best way to surpass differences between black and white was to ignore differences in skin color, cultural heritage, and history. We are all of one bond, so the theory went; only our commonalities should be acknowledged. While in principle, this message seemed constructive and tried to promote a melting pot ideal, in reality it led to further repression. Discussion of commonalities typically reflected the majority: European preferences in culture, history, literature, and art. In the process, African, Asian, and other views were benignly suppressed. Advocates for ethnic groups now realize this colorblind message actually created as much harm as it blended groups. Now, advocates encourage persons to proudly embrace their ethnic heritage. This would seem to be a justification for a person identifying with mental illness.

But wait a minute. We argued earlier that the experience of mental illness with stigma could not be compared to ethnic groups. In part, we based this on the comparison outlined in Table 3.1. Unlike persons of color, persons with mental illness seem to lack any affirmative aspects that define them. We found it difficult to identify any disabled group who embraced its disability as a positive force. Until about five years ago, that is, when CBS' 60 Minutes news magazine ran a story about the cochlear implant. It is an electronic device which, when surgically inserted, can radically improve hearing in people who are deaf. The interesting part of the story was not the rave reviews from parents whose children benefited from the implant. Rather, memorable was the rage from members of the deaf community who believed the cochlear implant was robbing them of their dignity. They believed that being deaf was no less a competent way of being than, for example, being black. Hearing impairments was not a problem for them within their community; they have a way of communicating (sign language) which permits the full range of expression. Embracing sign language is as noble an effort as enjoying African music or history. Sign language was the cultural experience that positively defined them.

To our knowledge, there has yet to be a similar movement in the mental illness community. Few persons admit that psychosis is an alternative, fruitful lifestyle, one to be respected. Not many advocates believe that medication, which rids the person of voices and delusions, is robbing the mental illness community of an essential way of being. Nevertheless, parallels between the deaf community and persons with mental illness remain. There are aspects to the experience of mental illness, and sharing this experience with peers, that defines who the person is. Admitting this, and acknowledging it to the rest of the world, may significantly enhance the person's self-esteem.

This kind of self-identification may also help people to further define their role in society. This point is more thoroughly discussed in Chapter 5—To Disclose or Not to Disclose. Public identification of oneself as having a mental illness helps people recognize peers with whom they can share their experiences. This kind of support helps people weather the storms of stigma and discrimination.

Labels: consumer, survivor, ex-patient.
Persons who identify themselves as currently having, or having had, a mental illness frequently adopt one of three labels summarized in Table 3.2. "Consumer" defines mental illness in terms of one's use of the mental health system. Typically, individuals who refer to themselves as consumers use such services as inpatient stays, crisis intervention, residential and vocational rehabilitation, and management of medications for psychoses and other severe disorders.

Table 3.2
Some Labels that Have Been Used to Respectfully
Refer to Persons with Mental Illness

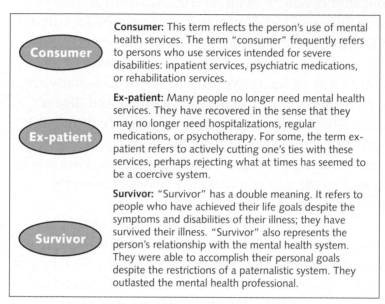

Consumer: This term reflects the person's use of mental health services. The term "consumer" frequently refers to persons who use services intended for severe disabilities: inpatient services, psychiatric medications, or rehabilitation services.

Ex-patient: Many people no longer need mental health services. They have recovered in the sense that they may no longer need hospitalizations, regular medications, or psychotherapy. For some, the term ex-patient refers to actively cutting one's ties with these services, perhaps rejecting what at times has seemed to be a coercive system.

Survivor: "Survivor" has a double meaning. It refers to people who have achieved their life goals despite the symptoms and disabilities of their illness; they have survived their illness. "Survivor" also represents the person's relationship with the mental health system. They were able to accomplish their personal goals despite the restrictions of a paternalistic system. They outlasted the mental health professional.

Some persons wish to be referred to as "ex-patients." This title clearly states that the person, while once struggling with mental illness, no longer needs such services. Ex-patient sometimes means the person has cut his or her relationship with the mental health system. Many people who use terms like ex-patient have experienced the mental health system as being coercive, unnecessarily restricting their life opportunities. People identify themselves as ex-patients in reaction to this mentality.

The term "survivor" actually has a double meaning that parallels the distinction made by ex-patients. On one hand, survivors are people who have overcome the symptoms and disabilities of their illness. Like the rest of the population, survivors are living their lives and accomplishing personal goals as they are encountered. On the other hand, survivors are persons who have beaten the barriers put up by a stigmatizing mental health system. In this case, they have survived a hostile treatment system.

Consumers, ex-patients, and survivors have formalized their existence into tangible organizations. They include such groups as the Mental Patients Liberation Project, the National Association of Psychiatric Survivors, On Our Own, the Anti-Insane Asylum Association, the Insane Liberation Front, and the Network Against Psychiatric Assault (specific information about groups like these is provided at the end of this book in *Learn More About It*). The role in which these kinds of advocacy and self-help organizations play in dealing with stigma is thoroughly discussed in Chapter 6, *Seven Ways to Foster Personal Empowerment*. The point here is that groups like these serve a very real need for a large group of people who identify themselves as having a mental illness. Namely, to address the concerns that have emerged as the result of their experiences with mental illness, the treatment system, and a sometimes hostile community.

Self-Identification is Not a Yes-No Question

We may have erroneously given the idea that identifying oneself as having a mental illness is a black and white decision. You either group yourself with others who have mental illness or you don't. Actually, the decision is a bit more gray. On some issues persons may identify with mental illness entirely (for example: the haunting impact of depression, dealing with the side effects of medication) while on other issues they do not (anger with a restrictive mental health system.) Moreover, ways in which we identify ourselves with mental illness change over time. Mental illness may have different significance to us depending on whether psychiatric disabilities are still present or whether a person has recently experienced the stigma of mental illness. We discuss the ways in which self-disclosure and personal identification vary over time in Chapter 5, *To Disclose or Not to Disclose.* We reviewed this point here merely to remind the reader of the further difficulties of labeling people.

In Summary: There are No Normal and Abnormal Groups

There is no litmus test, no clear marker, that allows us to sort the human race into those with mental illness and those who are without. We end this chapter, therefore, with the realization that there is no clean answer to the question that began it: Who does and who does not have a mental illness? Hence, the notion that there is an abnormal group of people that is easily distinguished from the rest of the world may not be true. Think how significant this statement is! Stigma rests on the assumption that persons with mental illness out there are clearly different from the rest of us. The stereotypes and prejudice of psychiatric stigma apply to these easily marked people.

What happens when we realize that this group does not really exist?... that there are no external markers that say Marie and Bennett have mental illnesses, Emil and Betsy do not?... that those "weird looking" people on city streets might just be poor, or drunk, or artists, or crooks, and not necessarily have mental illness? What happens? The foundation on which stigma is built erodes.

On A Personal Note

Who has a mental illness? This is not an abstract question for the authors of this book. In different ways, we have both struggled with this topic. Bob Lundin has grappled with mental illness for more than 20 years, with a history that is in many ways like Marie's (Bob's experiences are thoroughly discussed in Table 7.2, an example of a person's story that counters stereotypes about mental illness). He has been alternately diagnosed with bipolar illness and schizoaffective illness. Despite several hospitalizations, and about 15 years when Bob's life was ravaged by the symptoms and disabilities that result from these disorders, he has mastered his illness and now lives a full life. He is manager of the University of Chicago Center for Psychiatric Rehabilitation publications arm. He has championed the Awakenings Art Show, a collection of consumer artists from the Chicago area. And, central to our point here, Bob has decided to identify himself as a person with mental illness. He is out of the closet to let the world know that people like him make it!

The authors
share a golf
lesson:
Bob Lundin on
the left and Pat
Corrigan on the
right.

Are they
mentally ill?

Figure 3.1

Pat Corrigan has a history with mental illness
that is somewhere between Emil and Betsy. During college, he showed the signs of major depression and hypo-
mania. Despite some significant emergencies, he was
able to stay out of the hospital with the support of family, friends, mental health professionals, crisis programs,
and psychiatric medication. Nevertheless, his struggle
with mental illness took its toll. During a five year period, Pat dropped in and out of college and jobs, moving
repeatedly in the process, all in an effort to deal with his
depression and related symptoms. Despite this past, Pat
does not identify himself with mental illness. No doubt,
his professional interests in research and practice related to psychiatric disability and rehabilitation resulted
from his own experiences. Until now, however, Pat has
rarely discussed his own experiences with mental illness
in public.

Perhaps the pressure for mental health professionals (Pat is a licensed clinical psychologist) to seem
above the fray of mental illness has led to some of this

reluctance. Moreover, Pat has always felt that his struggles with mental illness were not as severe as the experiences that people like Bob had. Putting his experiences at their level might somehow lessen the stories of others. Finally, Pat believes that mental illness was only a small part of his life's past. Hence, while he might include his experiences with mental illness as part of the "I am" statements that describe Pat (I am a person who has been overwhelmed by depression. I am a person who has had to live with mental illness.), these kind of statements are far down on a list of ways in which he would describe himself. In some ways, Pat's identification with mental illness is much grayer and variable over time.

Like Marie, Bennett, Emil, and Betsy, Bob and Pat have lived with mental illness in various forms. And like them, who has a mental illness and how does one struggle with the stigma related to it are not questions that pose simple answers.

Chapter 4

Dealing with the Pain of Self-Stigma

> *"Let our first act every morning be to make the following resolve for the day: I shall not fear anyone on earth. I shall fear only God. I shall not bear ill will toward anyone. I shall not submit to injustice from anyone. I shall conquer untruth by truth. And in resisting untruth I shall put up with all suffering."*
>
> Mahatma Gandhi

In Chapter 2, we listed the various ways in which disrespectful attitudes and behaviors from the public destroy the life goals of persons with mental illness. Self-stigma delivers another equally wicked blow to this group. Being immersed in a society that perpetuates disrespectful images of mental illness, many persons with psychiatric disabilities *believe* these images.

> *"Everybody can't be wrong. Persons with mental illness must be morally weak."*

And once accepting this about mental illness, persons turn the belief on themselves.

> *"If persons with mental illness are morally weak, and I have a mental illness, then I must be bad."*

Reasoning like this is *self-stigma*. Many people with mental illness accept negative stereotypes and apply these stereotypes to themselves. In this chapter, we review the various ways which self-stigma haunts persons with mental illness. We then review some strategies which persons might use to deal with this kind of experience.

Self-Stigma and Franklin Goodman

Consider how self-stigma worsened the plight of Franklin Goodman. Despite the seemingly "good" intentions of his mother, ex-employer, and mental health care team, Franklin ended up out of a job, out of his apartment, and removed from his friends. After several weeks of failure, he begins to wonder whether they weren't right.

> *"Maybe I'm not able to care for myself. Dr. Hampton and my mom couldn't both be wrong. All that time working at the store, I was fooling myself. I'm nothing more than a psych patient. I should just accept that I'll never make it on my own, that I'll need a case manager for the rest of my life."*

Consider the impact of self-stigma, on top of the loss of opportunities that resulted from Franklin's hospitalization. If he is ever going to get back to work and live on his own, Franklin will need self-confidence and resolve. Instead, self-stigma has him buying into all the stereotypes about mental illness. His self-esteem is undermined:

"I'm nothing more than a mental case."

How can he hope to rebound in the future? His expectations are dismal:

"I should just accept that I'll never make it on my own. I'll need a case manager for the rest of my life."

Not only that, self-stigma robbed him of his past successes. Instead of viewing his years working and living independently as victories, he now says they are pipe dreams.

"Dr. Hampton and my mom couldn't both be wrong. All that time working at the store, I was fooling myself."

This kind of thinking is going to lead Franklin to the depths of self-doubt and depression. He must now overcome this, as well as the stigmatizing attitudes of his mother and mental health care team, to get back on his own once again.

Self-Stigma Assessment

Before discussing how self-stigma impacts persons, we provide a brief self-test. Readers should answer the questions in Table 4.1 to determine whether they beat themselves up with stigma. Alternatively, readers might administer this test to family members, clients, or peers who may struggle with self-stigma. The key for the test as well as the interpretation guidelines can be found on the next page. Complete the test fully before reviewing the key.

The test was divided into two sections. Section A determines whether readers identify themselves as individuals with past or current mental illness. Persons who have no history of mental illness, or who admit to no diagnosis or problems with psychiatric disability, are not likely to suffer from psychiatric stigma. This is not meant to imply that denying one's mental illness is a strategy for dealing with self-stigma. Rather, we are only alluding to the obvious: people who do not believe they have a mental illness are not likely to stigmatize themselves. Hence, if you did not answer yes to the statement in Section A, or are unaware of your diagnosis or disabilities, then you probably are not bothered by self-stigma.

Section B of the self-test provides two scores. The MI Stigma score represents how much you stigmatize others with mental illness. High scores on this scale (greater than 32) suggest you are prejudiced against mental illness and are likely to discriminate against persons with psychiatric disability. You would benefit from anti-stigma classes (see Chapters 7 and 8). The Self-Stigma score indicates the degree to which you turn

Table 4.1
Self-Stigma Assessment Scale

Section A

I currently, or in the past, have struggled with a mental illness.

(check one)

☐ yes ☐ no

If no, STOP here and proceed to the Interpretation Guide on the next page.

If yes, what was the diagnosis? _____

What problems or disabilities did you have as a result of this mental illness?

_____   _____

_____   _____

_____   _____

Section B

Now rank how much you agree with the following statements using this agreement scale.

strongly disagree	disagree	neither agree nor disagree	agree	strongly agree
1	2	3	4	5

_____ 1. Persons with mental illness are morally weak.

_____ 2. I am morally weak because I have a mental illness.

_____ 3. Persons with mental illness can't care for themselves.

_____ 4. I am unable to care for myself because I have a mental illness.

_____ 5. Persons with mental illness are dangerous and could snap at any minute.

_____ 6. I'm dangerous and could snap at any minute because I have a mental illness.

_____ 7. Persons with mental illness are no different than children.

_____ 8. I'm no different than a child because I have a mental illness.

_____ 9. Persons with mental illness can't handle responsibility.

_____ 10. I can't handle responsibility because I have a mental illness.

_____ 11. Who would want to live next to a person with mental illness?

_____ 12. Who would want to live next to a person like me with mental illness?

_____ 13. Everyone can plainly see persons with mental illness are weird.

_____ 14. Everyone can plainly see I'm weird because I have a mental illness.

_____ 15. Persons with mental illness are not worth the investment of time and resources.

_____ 16. I'm not worth the investment of time and resources because I have a mental illness.

Table 4.1 (cont.)
Self-Stigma Assessment Scale

Interpretation Guide for the Self-Stigma Assessment Scale

Section A

Self-stigma will have no impact on you if you have no current or past history of mental illness or do not admit to its impact. Hence, if you answered NO to the statement "I currently, or in the past, have struggled with a mental illness.", then self-stigma will have no impact on you. Moreover, if you are unaware of your diagnosis or believe that mental illness resulted in no problems or disabilities, then self-stigma will not likely hurt you either.

Section B

Scoring:

	Box 1		**Box 2**
Add up the scores of all the ODD numbered items and enter the total in Box 1.		Then add up all the EVEN numbered items and enter the total in Box 2.	
	MI Stigma		**Self-Stigma**

The total in Box 1 represents your tendency to stigmatize persons with mental illness. Scores in Box 1 that are greater than 32 suggest you stigmatize mental illness and are likely to blame persons with mental illness for their problems and disabilities. If you are an MI stigmatizer, make sure you read Chapters 7 and 8 to learn ways to change your attitudes and behaviors towards persons with mental illness.

The total in Box 2 represents your tendency for self-stigma, or how tough you will be on yourself because of your mental illness. Scores in Box 2 that are greater than 32 suggest you self-stigmatize and that you beat yourself up because you have a mental illness. Moreover, if the score in Box 2 is greater than the score in Box 1, you stigmatize yourself MORE than you stigmatize others because of mental illness. In either case, please read the remainder of Chapter 4 for ways to deal with self-stigma.

---

stigma against yourself and internalize negative statements about mental illness. High scores on this scale (greater than 32) mean you beat yourself up with self-stigma. You may need to learn alternative ways to handle stigmatizing self-statements before they overwhelm you. The strategies in the rest of this chapter are for you.

A note about using self-assessments.

The self-assessments included in this book—The Self-Stigma Assessment and the Personal Empowerment Self-Assessment Scale in Chapter 6—are provided to help persons understand themselves better. Sometimes, both test takers and professionals make the "grand error of truth" in using assessment information. They assume that if a test says so, then it must be true.

> *"I didn't think I self-stigmatized. But I scored higher than 32 so I must disapprove of myself."*

This kind of view is further compounded by concerns of self-doubt.

> *"I must be really screwed up if I was not even aware how much I hated myself."*

And self-doubt can lead to more self-stigma and more reason to give up control of one's life.

> *"I'm totally out of touch with myself. No wonder I'm such a bad person. I need a counselor to tell me these things."*

Information in these tests are meant to HELP people consider issues of self-stigma and empowerment. The final gauge of whether test information is right or wrong is the person taking the test. If the information makes sense or helps the person to stop and think over an issue, then it is probably useful feedback which the person may wish to heed. But, if test results seem to come out of left field and do not reflect the person's experience, then the information may be incorrect. Some tests just don't work right for some people. In these cases, it may be best to ignore the information altogether.

One final point about the assessments used in this book. Researchers spend many years developing tests that are reliable and valid. Unfortunately, these kinds of tests are frequently not useable by persons with mental illness; they tend to be cumbersome to score and difficult to interpret. Instead, we provide assessments that can be easily self-administered, scored, and interpreted. These measures are based on research conducted by investigators at our University of Chicago research center as well as by other experts in the field. Nevertheless, we encourage users to be cautious in interpreting the information provided by the self-assessments.

The Depth and Breadth of Self-Stigma

Self-stigma can be defined fairly easily. It is simply agreeing with the negative attitudes about mental illness and turning them in against one's self. As outlined in Table 4.1, these take the form of "I am" statements.

- *I really am unable to care for myself.*
- *I'm dangerous and could snap at any minute.*
- *I'm no different than a child.*

- *I can't handle responsibility.*
- *Don't give me money. I'll only blow it.*
- *I'm a bad person.*
- *Who would want to live next to a person like me?*
- *Everyone can plainly see I'm weird.*
- *I'm not worth the investment of time and resources.*
- *I have a weak personality.*

Note how the statements reflect several of the stereotypes and prejudices reviewed in Chapter 2. The difference here is that these statements do not represent an abstraction about other people. Rather, it's a personalized assertion about "me." Besides the self-test in Table 4.1, another way you can tell you self-stigmatize is by gauging your reaction to these ten statements. Persons who don't self-stigmatize tend to get angry at these statements.

> *"How could people believe this kind of rubbish! None of it is true."*

Conversely, people who self-stigmatize get sad or feel guilty after reading a list like this. It reminds them of the kind of comments they are hurting themselves with. These kinds of self-statements have a nasty impact on the person.

The Impact of Self-Stigma

Self-stigma has a broad and nasty impact on the person with mental illness which worsens the course of their disorder. Persons who self-stigmatize are likely to have more problems and disabilities with their mental illness than people who do not beat themselves up with statements like this. One reason is because people who self-stigmatize have poor self-esteem. Self-esteem means the person is confident that he or she is a good person. They basically have good intentions in life and mean to act on those intentions in a responsible manner. Think about persons who buy into self-stigma, however. They believe they are bad, or weak, or responsible for all of their troubles. They question their goals and have little confidence that they will act in a responsible manner.

> *"Not only am I less than normal people, I must be fundamentally bad."*

Many persons with low self-esteem believe they are not worthy: not worthy of their own respect, not worthy of recognition from others, and not worthy of support from peers.

> *"People are just wasting their time on me. I'll not amount to anything."*

This kind of feeling is accompanied by guilt. Persons search their life history to find out what they did wrong that brought on this damnation.

With the deprivation of self-esteem comes a loss of hope. Not only does the person believe they are not worthy of respect *now*, they believe things will not change in the future. Loss of hope and poor self-esteem feed each other in a continuous spiral, deepening over time. Persons with low self-esteem and little hope also lose confidence in their ability to succeed. This leads to a "why try?" attitude.

> *"Why try for a real job? Why try to live on my own? Why try to settle down and get married? I can't handle it. And if I get a job or a good place or a decent mate, I'll blow it."*

This kind of helpless and hopeless attitude affects the person's view of the world. Even successes are dismissed as quirks. Persons who self-stigmatize don't give themselves credit for their accomplishments. Instead, they attribute their successes to other people, while they see failure as their fault alone.

> *"I didn't get that job because of my abilities. They hired me because they wanted to hire a mental patient to show off to their friends."*

Self-stigma is truly crippling, undermining the person's abilities to pursue his or her goals and making each day another reminder of their unworthiness for being on this world.

Stereotype threat

Stigma can have an additional impact on oneself called "stereotype threat." Stanford psychologist Claude Steele argued that negative stereotypes undermine a person's identification with specific tasks (e.g., school, work, social interactions) and lessen the person's motivation to be successful in those tasks. Stereotype threat occurs when members of a stigmatized group (for example, African Americans, women, persons with schizophrenia) find themselves in a specific situation for which a negative stereotype applies. For example, a negative stereotype about African Americans suggests they are intellectually inferior and not likely to do well scholastically. Therefore, African Americans experiencing stereotype threat may feel anxious when faced with an achievement exam in school and perform poorly on the tests as a result. Over time, Blacks learn to not care about doing well on these kinds of tests.

> *"Why should I try to score well on the SAT? Everyone thinks I'll do poorly anyway."*

They no longer believe doing well in school is important.

Researchers at the University of Chicago have begun to study whether this principle applies to persons with mental illness. We wondered whether one of the reasons why persons with mental illness do poorly on cognitive tasks (for example, abilities to pay attention or remember) or fail to accomplish social roles—which of the following social roles have you achieved: competitive work, independent living, spouse, parent?—is because of stereotype threat. Stereotypes about persons with mental illness include the notion that they are not smart and are interpersonally incompetent. Persons with mental illness are as aware of these stereotypes as the rest of the population. After several years of hearing this, they are going to stop trying on cognitive tests.

> *"Why bother? Everyone thinks I'm a moron anyway!"*

They are going to give up on social tasks:

> *"No matter how well I do on the job,
> everyone is going to focus on my mis-
> takes."*

As a result, persons with mental illness will do poorly on these tasks even though they may be intellectually and socially capable of succeeding. Stereotype threat makes people look less competent than they are.

Stereotype threat is different than the kind of helpless and hopeless feelings that result from self-stigma. As the result of stereotype threat, people *disengage* from a certain task. After repeated notice that they are inept in a certain area, persons just don't care anymore. It's not that persons with mental illness are afraid of intellectual tasks, they just believe it's not important to them.

Is This Depression or Self-Stigma?

Many persons with severe mental illness are depressed; not just persons with major depression, but also persons with schizophrenia, those who abuse alcohol and other drugs, or individuals who suffer anxiety disorders. They have low self-esteem, feel hopeless and helpless, and give up on their goals. A full list of the signs and symptoms of depression is provided in Table 4.2. Note how several of these signs are similar to the pains experienced by persons who self-stigmatize. Moreover, persons who self-stigmatize often experience what mental health professionals call the vegetative signs of depression: not eating right, not sleeping right, or being fatigued. Like persons with depression, some who self-stigmatize are suicidal. This may show itself as being tired of living.

> *"I'd be better off dead than continue as a drag on my family and friends."*

Some persons who self-stigmatize may become very desperate and try to kill themselves. Clearly, self-stigma, like depression, can have serious consequences.

Table 4.2

The Signs and Symptoms of Psychiatric Depression Taken from the Fourth Edition of the Diagnostic and Statistical Manual of Mental Disorders (DSM-IV)

> Feels sad, tearful, or blue most of the time

> Lost interest or pleasure in most activities (I just don't enjoy anything anymore!)

> Feelings of worthlessness or excessive guilt

> Diminished ability to think clearly or concentrate

> Fatigue or loss of energy

> Frequent thoughts of death or suicide

> Not sleeping well or sleeping too much

> Not eating well or eating too much

> Not moving much (psychomotor retardation) or pacing a lot (agitation)

Given the similarity between depression and self-stigma, it may be unclear whether these signs represent a depression or the results of self-stigma. This distinction may be important to determine the best way to cope with each. Here are some strategies that help you tell the difference. One straightforward way to identify depression is when it occurs as the result of grief. Persons who experience a loss—a death of a loved one or sudden termination from a job—frequently mourn their loss and experience marked anguish. This kind of sadness typically goes away over time. Other persons have a biologically-induced depression; these persons experience severe depression, often for no apparent reason, as the result of imbalances in brain chemistry. One way to identify persons with biological depression is the repeated experience of depressive episodes. They might experience four to six weeks of deep sadness every year or two for decades. Still, other persons experience depression as the result of what they perceive to be a personal failure. They believe they are not as competent as others or are unable to reach their life goals, and they become sad. This kind of person is very similar to the individual who self-stigmatizes; they feel unworthy and hopeless about their future.

Many persons experience a mix of grief, biological depression, personal failure, and self-stigma. Some people, for example, suffer recurring depression due to brain biology and suffer periods of sadness due to perceived failures and self-stigma. This can lead to a chicken and egg question. Does biological depression cause self-stigma or do people who beat themselves up with stereotypes bring about relapses in biologically-based illnesses? Does grief lead to a sense of personal failure or are people who feel personally unsuccessful likely to experience grief more acutely? Although this may be an interesting question for researchers, deciding what came first is not essential for the person who is depressed and/or self-stigmatizes. Rather, they need to be mindful of the signs and symptoms of depression and self-stigma, seeking out help when these become overwhelming problems.

These various causes of depression—grief due to loss, brain biology, personal failure, and self-stigma—all respond well to help. Without this kind of intervention, persons risk continued sadness and a bleak future. Hence, the individual who self-stigmatizes, as well as all people with depression, may benefit from partnering with a mental health professional, peer counselor, or other helper in addressing these symptoms. All of these kinds of depression might significantly improve by taking anti-depressant medications, especially if the person is showing significant vegetative signs (not eating or sleeping well) or is contemplating suicide. Consulting with a psychiatrist may be useful. Moreover, persons who experience significant loss in life may benefit from grief counseling provided by the clergy or other pastoral counselors. Persons who struggle with depression due to perceived failure or self-stigma may benefit from talk-therapies and education efforts that challenge these notions. Some of these ways of coping are reviewed on the next several pages.

The purpose of this section is not to review the forms of depression and promote traditional therapies. Rather, the goal here is to point out to the reader the similarities between depression and self-stigmatizing. Both are potentially serious threats to persons and their goals. Both can be mended with appropriate interventions. One other point to keep in mind. Some of the so-called treatments for self-stigmatizing and related depression—like medication or talk therapy—can make self-stigma worse. Needing to see a psychiatrist might add to the person's conviction that they are unable to care for themselves and weaker than everyone else. We have only listed helping possibilities; it is up to the individual with self-stigma, and the person with depression, to decide what works best for him or her.

Some Strategies for Coping with Self-Stigma

Before reviewing ways to cope with self-stigma, here is an interesting point to consider. Research clearly shows that just because there are negative stereotypes about certain groups does not mean that persons from those groups usually agree with them or apply the stereotypes to themselves. For example, there are many disdainful images of African Americans in our history. Research suggests, however, that most black Americans do not agree with these stereotypes and do not view less of themselves as a result. They dismiss such statements like "blacks are lazy" as ignorance of the majority. Hence, applying this logic to mental illness, one might suspect that most persons with mental illness do not think less of themselves because of stereotypes about "psych patients." In fact, many persons with mental illness are able to keep from applying this stigma to themselves.

> *"Persons with mental illness are not all homicidal maniacs. And I'm not dangerous to society because I have mental illness."*

We do not mean to imply that these persons are not hurt by the scornful images of mental illness portrayed in the media and elsewhere. Rather we are saying that they neither agree with these images nor apply the stereotypes to themselves.

The point to remember is that having mental illness does not mean you *must* suffer self-stigma. Most persons with mental illness probably do not. If, however, you do fall victim to self-stigma, here are a couple of ways to beat it.

Table 4.3
Eight Myths and Corresponding Realities About Mental Illness

1   **Once crazy, always crazy. People don't get over it.** Long-term follow-up research suggests that many, many persons with the worst types of schizophrenia and other severe mental illness are able to live productive lives.

2   **All persons with mental illness are alike.** Persons with mental illness are as diverse a group of people as any other. Saying all persons with mental illness are similar is akin to saying all Latinos are the same. Not true!

3   **Severe mental illnesses are rare, just like lepers.** Actually severe mental illnesses like schizophrenia, manic-depression, and major depression may account for up to 8 to 10% of the population. That is about 640,000 people in a metropolitan area the size of Chicago, enough folks to fill Omaha, Nebraska and Des Moines, Iowa combined.

4   **The mentally ill are dangerous, one step away from a maniacal killing spree.** Very, very few people with mental illness ever murder someone. In fact, persons with mental illness are usually no more violent than the rest of the population.

5   **The mentally ill can never survive outside the hospital.** The vast majority of persons with mental illness live personally successful lives in their community.

6   **The mentally ill will never benefit from psychotherapy.** Carefully controlled research has shown that support and rehabilitation has significant impact on the lives of persons with mental illness.

7   **The mentally ill are unable to do anything but the lowest level jobs.** Persons with mental illness perform at all levels of work, just like the rest of the population.

8   **Bad parents and poor upbringing cause severe mental illness.** Schizophrenia and the other severe mental illnesses are biological diseases. They are caused by genetic or other embryological factors, not mom and dad.

This Table was adopted in part from an excellent paper by Courtney Harding and James Zahniser (1994) entitled Empirical Correction of Seven Myths About Schizophrenia With Implications for Treatment. The paper was published in the Acta Psychiatrica Scandinavica in Volume 90, Supplement 384, pages 140 to 146.

Learn More About Mental Illness to Counter Self-Stigma

There are many myths of mental illness which persons who self-stigmatize tend to believe. These are summarized in Table 4.3. Persons who self-stigmatize tend to agree with these myths and do not know the facts that contradict them. Self-stigma is weakened when people learn the research-based information which counters it. Chapter 8 reviews education strategies that help citizens change their attitudes abut mental illness. These strategies can be easily adapted to help persons with mental illness challenge their self-stigma. In this section, we briefly review these eight myths and facts that contradict them.

1. Once crazy, always crazy. People don't get over it.

Severe mental illnesses like schizophrenia and manic-depression were known as the "kiss-of-death" diagnosis. Once a person was so diagnosed, they were doomed; there was no getting over it. In fact, one of the great psychiatrists of the 20th century, Emil Kraepelin, believed that persons with schizophrenia inevitably end up demented, much like an elderly person with Alzheimer's Disease.

This issue has been studied carefully by several research teams in what is known as long-term follow-up studies. These researchers followed adults with manic-depression, schizophrenia, and other severe mental illnesses for 30 years or more. If Kraepelin was right, these persons should have ended up completely unable to take care of themselves, dependent on medication,

97

and tucked away on back wards. This is not, however, what researchers found. Rather they discovered the principle of thirds. About one third of the sample left hospitals and never turned back. They were able to achieve "normal" lives with no support from the mental health system. Another third left hospitals and were able to meet most of their life goals with support from family and counselors. The final third continued to struggle with their psychiatric disabilities. But even this final third did not have the horrible outcome predicted by Kraepelin. Very few required life-long hospitalization.

2. All persons with mental illness are similar

Another myth is that "they are all alike." Persons with mental illness all suffer the same foibles and all commit the same crimes. This, too, is wrong. Mental illness is only one characteristic that defines a person, just like skin color is only one attribute that describes African Americans. The similarity myth about mental illness is as false as saying all black people are alike or all women have the same goals. Citizens can only understand an individual by knowing their personal history and unique aspirations.

3. Severe mental illnesses are rare, just like leprosy

Persons with mental illness are scary because the disease is so rare. It's like leprosy in the Old Testament; God marked a handful of people with this disease because of their sins.

A quick review of the prevalence rates of mental illness suggests just the opposite. Severe mental illness is actually quite common. It is most likely that everyone knows someone who has severe mental illness. The citizen may not be aware of it because the person chooses not to disclose his or her psychiatric history. But research shows that people with schizophrenia, manic-depression, and major depression may account for up to 8 to 10% of the population. In a metropolitan area the size of Chicago that means 640,000 people are currently struggling with a severe mental illness. That is enough people to fill the cities of Omaha, Nebraska and Des Moines, Iowa combined. Severe mental illness is not rare.

4. The mentally ill are dangerous, one step away from a maniacal killing spree

This is probably the most damning myth: persons with mental illness are menacing and need to be locked away from society. There is a veritable rogue's gallery of murderers with mental illness that seem to support this falsehood: Theodore Kazinski (the Unabomber), John Hinkley (who shot President Reagan), David Berkowitz (the Son of Sam), Mark Chapman (John Lennon's killer), and Russell Weston, Jr. (the Capitol Hill assassin). Making the conclusion that all persons with mental illness are murderers based on evidence like this is a gross error in logic. It would be like concluding that all persons who wear fedoras are murderers because the Los Angeles police arrested three people last week wearing these hats. In truth, the vast majority of persons arrested, tried, and convicted for murder in the United States are NOT severely mentally ill. Very, very few persons with severe mental illness murder people or commit other serious crimes.

Still, a concerned citizen might retort, "But aren't all persons with mental illness dangerous, even if they don't kill?" The response here is somewhat complex. In general, persons with mental illness are no more violent than the rest of the population. Day in and day out, the person with schizophrenia is no more likely to harm someone than the average citizen. There are two exceptions to the rule.

● *Persons with mental illness who abuse drugs and alcohol are likely to be more violent than the rest of the population. Note, however, that this doesn't say anything unique about mental illness. Anybody—mentally ill or "normal"—who abuses drugs and alcohol is probably more violent than the rest of the citizenry.*

● *Persons with mental illness are more dangerous when symptoms flare up and they are in the emergency room. Keep in mind, however, that everybody in the ER— including those who are there for other physical illnesses—are frequently agitated and may be more violent than the average citizen.*

5. Persons with mental illness can never survive outside an asylum or hospital

This myth is a variation of the belief that persons with mental illness are not capable of living independently outside institutions. Sometimes, commentators point to the homeless problem as evidence that persons with mental illness cannot live on their own;

*"A failed mental health system has forced
the mentally ill into the streets. Homeless
shelters are full of maniacs and psychotics."*

This claim is false. Research finds no more than
40% of homeless persons as having mental illness. This
still seems high until two qualifiers are considered. A
large part of this group actually suffer alcoholism and
drug addictions, not the severe mental illnesses we have
been discussing here. Moreover, some of the persons in
the group may actually suffer *reactive* mental illness;
namely, they became depressed or anxious in reaction to
the homelessness. Less often do we find the person who
has a mental illness first and becomes homeless as a
result.

The long-term follow-up research shows that
more than two-thirds of persons with mental illness who
once had to live in state hospitals end up on their own
in the community. Moreover, research on community-
based rehabilitation shows the majority of persons in
that final third can live in their own homes and go to
some kind of work each day when provided intensive
support and counseling.

6. People with mental illness will never benefit from psychotherapy

Persons with mental illness are different than
everyone else. Only medication works on people with
mental illness. They do not benefit from psychotherapy
or interpersonal support because they are fundamentally limited in their ability to build relationships with
therapists.

This is also a myth. Research shows that persons with schizophrenia, manic-depression, and depression benefit from close working alliances with counselors who try to help them meet their life goals. They also receive great gains from peer support. There is some evidence that persons with mental illness do not benefit from insight-oriented therapies like psychoanalysis which investigates the childhood routes of their problems. But then, there is also ample evidence that these insight-oriented therapies do not provide much help for anyone, so this limitation is not unique to severe mental illness.

7. People with mental illness are unable to do anything but the lowest level jobs

At this point, the reader may acknowledge that persons with mental illness can live in the community. But there is still the myth that persons with severe mental illness can only work in sheltered workshops or entry level jobs like janitorial work or food service.

There are two things to keep in mind about this false statement. First, much of the population works in these entry-level jobs and are able to provide for themselves in the process. So, this belief, once again, is not unique to severe mental illness. Second, many persons with severe mental illness work in top-notch jobs. Schizophrenia and depression do not doom persons to the lower vocational rung. Table 4.4 lists persons with mental illness who are quite successful; the list includes notables from history as well as persons that are prominent today.

Table 4.4
A Sampling of Persons with Severe Mental Illness who Have
Successful Careers

PERSON	MENTAL ILLNESS	CAREER
Samuel Becket	Depression	Writer
Clifford Beers	Manic-Depression	Humanitarian
Menachem Begin	Depression	Israeli Prime Minister
Truman Capote	Depression	Writer
Winston Churchill	Depression	Prime Minister (U.K.)
Calvin Coolidge	Depression	U.S. President
Patti Duke	Depression	Actress
Daniel Fisher	Schizophrenia	Psychiatrist
Fred Frese	Schizophrenia	Psychologist
Phil Graham	Manic-Depression	Owner, Washington Post
Audrey Hepburn	Depression	Actress
Ernest Hemingway	Depression	Writer
Kay R. Jamison	Manic-Depression	Author and Researcher
Randall Jarrell	Manic-Depression	Poet
Vivien Leigh	Manic-Depression	Actress
John Lennon	Depression	Musician
Jack London	Depression	Writer
Robert Lowell	Manic-Depression	Poet
Robert Lundin	Schizoaffective	Author and Artist
Burgess Meredith	Manic-Depression	Actor
Thelonious Monk	Depression	Jazz Musician
John Forbes Nash	Schizophrenia	Nobel Laureate
Vaslav Nijinsky	Schizophrenia	Ballet Dancer
Richard Nixon	Depression	U.S. President
George Patton	Depression	U.S. General
Jackson Pollock	Depression	Artist
Diana Spencer	Depression	Princess of Wales
Rod Steiger	Depression	Actor
Mike Wallace	Depression	News Reporter
Tennessee Williams	Depression	Writer
Virginia Woolf	Manic-Depression	Writer

Lists like this may support another myth: although there are some persons with the spark of genius, this is a rare breed. Persons with mental illness, for the most part, still fail to obtain real jobs and successful careers. What Table 4.4 does not include are the thousands of lawyers, doctors, teachers, engineers, and business persons who also have severe mental illness.

8. Bad parents and bad upbringing cause severe mental illness

This myth is especially troubling to families. Some people believe persons with mental illness are born normal but become victims of mental illness because of bad parents. Hence, adults troubled by mental illness are walking witnesses to evil mothers and fathers. The bad parenting myth has its routes in the mental health professions. Sigmund Freud, and other psychoanalysts, believed that most mental illness is caused by bad parenting; in particular, a cold and uncaring mother. This mother was incapable of providing the love and support her child needed so the child grew up disturbed.

Now research has shown that severe mental illness is caused by biological factors, not parental error. Bad genes or misfortunes during pregnancy lead to mental illness. There is no evidence that the problems experienced by adults with schizophrenia, manic-depression, and depression can be traced back to childhood and bad parenting.

Reviewing myths to challenge self-stigma.

Reviewing these myths can help many persons with self-stigma change opinions about their mental illness. This kind of opinion-change-through-education program can be conducted in one-to-one therapy settings. Professional counselors can walk their clients through the myths in Table 4.3. This kind of effort can also be conducted in a group setting, where peers can

discuss their reactions to these myths. Perhaps an equally powerful way to review misconceptions about mental
illness is in a peer counseling or mutual help setting.
Persons with mental illness who have resolved their
reactions to self-stigma might lead peers through a discussion of the myths and facts of mental illness. Many
self-help and advocacy programs listed at the back of
this book have developed programs just like this.

Some persons might want additional information
about mental illness to challenge these facts. In Chapter
8, we extensively reviewed a variety of details about
mental illness that can be incorporated into an education program. Some persons with mental illness might
want to lead or participate in these programs to learn
more about the impact of their disability and effective
strategies for improving it.

Directly Countering Self-Stigmatizing Attitudes

Despite learning facts that counter myths, some
persons still beat themselves up with self-stigma.
Fortunately, there are ways to directly challenge these
hurtful attitudes, replacing them with beliefs that do not
undermine the person's self-esteem. This kind of
thought-changing approach, outlined in Table 4.5, was
originally developed by Aaron Beck and has been studied by researchers for more than 30 years. The interesting thing about this model is that its impact is much
broader than the negative impact of self-stigma. It
explains how irrational attitudes experienced by *everyone* lead to hurtful feelings.

Table 4.5
A Model Outlining the Negative Effects of Hurtful Attitudes

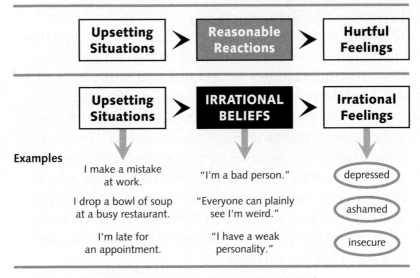

Examples

I make a mistake at work.	"I'm a bad person."	depressed
I drop a bowl of soup at a busy restaurant.	"Everyone can plainly see I'm weird."	ashamed
I'm late for an appointment.	"I have a weak personality."	insecure

The Two Truth Assumptions that Underlie Irrational Beliefs

> 1. Irrational beliefs must be true.

> 2. Because these beliefs are true, other people would agree with them.

Subsequent Assumptions About Changing Irrational Beliefs

> 1. We are more likely to give up irrational beliefs when we find out others, especially "respected" others, disagree with them.

> 2. Once we have challenged these beliefs, we should develop counters to use against them in the future.

As outlined in Table 4.5, Beck and others believed that hurtful feelings typically arise from reasonable reactions to upsetting situations. Reactions to situations are called "reasonable" when it is the kind of reaction that almost everyone would display.

- *A loved one dies and the person is deeply saddened.*

- *A patient is having surgery and is nervous.*

- *A customer is ignored by a waitress and is angry.*

Most people would respond to each of these situations with the corresponding hurtful feeling. It might be considered the reasonable emotional reply to these situations.

Sometimes people seem to respond with irrational emotions to situations. For example, Damita makes a mistake at work. She misfiles a customer's chart. As a result, she gets deeply depressed. Or, Leon spills a bowl of soup at the neighborhood diner. He becomes so embarrassed that he won't eat there the following month even though everyone from Bible study is going there for brunch. Both of these responses don't make sense, at least to the outside observer. Sure, Damita might be momentarily concerned about her mistake, but to become tearful and deeply sad? And it might be reasonable for Leon to be embarrassed about his accident at the diner, but to the point that several weeks later he won't go back because he is ashamed? These kinds of emotional responses seem irrational. Keep in mind that we are calling the emotional response irrational, not the person. Everyone has these kinds of irrational responses at one time or other in their life, not just persons with mental illness.

Wait a minute, how can emotional responses be irrational? Aren't they the automatic responses to situations? Grief after the death of a loved one is sincerely painful. Would Aaron Beck call this irrational?

107

Beck believed that some emotions were irrational or damaging when they were *extreme.* There is
nothing about grief (or sadness, or rage, or shame) by
itself that is damaging. In fact, having these "negative"
emotions allows humankind to appreciate the breadth
of our life experiences. Some events are joyful, others
are glum. However, any emotion taken to an extreme is
what Beck considered irrational or damaging. Extreme
means an emotion is experienced in too much depth
compared to the situation or for too long a period after.
The reasonable person would agree that deep depression in response to a clerical error is irrational. Grief
over the death of one's father is reasonable. Grief in
response to misfiling a record is not. The reasonable
person would concur that several months of shame after
the conviction for a bad crime might be reasonable.
Several weeks of embarrassment after spilling soup is
extreme.

The second line of Table 4.5 is the essential
insight of Beck's view. Irrational emotions do not occur
because of a situation; they occur because of a mediat-
ing belief. Damita did not get depressed because she
erred at work; she became sad because she somehow
learned in the past that work mistakes are more evidence that "she is a bad person." Put yourself in her situation. Being reminded that you are fundamentally no
good is going to make you depressed. (Many readers
will say this doesn't make sense. Of course it doesn't,
that's why Damita is being hampered by irrational
thoughts and feelings.) Leon's being ashamed does not
occur because he dropped the soup. It's because else-

where during his life, he has associated gaffes like this with the belief that he's weird. "Everyone can tell. I'm an oddball." Dropping the soup only reminds him of this belief and leads to feeling ashamed several days later.

Here is how Beck's theory is related to the central point of this chapter: **self-stigma is a type of irrational belief.** Lumping self-stigma into the same category as irrational beliefs normalizes the experience of self-stigma. Self-stigma is not something experienced just by crazy people. Everyone is plagued by these kinds of thoughts. In fact, the irrational beliefs used as examples in Table 4.5 –

● I'm a bad person;

● Everyone can plainly see I'm weird;

● I have a weak personality—

were borrowed from the list of self-stigma provided earlier in this chapter. Realizing that everyone beats themselves up with hurtful thoughts can be destigmatizing in its own right.

> *"You mean having this kind of self-stigma isn't proof I'm nuts? Everyone thinks this way at one time or another? That's a relief!"*

Moreover, grouping self-stigma with irrational beliefs provides the person with tools that have been shown to stop damage from these kinds of beliefs.

Assumptions about changing irrational beliefs.

Irrational beliefs and self-stigma are not created in a void. They are learned over the course of the person's life. They also rest on two Truth assumptions which, if challenged, help the person to better manage the irrational feelings which result from these beliefs. These assumptions are summarized at the bottom of Table 4.5. First, persons assume that all their beliefs are true; that's one reason why they can't ignore them. If the person who said, "Everyone can plainly see I'm weird." believed this was false, "There's nothing wrong with the way I look." he or she could easily ignore the statement and wouldn't feel ashamed.

Say this statement to yourself right now: "Everyone can plainly see I'm weird." Did you experience embarrassment or shame? No, because you think this kind of self-stigma is bunk. Persons who hurt themselves with self-stigma don't recognize the statement is wrong. It ranks on the same level as other statements of fact:

- *The sun will rise in the morning.*
- *Murderers are bad.*
- *I'm weird looking.*

The second assumption is that most reasonable people agree with the truth of these beliefs. Just as most people agree that the sun will rise tomorrow and murderers are evil, they would concur, if asked, that yes, "I'm weird looking!" This assertion—most people agree with the truth of a belief—echoes the statement made above. Namely, irrational thoughts do not develop in a vacuum. Take, for example, the "I am weird looking." statement. People learn at a young age from television, news stories, comic books, talk radio, and other media sources that persons with mental illness are poorly dressed, talk to themselves, eat garbage, and have nervous tics. We come to equate mental illness with looking weird in public. What happens then when a person is saddled with the mental illness label? He or she may believe that, like the rest of the world of persons with mental illness, they, too, look weird. They now have developed a self-stigma that is making them feel ashamed for no legitimate reason. Moreover, ask individuals who think they look weird whether they believe the rest of the world agrees, they likely would say, "Yes. It's obvious to me and to most everyone else."

Fortunately, persons can use these two truth assumptions to challenge irrational beliefs. What if people who believed an irrational thought found out that the rest of the world did not agree? Consider how Damita might feel if she found out that others did not concur that a filing error meant she was a bad person. Or, how might Leon change his reaction if he knew that his friends disagree that dropping a bowl of soup meant he looked weird? Or what might Franklin Goodman have thought if others challenged his assertion,

> *"I'm nothing more than a mental patient. I should just accept that I'll never make it on my own, that I'll need a case manager for the rest of my life."*

The best way to change irrational beliefs or self-stigmas is to test them out. Collect evidence that challenges the truth of an assumption. This can be done in several different ways.

1. Persons can check out whether the irrational belief is true by surveying friends, co-workers, and others. They would literally poll people: "Do you think I look weird because I'm mentally ill?" People should carefully consider who to include in this survey, asking people who are likely to be supportive, not individuals who might say mean things in retaliation.

> *"I think people in my book group are reasonable people. I'll ask them. No point trying this at work. Those guys wouldn't take it serious. They'd all rib me."*

2. Most people have personal mentors, individuals we believe have things figured out in life. These might be our pastors, an older brother, a wise friend, or a quiet co-worker. Asking these persons can be an especially powerful way to challenge irrational beliefs.

> *"Reverend, do you think all persons with mental illness are morally weak?"*

3. Sometimes irrational beliefs can be challenged by directly testing them. For example, Amy thought she, like most people with mental illness, was weird looking. To test this, she showed pictures of five acquaintances— two with mental illness and three without—to a group of co-workers, asking them to pick out the "weird looking people with mental illness." They couldn't do it, which helped to challenge the self-stigma that "I must be weird looking because I have a mental illness."

Even when people are able to undermine irrational thoughts by finding out others believe they are false, these irrational beliefs are stubborn. They tend to return to hurt the person in the future. Hence, individuals who have been able to challenge self-stigma and irrational beliefs need to develop *counters*. These are comebacks to the irrational beliefs that keep them in check.

- *I'm not bad because I misfiled that chart. It was a mistake like most people make.*

- *I don't have a weak personality because I was late for an appointment. Everyone is late once in a while.*

This kind of talking back to irrational beliefs provides control. It normalizes the event instead of letting it spiral into the kind of irrational and hurtful feelings that torment people. People frequently write the counters down on a small card and keep it in their wallet. Then, they can pull out the card when they are beating themselves up with self-stigma and remind themselves that the stigma is false.

> *"People don't look at me and say I look weird because I have a mental illness. Most people do not even know my history with mental illness."*

Are we rational beings?

This kind of approach to changing irrational beliefs and self-stigma is frequently criticized. Humans are not rational beings, we are sentient organisms that react to situations based on our emotions, our wants, and our whims. This kind of talk about rational and irrational thoughts ignores our feeling and caring core, trying to replace it with a view of people as computers. People are more than the sum of their thoughts. This kind of notion only further stigmatizes people.

We agree that this concern further diminishes a fully rounded picture of persons. By saying persons have rational and irrational thoughts and can control those thoughts through checking out the experiences of their peers, we do not mean to deny the power of their emotions and motivations. However, we also know that humans are, among their many complex sides, thinking beings. Sometimes thoughts cause us unnecessary pain. The thought-countering methods discussed here are only provided for limited goals. They are meant to help people deal with self-stigma and other irrational cognitions that overwhelm them, cause unyielding hurtful feelings, and interfere with their life goals.

The Stopping Self-Stigma Worksheet.

The various assumptions about irrational beliefs and changing these beliefs are summarized as a "Stop Self-Stigma" Worksheet. A blank version is provided in Table 4.6 which readers are welcome to photocopy for self-stigma that may haunt them or friends. We also provided a completed version of the worksheet in Table 4.7 as an example of how to use it; this was filled out by Edgar who was troubled by the self-stigma that he was a morally weak person because he had been hospitalized for depression twice. The worksheet comprises five steps. First, we begin with a clear statement of the hurtful attitude using the formula:

I must be _____ because _____ .

Albert Ellis said that irrational thoughts are often marked by *mustabatory* thinking. "I *must* do X to be a good person." "I *must* have done Y as a sign that I am bad." Talking about yourself with *musts* leads to irrational feelings. This kind of formula helps persons put their irrational thoughts into words. Like many persons with mental illness who self-stigmatize, Edgar believed he was a weak person because he was overwhelmed by his mental illness sometimes.

The next step is to further define the mustabatory statement as a true-false assumption. One way to do this is to change the statement from a personal "I" belief to a statement that includes "all people like me." With this in mind, Edgar broke his hurtful belief into:

● *All strong people don't have mental illnesses.*

● *Weak means bad. All people who have problems are bad.*

The truth of I statements is not always clear; however, change it to a general statement about humankind, and its falseness becomes evident.

Next, the person challenges these assumptions by asking others whether they believe the two attitudes are true. First, Edgar sought out a circle of trusted people for feedback, in this case a group from After Hours, an adult social club he attends weekly. Edgar also decided

Table 4.6
Stop Self-Stigma Worksheet: Complete All Five Steps

---

1. **State the Hurtful Belief**

I MUST BE _____ BECAUSE _____
_____

---

2. **Define the True-False Assumptions**
_____
_____

---

3. **Challenge the Assumptions by Checking Them Out with Whom?**

_____   _____

_____   _____

---

4. **Collect Evidence that Challenges the Assumptions**
_____
_____

---

5. **Restate the Attitude so It Does Not Injure Me. This is a COUNTER.** ∨
_____
_____

---

to check with his older sister, Connie, mayor of his hometown and someone in whom he has confidence. Edgar was surprised by the response from people at After Hours. Not only did they disagree with the statement that "Strong people don't have mental illnesses," to a person, they all relayed some experience with depression or anxiety. Two friends, in fact, had been hospitalized like Edgar. Members of After Hours also took exception that struggling with personal problems meant a person is bad. Edgar was especially moved by what Connie said.

Table 4.7
Sample Worksheet: Edgar's Attempt to Change Hurtful Beliefs

---

1. State the Hurtful Belief

I MUST BE *a weak person* BECAUSE *I have a mental illness.*

---

2. Define the True-False Assumptions

Strong people don't have mental illnesses.
Weak means bad. All people who have problems are bad.

---

3. Challenge the Assumptions by Checking Them Out with Whom?

I'll ask people in my After Hours social group.
They've been friends for a while and will give me an honest answer.

My older sister. She is smart and always tells me the truth.

---

4. Collect Evidence that Challenges the Assumptions

− All my friends in the social club said they've had psychiatric problems
like mild depression or anxiety and they don't believe they're weak.
− They said struggling with problems and being bad are clearly
two different things.
− My sister said dealing with psychiatric problems is a sure sign of
strength, not weakness.

---

5. Restate the Attitude so It Does Not Injure Me. This is a COUNTER. ✓

I'm not weak or bad because of my mental illness.
In fact, I'm a hero for hanging on.

---

*"Are you weak because you struggle with
mental illness once in a while? No way
Edgar. If anything, what you've overcome
means you're a hero. Few people can contend with the symptoms, the hospitals, the
side effects, and get back on their feet as
well as you."*

117

Not only was Connie's feedback supportive, it countered his belief about being of weak mind because of his past psychiatric problems.

The final step is to translate Worksheet findings into an attitude that *counters* future hurtful beliefs. Even though Edgar benefited greatly from feedback by his friends and sister, he's likely to struggle with these self-stigmatizing beliefs again. It's the nature of irrational beliefs to come back and try to hurt us. Hence, Edgar put together the various things people said about not being weak into a counter statement he could use against that stigma in the future.

> *"I'm not weak or bad because of my mental illness. In fact, I'm a hero for hanging on."*

Edgar actually wrote this counter on the back of the calendar listing his monthly After Hours meetings. When he was alone and feeling ashamed, he'd pull out the card and read this message to himself.

Implementing this worksheet.

There are a variety of ways in which the Self-Stigma Worksheet might be used to control hurtful beliefs. Some readers may be able to copy this worksheet out of the book and use it to directly stop their self-stigmatizing beliefs. Others might want to work with a helper or counselor and review the steps one at a time. An especially useful way to use this worksheet is for a group of persons who self-stigmatize to regularly gather and share their counters to these kinds of stigma. Many persons are tormented by the same kinds of self-stigma. Sharing from the worksheet in this manner can help the entire group. Moreover, this kind of group activity facilitates an individual's sense of personal power.

Gaining Personal Power

People with mental illness who have personal power over their disability AND the various ways in which they are dealing with their mental illness do not self-stigmatize. In fact, we view personal power as the polar opposite of self-stigma. Hence, the seven ways to foster personal power (discussed in Chapter 6) are an excellent means for overcoming self-stigma. These include involvement in mutual help programs where individuals provide guidance and support so that peers can not only overcome the disabilities of severe mental illness but the various forms of stigma and discrimination they may experience each day. They may also include participation in advocacy programs where persons with mental illness face head-on the various prejudices in their communities. Persons involved in efforts like these gain significant power from their peers and soon lose the self-stigma that may have been haunting them.

Other Ways to Deal with Depression

As we said earlier, persons who self-stigmatize suffer many of the problems of persons coping with major depression. Hence, in addition to coping with the self-stigmatizing beliefs, anything that helps the person cope with depression will help him or her deal with self-stigma. Reviewing the broad set of strategies that help people cope with stigma is beyond the scope of this book. Instead, we wish the reader to consider two important references both by David Burns:

- David D. Burns. 1990. *The Feeling Good Handbook*. New York: Avon Books.

- David D. Burns. 1999. *Feeling Good: The New Mood Therapy*. New York: Avon Books.

These books are easily read and understood by the public. The Handbook is chock-full of exercises that accompany the conceptual discussion of how to cope with depression found in the New Mood Therapy.

Stigma Is NOT Solely the Problem of the Person with Mental Illness

We reviewed ways to identify and cope with self-stigma in this chapter. As an end, we repeat a theme that is prominent in this book. Namely, the effects of stigma (be these self-stigma, prejudice, or discrimination) are not solely the problem of persons with mental illness. By focusing on how persons can handle self-stigma, we may be miscommunicating that they alone are responsible for coping with stigma. Wrong! Mental illness stigma is the creation of society as a whole. It is the responsibility of all humankind, therefore, to find ways to erase it.

Chapter 5

To Disclose
or Not
To Disclose

*"In all things that are purely social we can be
as separate as the fingers, yet one as the hand
in all things essential to mutual progress."*

Booker T. Washington

Most persons with mental illness can choose to keep their disability a secret. Unlike the stigma experienced by persons of color or by physical disability, mental illness can be kept private. People you meet everyday—from the conductor on the train, to the clerk at the bakery, to your co-worker at the office—don't know whether you struggle with a psychiatric illness. Hence, each person who feels victimized by the stigma of mental illness must decide whether to disclose their experiences to the public, and if so with whom. They need to consider how disclosing their mental illness will benefit them and how it may harm.

Disclosure is not a black and white choice. Mental illness is a complex experience. People need to decide which parts of this experience to disclose.

Moreover, disclosing mental illness is a very personal decision. Hence, we decided to write this chapter in second person, to YOU the readers who are actually struggling with disclosure decisions. What can you do to answer questions about whether you should disclose your psychiatric history and to whom? However, we also think the points in this chapter are important for family members, service providers, and others who may help persons with mental illness consider the kind of challenges which disclosure poses.

Secrets Are a Part of Life

Deciding to disclose your experiences with mental illness is not an easy decision. Sometimes, this choice is made harder by the guilt people feel about having a secret,

> *"I must be a bad person to have to hide part of who I am."*

This kind of guilt doesn't make the decision process any easier. Persons with mental illness feel like people with leprosy because they have these secrets. However, many persons are consoled with the knowledge that most adults must contend with secrets. They include:

- persons who struggle with coming out of the closet: gays and lesbians, persons with AIDS, and persons from some non-traditional religious denominations.

- individuals with family members and friends who are associated with stigmatized groups. Parents, brothers, and sisters may choose not to share this with the public.

● individuals who make life choices which they wish not to discuss with others. They may work a job which others might criticize or live in a neighborhood which is not considered fashionable. Smokers who work around health-conscious co-workers may not want peers to know.

There is some comfort realizing that many of the strangers you meet each day—people from whom you are trying to keep your mental illness—are withholding a secret from you. You do not struggle alone.

Despite information like this, some persons still beat themselves up about their evil little secret; "I must be wrong if I have to keep my psychiatric history private." This kind of attitude can have an insidious effect on the person. In Chapter 4, we discussed ways to cope with bad attitudes about ourselves; this same method applies here and is recapped in the Worksheet in Table 5.1.

There are five steps for changing attitudes about ourselves and our secrets. First, we begin with a clear statement of the hurtful attitude using the formula:

I must be _____ because _____ .

"I must be a bad person because I have a secret about my mental illness."

In further defining this attitude, two key components seem to account for the bad feelings: (1) thinking that

123

your mental illness should be kept private and (2) believing that normal people don't keep such secrets.

Table 5.1
The Self-Stigma Worksheet Applied to "the Secret of Mental Illness"

---

1. State the Hurtful Belief

I MUST BE _a bad person_ BECAUSE _I have a secret about my mental illness._

---

2. Define the True-False Assumptions

Secrets are bad because normal people don't have them.
I should keep my mental illness a secret.

---

3. Challenge the Assumptions by Checking Them Out with Whom?

I'll ask people in my bible study group.
They're normal and will give me an honest answer.

I'll ask my pastor. He's a straight shooter.

---

4. Collect Evidence that Challenges the Assumptions

– Six out of seven people in my bible study group admitted to having a secret at some time in their life.
– My pastor has even had secrets.

– Everyone said it's up to me to determine whether to keep something a secret.

---

5. Restate the Attitude so It Does Not Injure Me. This is a COUNTER.

I'm not bad for having secrets. Everyone does.

Next, you want to challenge these assumptions by asking others whether they believe the two attitudes are true. According to the discussion in Chapter 4, persons are likely to give up hurtful attitudes when they discover underlying assumptions are actually false. First, you seek out a circle of trusted people for feedback, in this case a bible study group. You also decide to check with your pastor, who you think is reliable and a "straight shooter." From your bible study group you learn that six out of seven people admitted to keeping a secret at some time in their life. Then your pastor tells you that at times he has kept secrets. Both your pastor and the people in your bible study group said there is no reason why you should not keep a secret as long as you do not hurt others in the process.

The final step is to translate these findings into an attitude that *counters* the hurtful belief.

> *"I'm not bad for having secrets. Everyone does."*

You may wish to write it down on a card so you can better remember. Then, the next time you're questioning your integrity for having a secret about mental illness, pull out the counter. Remind yourself that everyone keeps secrets. There is nothing wrong with it.

Your Protection Against Disclosure

Even though people choose to keep it private, most persons with mental illness have already disclosed their experiences. They have told mental health professionals about their disabilities. The way in which professionals respond to knowledge about your psychiatric past gives you some sense how others may react to this information, though mental health professionals generally are more understanding about your story than the average man on the street. Still, in making decisions about disclosing your experiences with mental illness, you first need to consider how your right to privacy is protected. All states in the Union have passed laws

Table 5.2
A Fact Sheet about Confidentiality Laws

All states in the Union have legislation that requires mental health workers to **NOT** disclose any information about you without your permission. Depending on the State, this generally means the following for adults.

> Every interaction you have with a mental health organization is considered confidential and may not be disclosed without your permission.

> > This includes obvious issues like individual and group psychotherapy, meetings with a psychiatrist, participation in community meetings, and physicals by a nurse practitioner.
> >
> > But, this literally means every interaction. Talking to the receptionist, waiting in the lounge, riding on the agency van, bumping into the janitor are all interactions which are confidential. No one has a right to know about anything you do at a mental health organization without your prior written permission.
> >
> > In fact, no one has the right to know you ATTEND a mental health organization without your permission.

> Confidentiality laws also apply to all records: written charts, videotapes, or computer files. They may not be disclosed without your permission.

> Confidentiality applies to everyone who works for an organization: from the medical director to the gardener to even volunteers.

> No one may obtain confidential information about you without your written permission including your employer, landlord, or family members.

> Your confidentiality is protected forever, even after you die. Employees of a mental health organization have to respect your confidentiality forever, even after they leave the organization.

> You may choose to disclose any part of your record or interactions with a mental health organization. You can only do this when you sign a written release of information that specifies what materials are to be released (John Doe's history in the Opportunities Vocational Program from October 1 to December 1, 1998) and where it is being sent (to Dr. Jones at Blackhawk Mental Health Center).

> The only authority that can order a mental health professional to violate your confidentiality is a judge in a court of law when you are involved in civil or criminal proceedings.

which guarantee that interactions with mental health professionals remain confidential. A fact sheet summarizing key points of these laws is provided in Table 5.2.

Confidentiality Laws

Not a state in the union allows mental health professionals to disclose information about your history without your permission. This includes clinical interactions with the mental health system such as psychotherapy, group therapy, and participation in community meetings. But it also means every interaction you have in a mental health setting such as a conversation with a receptionist or while riding in the hospital van to an outing. No one has the right to know that you have ever been in a hospital or attended a community mental health center without your prior written permission.

After you leave a hospital or a community program, confidentiality applies to all of your records. They cannot be released without your explicit permission. These include written charts, video tapes, even computer files. Similarly, anyone seeking your medical charts will be rebuffed unless they have your permission, such as landlords, your employer, or even your family members. Your records are kept from everyone, even after you die. You may release your records to another mental health organization, but only with a prior, written release. Consider the two stipulations here. Permission must be obtained prior to the release of information; it is rarely legal to do so after information has been shared. Mental health agencies cannot ask you to sign a release when they have already given material about you to someone else. In addition, this permission must be written, specified as to what information is to be

Figure 5.1

A copy of the standard form used at the University of Chicago to obtain a release of information for persons participating in our programs.

UNIVERSITY OF CHICAGO HOSPITALS
MEDICAL RECORD DEPARTMENT
5841 S. Maryland Avenue M/C 0978
Chicago, Illinois 60637

RELEASE OF MEDICAL RECORD

Note to Requestor of Records:
There may be a charge for copies of the medical record.

Note to Recipient of Records: The patient's medical record is privileged information which is protected by various State and Federal Laws. Such information may not be further disclosed to other persons without a separate written authorization from the patient.

1. I, _____ born _____
   (Patient's Name)   (Date of Birth)

   _____
   (Street Address)   (City)   (State)   (Zip Code)

   Authorize The University of Chicago Hospitals to release to the party listed in paragraph 2 the following information from my medical records:
   (Check and/or circle appropriate items)
   ❏ Complete record
   ❏ Abstract (face sheet, history and physical, operative report) discharge summary, consult)
   ❏ Diagnoses
   ❏ Surgical (operative report, pathology report)
   ❏ Test results (lab, radiology, cardiology, neurophysiology, respiratory)
   ❏ Psychiatric and/or substance abuse evaluations and treatment
   ❏ Aids and/or aids related diagnoses, evaluations and treatment
   ❏ Therapy notes (physical, occupational, speech, chemo, radiation)
   ❏ Clinic visit notes
   ❏ Other _____

   for the following dates of treatment: _____

   _____

2. My medical record may be inspected by and/or copies may be released to:

   _____
   (Name of Person)   (Name of affiliated Organization)

   _____
   (Street Address)   (City)   (State)   (Zip Code)

   for the purpose of _____

3. I may revoke this authorization in writing at any time (except to the extent that actions have been taken in reliance upon it).

   Unless revoked or renewed in writing, this authorization will expire on _____ .
                                                                          (Date)

   If the expiration date is not specified above. this authorization will automatically expire 90 days from the date signed below.

4. If I wish to inspect or have a copy of my hospital record (after discharge and for which there may be a charge), I may contact the Hospital's Medical Records Department.

   _____
   (Patient's, Signature)   (Date)

   If the patient is a minor, subject to guardianship or is deceased, I have signed my name below on behalf of the patient and myself.

   _____
   (Patient's Legal Guardian's or Agent's Signature)   (Date)

   I witnessed the signature on this form: Name of Witness: (Please Print) _____

   _____
   (Witness Signature)   (Date)

   REFUSAL: Since I refuse to authorize disclosure of my medical record to the party listed in paragraph 2, I will be solely responsible for the

   following consequences: _____

   _____

   _____
   (Signature)   (Date)   (Print Name)   (Date)

released, where it is being sent, who will receive it, and when the release will no longer apply. By the way, you are entitled to a copy of that release and may take it back later if you change your mind; a copy of the standard form used to obtain release of information at University of Chicago services is provided in Figure 5.1. Also, the agency cannot pressure you in any way to sign the release of information.

A judge presiding over a civil or criminal case in which you are involved is the only person who can override this system of confidentiality. He or she can order your mental health agency to provide information about you in matters before the case. You can decide to appeal this decision (usually with the help of an attorney representing your interest). Nevertheless, the final decision in these cases lies with the court.

Who the laws do and don't apply to

Confidentiality laws clearly apply to psychiatrists, psychologists, social workers, nurses, and other staff providing mental health services. In fact, these laws apply to all paid employees; receptionists, bus drivers, food service workers, and housekeeping staff must all obey it. In addition, these laws apply to unpaid workers associated with the mental health program: recreation volunteers, therapy students, outside advocates, and members of the board of directors. Note however, that laws do not apply to one group of people you regularly encounter at a mental health program: other persons receiving services. Fellow "consumers" whom you meet in a psychiatric unit of a hospital, or in group therapy at a community program, are not bound by confidentiality laws. Nor must family members attending therapy sessions protect your confidentiality. Certainly, staff will request that fellow group members respect your confidentiality—they probably wish the same protections for themselves—but there are no laws requiring that be so.

Other state and federal laws protect your privacy outside mental health institutions. Defamation, slander, and libel are statutes that prevent falsehoods about you from being published or otherwise disseminated. Title 18 of the U.S. Code prevents people from learning about you by reading your mail. Hence, correspondence from your psychiatrist is protected by law. The Americans with Disabilities Act (the ADA) prevents employers from sharing information about your psychiatric disability with others. More information is provided about the ADA in Chapter 9.

There are clearly many legal protections of your privacy. Unfortunately, these protections are not absolute; gossip, for example, may always spread. There are no laws that prevent co-workers from telling stories. Neighbors and friends may pass out information about you in a spiteful manner. Hence, you will need to make an explicit decision about whether you wish to disclose your experiences with mental illness.

The Pros and Cons of Disclosure

There are both advantages and disadvantages to disclosing your mental illness. Consider the stories of George and Susan.

George never talks about his illness. He never voluntarily discloses it. George has

*worked for years as a congressional aide
with frequent episodes of depression. He
has never breathed a word of it to his children, friends, colleagues, the press, or his
boss. Why is George so secretive? He is in
a highpowered job where showing so much
as a glimmer of weakness could be fatal to
his career. His symptoms are tolerable, so
he carries on in silence.*

*Susan, on the other hand, lives in a nurtur-
ing group home. Her mental illness is discussed freely and openly. Gathering
strength from group support, Susan is
actively encouraged to disclose her
schizoaffective disorder. Susan has made
great strides in managing her illness. She is
proud and gets praise for sharing her
recovery from the depths of psychosis and
depression.*

Some Costs and Benefits of Disclosure

There are a variety of reasons why a person
might disclose his or her experience with mental illness.
These could be considered in terms of *costs* (reasons
why you may regret disclosing) and *benefits* (reasons
why disclosure will help you). Several of these are summarized in Table 5.3. Let us consider the benefits first.
These are the reasons why letting other people know
about your psychiatric disabilities may help you.

Table 5.3
The Costs and Benefits of Disclosing Mental Illness

Benefits	Costs
you don't have to worry about hiding your mental illness	others may disapprove of your mental illness or your disclosure
you can be more open about your day-to-day affairs	others may gossip about you
others may express approval	others may exclude you from social gatherings
others may have similar experiences	others may exclude you from work, housing, and other opportunities
you may find someone who can help you in the future	you may worry more about what people are thinking about you
you are promoting your sense of personal power	you may worry that others will pity you
you are living testimony against stigma	future relapses may be more stressful because everyone will be watching
	family members and others may be angry you disclosed

The Advantages of Disclosing

One advantage to telling others is that *you won't have to worry any more about your secret getting out.* The minute others know, the secret is gone. It frees the person of the fear related to keeping secrets as well as the resentment that you have to hide part of yourself. Disclosing to other people *helps you to feel more open about day-to-day experiences.*

> *"Wow, I used to lie to the guys on the job so they wouldn't find out that I was leaving work early to see my psychiatrist. Now, it doesn't matter. Instead, I can complain to them about how I hate to wait for the doc*

just like how you might gripe about waiting for your dentist."

Your fear is that others, when they find out, will disapprove or humiliate you. A pleasant benefit of disclosure might be the contrary, *receiving approval and support from others.*

"Oh my gosh, Carolyn. I didn't know you struggled with depression. I'm really impressed with how well you manage."

Most people are coping with some kind of personal trial or tribulation, even if it is not mental illness. They may be fascinated by your ability to cope and respect you for it.

You may be pleasantly surprised to find out that *others have similar problems.* Frequently, persons discover that when they admit to their psychiatric problems, others respond "me too." Given that more than 20% of the population are struggling with some kind of mental illness at any one time (8% of the population are dealing with severe mental illnesses like schizophrenia or manic-depression), it is likely that you will have "me too" experiences when you tell your story.

You may build friendships with those who have similar problems. These friends can then be available to *help you in the future.*

"Betty told me she gets depressed sometimes, too. That really helped. Next time I was feeling a little sad at work, I'd drop by Betty's desk and we talked. She was able to say the kind of things that would get me through the day."

Disclosing your experiences with mental illness is often the first step to finding an entire support network of persons with like problems. Self-help groups provide a place where you can let your secrets out. They are places where persons with mental illness can be with kindred spirits, not worry about disclosure, and get support. Alternatively, finding a small group of friends who know your problems can be equally liberating.

Keeping a secret about mental illness fosters a feeling of shame. *Telling your story promotes a sense of personal power.* As we will discuss in the next section of the book, a feeling of personal power is the opposite of being victimized by shame.

> *"I was surprised when I told the writers group about my history of manic depression. I didn't feel like a wimp anymore. I had something to say, I looked them in the eyes, and I said it."*

This sense of power over your life is a major step towards dealing with stigma.

Finally, telling your secret actually challenges many of the stigmatizing attitudes others have about mental illness. You are living testimony against many of the said and unsaid myths about psychiatric disability.

> *"It was an education working next to Jim. I thought mental patients were all dangerous or homeless. Jim was the best employee in the shop and one of the nicest guys you could meet."*

The Costs of Disclosing

Although there are several benefits to disclosing your experiences, you need to consider the costs as well. These are the reasons why you currently are not telling persons about your experience. They are also reviewed in Table 5.3 and must be carefully considered so that divulging your secret does not end up harming you. One big group of reasons why you may not disclose is the repercussions from others. Some persons may disapprove of you for telling your experiences. They fear mental illness or are offended by people that have been hospitalized. They may turn these emotions against you. Others may resent you for asserting your right to tell.

> *"I'm sick and tired of all these oppressed people whining. Blacks, Latinos, guys in wheel chairs, and now Sid because he's mentally ill. Why do I have to bleed for all these other guys?"*

Persons might start talking about you. Gossip is the bane of offices and neighborhoods. Telling persons about your experiences with depression, hospitals, or medications provides juicy stock for the gossip line. Some persons are going to shun you at social gatherings when they hear your story. They may have ignorant views about persons with mental illness being dangerous and want to protect themselves. Some persons may actually exclude you from work or housing opportunities. A supervisor might keep you from a good job because of hostility; "I'm not having that crazy on my squad." Or the supervisor might become overly protective. "I was going to promote him to the day shift but I don't think he can handle it."

The costs of disclosure are not limited to others. You may also have trouble with it. Some of you may worry what others think of you because you told your secret. You wonder what people mean when they ask "how are you?" or say they "can't join you for lunch." Others may be concerned that people who find out will pity you.

> *"It was bad enough to have to keep my*
> *history a secret. But I told a couple of guys*
> *from the local greasy spoon and they were*
> *patronizing. 'Don't stress yourself, dear.*
> *Don't work too hard, buddy.' I would have*
> *rather had their scorn."*

Some persons who disclose may find future relapses harder. Rather than attending to their needs, they may be worrying about what their co-workers, neighbors, or friends are thinking.

Finally, some persons might experience family anger about disclosing their mental illness.

> *"I didn't want everyone to know you had*
> *been hospitalized. Now, all the guys at the*
> *yard have started whispering about my*
> *psycho wife."*

Families have their own troubles with stigma which will be affected by your decision to disclose.

The impact of disclosing in large cities and small towns

The size of your community needs to be considered when deciding to disclose your experience. It is fairly easy to be anonymous in a large city. There is truth to the stereotype of neighbors not knowing neighbors or citizens not caring about other's business in huge metropolitan areas. Conversely, information seems to spread quickly through small towns and rural areas. These communities typically have a small network and long history with one another. Hence, new information about someone tends to have a big impact on the network and quickly spreads to all points. Telling your story in a place like New York City will have a more limited impact than sharing your experiences in Smalltown, Illinois. You need to consider how information might spread to others when deciding whether or not to disclose.

This effect is not limited to urban and rural communities. Even if you work in a large city, information will quickly spread through a work place, a church, or any small social group where members are familiar with each other. Just like comparing Smalltown, Illinois to New York City, information about a person's mental illness can spread much faster in a small business, like the "Corner Restaurant," than in a large factory or package delivery company. Consider Ruth, who works for a telephone manufacturing company which employs 2,000. As long as her quotas are met and her absences are kept within permissible levels, her personal health problems are not of concern to management. Janice, on the other hand, works as a waitress in a small eatery. With no more than 12 employees, Janice's behavior is readily scrutinized, and her mood shifts and frequent absences are noted by her co-workers and the boss.

Weighing the Costs and Benefits of Disclosing

Only you can judge what the various costs and benefits mean for a decision about disclosure. The Cost and Benefits Worksheet in Table 5.4 is provided as a way to help you make this decision. You'll notice the worksheet has two columns. List the benefits for disclosure on the left side and the costs on the right. Remember, benefits are the reasons why you would want to disclose. Ask yourself the question, *"How will letting other people know about my mental illness help me?"* Costs are the disadvantages to disclosing experiences with mental illness: *"How will talking to others about my experiences hurt?"* Some people like to carefully consider all the benefits, first listing as many as they can think of. They then write down the costs. Others just start writing down costs and benefits as they come to mind until they have them all listed.

You will notice that the cost and benefit columns are divided into short and long-term sections. The impact of costs and benefits are sometimes relatively immediate and other times delayed. For example, Betty identified short-term costs:

> *"If I tell my co-workers that I have been hospitalized for schizophrenia they may not want to ever meet me for lunch."*

Table 5.4
The Costs and Benefits Worksheet for Disclosing My Mental Illness

Setting: _____

Don't censor any ideas. Write them all down.
Put a star (★) next to costs and benefits you think are especially important.

Short-Term Benefits	Short-Term Costs

Long-Term Benefits	Long-Term Costs

Given these costs and benefits:

☐ I have decided **to disclose** my mental illness.

☐ I have decided **NOT to disclose** my mental illness.

☐ I have decided **to put off** my decision.

and short-term benefits:

"Perhaps other people in my office could help me deal with the boss if they new about my mental illness."

She also identified long-term costs:

> *"If I tell my supervisor I have regular*
> *bouts of depression, he may pass over my*
> *promotion next year."*

and benefits:

> *"If I tell, my boss may be willing to provide*
> *me some on-the-job help after inventory is*
> *complete."*

Generally, people tend to be more influenced by short-term costs and benefits because they happen sooner. However, long-term costs and benefits frequently have greater implications for the future. So, make sure you carefully consider them, too.

Sometimes people censor themselves as they list costs and benefits.

> *"I'm worried that people won't have lunch*
> *with me if I tell... Nyah, that's a dumb idea.*
> *I'm going to take that off the Worksheet*
> *list."*

Don't dismiss any cost or benefit no matter how silly it may seem. Put them on the list so you can consider all advantages and disadvantages together. Sometimes the items you want to censor are actually important; you may just be embarrassed about the issue. If the item is really irrelevant, you'll ignore it in the final analysis.

After listing all the costs and benefits, put a star next to one or two that seem particularly important. Important items are the ones you spent a lot of time thinking about. You may want to star the items that make you nervous when you think about them: *"If I tell my buddies about seeing a psychiatrist, they'll laugh at me just like they give Harvey a hard time about seeing a foot doctor."* Or you may mark items that suggest a lot of hope: *"Maybe if I tell people on my softball team, my buddies will understand better why I don't go to bars after the games; I can't mix alcohol and meds."* Some persons consider the list of advantages and disadvantages in Table 5.3 for additional ideas about possible costs and benefits. However, don't limit yourself to these options. Frequently, you will come up with a cost or benefit not in the list that is especially relevant to you.

Your decision depends on the setting

Costs and benefits of disclosing your experience vary by the situation you are in. Telling persons your history with psychiatric experience is a lot different at work than in your neighborhood or with your softball teammates. You could conceivably decide to tell persons at work but not in your neighborhood, or tell your close friends but not tell your son's teacher. Hence, you need to list costs and benefits of disclosing your mental illness separately for each setting that is important to you. You can do this by making copies of the Costs and Benefits Worksheet and enter the name of each setting on the first line at the top of the form: work, neighborhood, social groups, synagogue, or family members that don't know. Then write down the costs and benefits for disclosing to people at that setting.

Actually, costs and benefits of disclosure might differ within a setting. A supervisor may react differently to your disclosure than members of the construction team. Hence, you may have to define the setting even further. Look at the different settings Edwina considered in making her decision about disclosure.

> *"There are four different groups of people to consider at church. First, my pastor is a very dynamic woman and a clear moral leader. She'll respond differently than the second group, people in the choir, especially the choir master. And I know people in the third group, my bible group, real well. We've been meeting weekly for the past year. Finally, I don't know what to expect if I stand up and give witness to the congregation during service on Sunday."*

What is your decision?

The purpose of the Worksheet is to yield a decision about whether to disclose your mental illness. Two decisions are straightforward.

- Yes, I want to let some people know about my experiences with mental illness.

- No, I don't want people to know about my mental illness.

Although the options are clear, there is no easy way to add up the costs and benefits and come up with a decision. Good decisions are more than the sum of the right and left columns in Table 5.4. Clearly, some advantages or disadvantages will be more important and therefore should weigh far more in the decision. These are the items you starred in the list.

> *"Okay, on the worksheet I show three benefits for disclosing and nine disadvantages. I don't care, I still want to disclose; I need to get out there and advocate for the mentally ill—meet other people with mental illness. I'm going to tell the people at work tomorrow!"*

Some people may not be able to make a decision about disclosing after reviewing costs and benefits; they may need to decide to postpone the decision. They may choose to use this time to gather more information about disclosure.

Can someone help you with the decision?

Disclosing a mental illness is a difficult decision to make alone. Since there are so many emotion-charged factors to take into consideration, it is hard for a person to calmly and rationally weigh the pluses and minuses. You may want to consider the judgement and advice of others before you plunge into disclosing. Remember, though, that if you decide to seek counsel, you are going to have to disclose your illness to the people from whom you seek advice.

Family members may be good sources of advice. Don't forget your decision may impact them and their standing in the community as well as yours. They may try to protect you from the potential pain and downfalls of disclosure. Some families may not be supportive. Others, however, will understand the benefits of disclosure and understand your right to disclose; they may encourage you. Your family members may give you great emotional and personal support just when you need it. Counselors are also a good source for advice on your decision to disclose or not. Experienced counselors have advised many people with mental illness, and they have seen the successes and problems of disclosure.

Your friends who have mental illness, especially those who have disclosed, may offer positive advice or possibly a warning, depending upon their experience disclosing a mental illness. Those who are advocates and have succeeded in organizations like NAMI, will likely advise you to tell. Those who have had failures on account of disclosure, such as loss of a job or failure of a broken marriage, might tell you to keep your lips sealed.

Disclosure is a journey

Disclosure is not a one-time decision. Depending on life circumstances, you're interests in disclosing are going to change over time. You may decide today not to disclose but change your mind in a month.

> *"You know, after I heard that advocate from the Empowerment Center talk about her experiences disclosing mental illness, I decided I wanted to let other people know about my illness."*

Conversely, you may decide to disclose today but pull back later.

> *"People at my old job know I have an ill-*
> *ness, but, I'm starting a new job next week.*
> *I don't know whether I can trust them."*

Disclosing your experiences with mental illness is a *journey*, just like any important life decision. You must constantly decide how much energy to spend on your friends, family, work, and God. Sometimes you're invested in work and ignore recreation. Other times you focus on family and hobbies. You must do the same with disclosure. Hence, you may find yourself filling out the Costs and Benefits Worksheet several times in your life, coming up with different conclusions each time.

How to Disclose

Depending on your decision, there are a variety of ways in which you might disclose, or not disclose, your experience with mental illness; see Table 5.5 for a short list. You will likely select from these approaches depending on the situation. For example, some persons may choose to selectively disclose in certain situations (tell my church group and immediate supervisor at work), keep it a secret in other situations (not tell any of my co-workers), and avoid a third set of situations altogether (not go to bars after work—some of those people would make fun of me if they found out). Table 5.5 lists five ways you may decide on handling the issue of disclosure.

Table 5.5
Five Ways to Disclose or Not Disclose

1. SOCIAL AVOIDANCE

Altogether avoid persons and places that might stigmatize or otherwise disrespect you because of your mental illness.

Benefit	**Cost**
You don't encounter people who will unfairly harm you.	You lose the opportunity to meet new people who possibly may be supportive.

2. SECRECY

Don't tell persons at places you work or live about your mental illness.

Benefit	**Cost**
Like social avoidance, you withhold information from people you don't know and trust. But, you don't have to avoid important settings like work or the community in the process.	Some people feel guilty about keeping secrets.

3. SELECTIVE DISCLOSURE

Tell some persons who you believe will be supportive about your mental illness.

Benefit	**Cost**
You find a small group of people who will understand your experiences and provide support.	You may disclose to some people who hurt you with the information. You may have difficulty keeping track of who knows and who doesn't.

4. INDISCRIMINANT DISCLOSURE

Don't be concerned about who knows about your mental illness. Tell anyone you encounter.

Benefit	**Cost**
You don't worry who knows about your problems. And you are likely to find people who will be supportive.	You are likely to tell people who hurt you with the information.

5. BROADCAST YOUR EXPERIENCE

Purposefully communicate your experiences with mental illness to a large group.

Benefit	**Cost**
You don't have to worry who knows about your history of mental illness. You are promoting a personal sense of empowerment in yourself. You are striking a blow against stigma.	You are going to encounter people who may try to hurt you with this information. You are also going to meet people who disapprove of your political statement.

1. Social Avoidance

Ironically, the first way to handle disclosure may be to not tell anyone. This means avoiding situations where people may find out about one's mental illness. People who are victimized by stigma may choose to not socialize with, live near, or work alongside persons without disabilities. Instead, they only associate with other persons who have mental illness. This may include persons with mental illness living in a therapeutic community, working in a sheltered or supported work environment, or interacting with friends in a social club developed for mental illness. In this way, the person can avoid the "normal" population that may disapprove of their disabilities or actively work to keep them out.

In some ways, this approach is similar to the old notion of *asylum*. A few persons have such severe psychiatric disabilities that they need a safe and pleasant place to live and work, a place where they can escape the pressures and disapproval of society. What was known as the "moral view of psychiatric care" originally envisioned state hospitals for this purpose: nice homes, rural settings, and supportive caretakers who help persons with extreme disabilities escape the stresses of society and, by the way, citizens in society who will stigmatize them. Unfortunately, very few hospitals ever achieved this goal, in part because most state and private facilities are dominated by persons with acute symptoms, some of whom might be potentially dangerous to self or others. The predominant concern for protection of people with mental illness from violence frequently overrides many of the "pleasant" aspects of hospital living.

This kind of asylum could be more appropriately accomplished in community-based programs. Persons with profound disabilities, who choose not to address their community's prejudice against mental illness, could live in pleasant compounds and work in sheltered settings away from the rest of their neighbors. Persons could learn to cope with their symptoms or achieve their interpersonal goals in a setting relatively free of disapproving neighbors or co-workers.

Unfortunately, there are also several negatives to social avoidance. Persons who choose to avoid the "normal" world lose out on all the benefits it brings: free access to a broader set of opportunities and citizens who support your experience with mental illness. Moreover, social avoidance in some ways promotes stigma and discrimination. It endorses the idea that persons with mental illness need to be locked away from the rest of the world. Persons who choose to avoid social situations may be putting off a challenge they must eventually face. Social avoidance may be a useful strategy during times when symptoms are intense and the person needs a respite from the demands of society. But avoiding the normal world altogether will most likely prevent most persons from achieving the breadth of their life goals.

Recognizing persons to avoid

A more moderate approach to social avoidance might be steering clear of certain groups of people—those who stigmatize—rather than your community as a whole. This requires you to be alert for people who would be intolerant of persons with psychiatric disability. Table 5.6 lists several themes that bigots are likely to spout. You may wish to avoid social interactions with these kinds of people.

Table 5.6
Bigots You Should Avoid: You Can Tell Them by What They Say

General Bigots: People Who Disrespect Everyone

> Those black people; they're all lazy.
> Jews will take your money.
> Irish are all drunks.
> Why do people in wheel chairs get all the breaks?
> Homosexuals deserve to be punished with AIDS.

Thoughtless Speakers: People Who Use Disrespectful Language

> Frightening language
> What do you expect from wackos?
> Crazies can't take care of themselves.
> Murderers are all maniacs.
> Inappropriate humor
> Split personalities have two people to talk to.
> I'm a wild and crazy guy.

Fear Mongers: People Who Say Social Problems Are Caused by Mental Illness

> Many famous people are killed by psychos who should be locked up.
> The homeless are all displaced mental patients.
> Pedophiles are all mentally ill.
> Schools are dangerous because of all the crazies.

People Who Oppose Fair Chances

> I don't want a halfway house in my back yard.
> I'm against laws that protect the rights of mental patients.
> I'd never hire a mental patient.

Avoid the bigot who looks at all people, especially minorities and disadvantaged groups, from a stereotyped, cruel and disrespectful perspective.

> *"All blacks are criminals, all Jews are money-hungry, the Irish are drunks, and gays deserve AIDS."*

Stay away from these people. Persons with mental illness are derided by bigots who have contempt for everyone outside of their own narrow spectrum of acceptable people or races.

People with mental illness are sometimes heckled by citizens we might refer to as "thoughtless speakers"—another narrow-minded and disparaging group of bigots. These people may pepper their language with incorrect and insensitive words such as "wackos," "crazies," "psychos," and "maniacs." Worse, thoughtless speakers perpetuate myths about mental illness with phrases like "Wackos oughta be locked up and the key thrown away!" or "Look, that guy needs his head shrunk!" Unfortunately, many talk radio shows are overrun with these kinds of thinkers.

There are also people we refer to as "Fear Mongers." Their negative attitudes toward mental illness emerge when they alarm friends and neighbors about supposed dangers. They might think that the streets are full of psychos who, since they're not locked up, will try to assassinate presidents or other public figures. According to their limited perspective, the population of the homeless is completely mentally ill and child molesters are invariably psychotic.

And finally, there is a population of people to avoid who do not want to give persons with mental illness a fair chance. "I don't want a group home on my block," they might say. They write their congressperson and tell him or her not to pass laws that benefit persons with mental illness. They may tell their boss that they don't want to work next to co-workers with mental illness. Since they appeal to everyone's prejudices, people who oppose fair chances can inflict a lot of damage.

2. Secrecy

There is no need to avoid work or community situations to keep your experiences with mental illness private. Many persons choose to enter these worlds but not share their experiences with others. Ed was a popular employee at a large food store for six years and never told co-workers he had been hospitalized for schizophrenia. Cynthia carpooled her kids with neighbors for 18 months and never let them know about her depression. Abdul went to mosque weekly and never let others know his history with manic-depression. It wasn't too hard to hide their psychiatric history.

But can't they tell I'm mentally ill?

Sometimes, it seems like everyone can tell you are struggling with symptoms. The reality, however, is that your experience with mental illness can be hidden. Keeping mental illness a secret is much easier than hiding one's gender, ethnic background, or physical disability.

- *Many of your experiences with psychosis and depression are private.* Most people do not know if you are hearing voices. They don't know your beliefs. They cannot determine whether you're sad or worried... unless you tell them!

- *Many of the signs of mental illness are overlooked.* Co-workers may think your depression is temporary blues. Neighbors may think your confusion is being sleepy-headed. There is a central tendency in the human condition that protects your privacy; namely, most everyone is tuned into themselves and misses much of what is going on around them.

- *Many of the signs are misunderstood.* The public misunderstands mental illness and frequently labels eccentric or unusual conduct wrongly: people who are dressed poorly are homeless and have a mental illness; individuals who punk their hair or pierce their ears are crazy. If you dress within customary bounds, you'll be overlooked.

How do I keep it private?

There are two parts to keeping your experiences with mental illness a secret. The first part seems easy: *don't tell anyone.* Don't share your history of hospitalizations, doctors, medications, and symptoms.

"I'd been playing in this poker group for seven years. We'd talk about work, wives, our kids, hobbies, our college years. But whenever we touched on the time after college—those few years I was in and out of the hospital before my mania was under control—I clammed up. Or better yet, I asked my buddy a question about his days in the Army. I could always count on Sol taking off on a topic."

For some people, not talking leads to big gaps in their life story. Work résumés have blank years when you were in the hospital. Photo albums do not include years of pictures when you were coping with your illness.

There are several costs to not talking about your experiences. You may find it difficult to always have to be vigilant to what you say about yourself. This kind of vigilance may lead to resentment.

> *"I've done nothing wrong. How come I have to be so careful all the time?"*

Nevertheless, this simple act of keeping parts of your experience to yourself may greatly open up work settings and communities.

> *"If I kept it to myself, I could go to the job and not worry about people thinking I was crazy."*

The first strategy for keeping your experiences secret is an act of omission; the second is an act of commission. You may need to fill in some gaps in your past and current experience. For example, many persons wrestle with holes in their work history. Consider Tamiko's experience; she had two years, between discharge from the Navy (she was in computer operations) and her 26th birthday, when she was in and out of hospitals for depression. Instead of leaving these years blank on her résumé, she wrote "advanced training in computers." When asked during job interviews what this training meant, she truthfully discussed the adult education courses she completed in systems management. She did not, however, talk about how these courses were interspersed with psychiatric hospitalizations.

You also must decide how to discuss current experiences related to your mental illness.

● *"Why do you leave early to see a doctor every month? What are those medicines you take at lunch for?"*

Table 5.7
Sample Answers to Questions About Activities Related to Your Mental Illness

Situation

You are heading out the door to your monthly psychiatrist's appointment.

? **Question:** Where are you going?
Response: I have a doctor's appointment. **!**

Situation

You are on your way to your weekly therapist's appointment.

? **Question:** Where are you going?
Response: I have a weekly appointment for my hair. **!**

Situation

You are taking some pills at lunch.

? **Question:** What are those for?
Response: A long standing health problem. **!**

Situation

You are one of the few people not drinking at a party.

? **Question:** C'mon, have a drink.
Response: No, I'm the designated driver. **!**

Situation

Your depression has returned and you are a little tearful at work.

? **Question:** Why are you crying?
Response: I had a loss in the family. **!**

Situation

You are a little more disoriented and having trouble with your job.

? **Question:** What's wrong?
Response: I'm a little dizzy from not sleeping well last night. **!**

● *"How come you never drink alcohol at
company parties?"*

Without answers, these current gaps may stick out for
some co-workers or neighbors. Table 5.7 provides examples of common questions and possible answers that
you might want to use in situations like this.

Friends and family members, familiar with your
experiences, may need to be included in the secret. At a
minimum, you cannot permit your parents to tell co-
workers or neighbors your psychiatric history if you are
trying to maintain your privacy. In addition, you may
want them to join you in your subterfuge.

> *"Dad, I told everyone at the office that I
> take you to the doctor once a month, rather
> than telling them that I go to my psychia-
> trist. I need you to back me up when Sally
> from work comes to the party tonight."*

For some, these acts of commission are a disadvantage to secrecy; "Why do I have to lie about my
mental illness?" It can be even harder for some when
they ask family members or friends to participate in the
secret. Many people, as a result, choose to forego this
aspect of secrecy. Others, however, see filling in the gaps
less as a lie and more a process of telling one's life experiences in a manner that is palatable to people. Recall
Tamiko's work résumé? She did not lie about her time
in the psychiatric hospital. Rather, she focused on something positive she did during that time: complete some
courses on computers. It's a matter of refocusing your
story on information that will not lead to stigmatizing
responses from others.

3. Selective disclosure

When you keep your experiences with mental illness a secret, you are not able to take advantage of the
support and resources of others. To rectify this problem,
some people take a chance and disclose their mental illness to selected co-workers or neighbors. These people
are taking a risk, however; those who find out may shun
them.

- *"I don't want to work next to a mental patient."*

- *"I don't want someone who had to be locked up in my bible group."*

- *"I'm pulling my kid out of the car pool. You can't drive safely when you take meds."*

With the risk comes opportunity. Persons who
disclose may find people who are supportive. "Now that
I told Mary about my depression, I can talk to her about
the side effects to my medications." Moreover, you
won't have to worry about keeping a secret near those
you've disclosed to. "Once Annette knew, it was such a
freeing feeling to open up to her."

Who might you disclose to?

Selective disclosure does not mean sharing your
experiences with everyone. You need to identify people
who are likely to respond positively to your message.
Table 5.8 lists the three reasons why you might disclose
to one person and not to another.

Table 5.8
Three Reasons Why You Might Disclose to Someone

---

1. Functional Relationship

The person provides some function with you where knowing your experiences with mental illness might help accomplish the function.

Sample functional relationships include:

psychiatrist	supervisor
doctor	co-workers
minister	teacher
car pool member	team member

2. Supportive Relationship

The person seems to be friendly and will provide support and approval to you when they find out about your experience.

Characteristics of this kind of person include:

pleasantness	open-mindedness
concern for others	loyalty
trustworthy	helpful

3. Empathic Relationship

Some people to whom you might disclose have had similar, though perhaps less painful, experiences. "I know what it's like to be depressed."

These kinds of persons can provide an empathic relationship. Their characteristics include:

willingness to listen	seem to understand
kindness	honesty

The *functional* relationship represents an association with some person where your mental illness serves as a conduit for establishing that relationship. Your relationship with a psychiatrist is an example. He or she sees you to diagnose and treat your mental illness. Thus, addressing the mental illness is the grounds for developing the relationship. The same type of relationship might be true with your family doctor, a minister, a teacher, or even your supervisor at work.

You might also consider disclosing to a person with whom you have developed a *supportive* relationship. You can be fairly certain that the friendly and kind person will support you when they discover that you live with a mental illness. You may discover supportive people by their pleasantness, concern for others, and open-mindedness. When someone takes interest in you, and seems to want to know more about you than your name and hometown, they may be a good candidate for developing a supportive relationship.

Then there are others who *empathize* with you. Often they've lived closely to people with similar experiences, or have a mental illness themselves.

> *"I know what the humiliation is," they might say. "I've had my depressions, too."*

Look for people that seem to be willing to listen, to understand, and who have a look of recognition when they hear talk about mental illness.

This demonstrates one facet of consumer empowerment which is gaining increasing acceptance in today's mental health world: self-help groups. Mental illness can be a very lonely disease. It behooves people with mental illness to seek out and develop friendships with other people with similar disorders. There are many organizations where this can be done including the National Alliance for the Mentally Ill, the Depressive Manic-Depressive Association, Emotions Anonymous, GROW, and others. The *Learn More About It* section at the back of the book provides contact information for groups like these.

What will you disclose?

A decision to disclose to someone does not mean you must disclose everything. Choosing to disclose does not mean giving up all your privacy. Rather, you are sharing information to break the secret, get some help, and enjoy some interpersonal closeness. Hence, just as you decided to whom you might disclose, so you must decide what you will and will not share. You need to determine what from your *past* do you wish to discuss and what *current* experiences do you want to keep private. The purpose of disclosing your past is to give people some knowledge of your problems with mental illness. The goal is not confession. Don't feel compelled to share things you are embarrassed about. Everyone has skeletons in their closet; you do not have to air these to get others to understand you have recovered from a severe mental illness. Specific issues you may wish to share include your diagnosis, symptoms, history of hospitalizations, and medications.

> *"I have a serious mental illness called schizophrenia. As a result, I have heard voices, had some strange beliefs, and been agitated. I was hospitalized four times in two years because of this. My psychiatrist and I have tried several different medications. Right now, my symptoms are managed well by a drug called Zyprexa."*

Remember! Don't share past experiences that make you feel embarrassed or ashamed.

The purpose of sharing current experiences with mental illness is twofold. First, you may want to impress upon the person that the severe mental illness of long ago has much less impact on you now. You want to let the person know you can control small problems that occur in your life.

> *"No, I'm not still mentally ill in the sense*
> *that I need to be hospitalized. Sometimes I*
> *get a little depressed. But I can handle it."*

The message here is that mental illness may not entirely go away. However, persons like you are still able to work, raise families, and be responsible members of society.

The second goal of sharing current experiences is to alert the person that you may have troubles in the future and need some assistance. Some persons may respond with empathy; "I know what it's like to have problems with depression, and I'm here for you." Others may offer support; "What can I do for you when you're having a panic attack?"

Disclosing is a process, not a one time act. Hence, as you get to know the person with whom you shared information, you may decide to provide more detail.

> *"As I got to know Mike, I told him more*
> *and more about my hospitalization. He*
> *had never been hospitalized but he still*
> *knew what I was talking about. He was in*
> *the Army and felt pushed around—told*
> *what to do there."*

Conversely, you may decide to withdraw from persons who disappoint you after disclosing to them. Deciding to share information doesn't prevent you from deciding to stop later.

"I made a mistake with Ray. I thought he was open-minded. But it didn't seem like he could handle it. So I guess we just fell apart. He stop sitting with me at lunch and I stopped sharing my experiences with mental illness with him. I was cordial but became a bit more distant."

Why I wanted you to know?

It may not be enough to tell your private history. You also need to tell persons what you want for letting them in on your secret; "Why I want you to know?" You will then be able to judge whether telling your story was successful by comparing the person's response to your hopes.

"I was scared about letting people know at work. I wanted Marie and Francie in the steno pool to understand why I had to leave work early on Wednesdays for my therapist's appointment. More importantly, I just didn't want to have to keep my illness a secret to them any longer. Their reaction was a pleasant surprise. Francie has sought me out since then to discuss my trips to Doctor Harrison's office. And Marie told me that sometimes she suffers from depression. I feel much less alone."

This means you need to carefully consider your reasons for telling others about your mental illness. You may have touched on these reasons when you listed the benefits of disclosure (the Worksheet in Table 5.4). They need to be translated into requests. Other common reasons and requests for telling peers are summarized in Table 5.9.

Table 5.9

Some Reasons Why People Decided to Disclose Their Mental Illness

---

To Tell the Secret

"I just wanted someone else to know that I get hospitalized for manic-depression."
"I don't want to have to feel like I'm sneaking around with a secret."
"I felt bad for having to keep a secret. I don't want to feel bad any more."

Understanding

"I'm hoping others will understand not only my mental illness, but the difficulty trying to keep it a secret."
"I'd like someone to say to me, 'I've had problems too.'"

Support and Assistance

"Sometimes I get sad. I'm looking for friends who can be supportive."
"Can I get a ride to the doctor?"
"Sometimes, I just need someone to talk to."

Reasonable Accommodation

"It's a law. When I ask for sensible help at work, you need to give it to me."
"Can I come in a half hour late this week? I'm feeling a little down. I'll make it up next week."

Many people with mental illness are moved to disclose their condition as a way to disperse their secret. They don't like to keep the secret of having a mental illness to themselves. They feel relieved to have the secret off their shoulders. Others disclose with a hope to gain understanding. They want others to comprehend their condition and in doing so understand *them*. A person with mental illness hopes that he or she might tap into a vein of empathy, where someone else might disclose to them that they, too, have a mental illness.

A person with mental illness might hope for support and assistance when disclosing a mental illness. This might be direct assistance as simple as asking for a ride to the community center. It might be emotional assistance like someone to talk with about their illness. Finally, there can be legal reasons for disclosing a mental illness. The Americans with Disabilities Act says businesses must give reasonable accommodation to persons with disabilities if they request it (See Chapter 9 for more about the ADA). Before reasonable accommodation can be requested, an employee with a debilitating mental illness needs to disclose the condition to their employer.

4. Indiscriminant Disclosure

Selective disclosure means there is a group of people with whom you are sharing your mental illness experiences AND a group from whom you are keeping the information secret. More than likely, the group who is not in on the secret is much larger than those you have shared the information with. This means there is still a large number of people who you have to be wary of; individuals who you don't want to find out about your experiences. Moreover, this means there is still a secret which could represent a source of shame.

> *"Even though I told my boss, guys on my work team, and my best friend, most people don't know. Every time I meet someone, it seems like there is this big secret between us. I have to be careful about what I say."*

People who choose indiscriminant disclosure abandon the secrecy. They choose to disregard any of the negative consequences of people finding out about their mental illness.

> *"I got tired of wondering who knew and who didn't. I finally got to the point where I didn't care. I stopped trying to keep my past a secret. I stopped concealing my meds and doctor appointments."*

The decision to no longer conceal your mental illness is not the same as telling everyone your story. Not keeping a secret means you are no longer trying to hide it. The person is relieved of the burden posed by the secret.

If you choose indiscriminant disclosure, you must still identify persons to seek out and actively share your experience. Not everyone will respond to your message well. Hence, the three reasons why you might disclose (in Table 5.8) are still relevant for selecting persons to tell. The difference is that you no longer worry about hiding your history from the world.

Reframe your experience

Most persons have to change the way they view their mental illness if they are to opt for indiscriminant disclosure. This may mean adjustment in a lifelong attitude about the place of mental illness in society. In the past, you probably viewed it as something that is disparaged by others and, therefore, should be kept secret. The desire to keep it a secret needs to change radically for you to partake in indiscriminant disclosure.

This redefinition may require accepting mental illness as part of *who you are*. Mental illness is not a bad part of you that needs to be rejected. It is one of many qualities that describe you: right-handed, brown haired, skilled in math, fair skinned, blue eyed, tall, poor at sports, and having schizophrenia. We are not making light of your mental illness; it clearly affects your life and life goals. But it is still only a small part of what defines who you are and what your future portends. If mental illness were all that mattered, then all persons with schizophrenia would be alike. As we've said earlier in this book, persons with schizophrenia are as diverse a group as African Americans, artists, and Anglicans. Your other qualities would have no relevance—which is wrong—your ability to cope greatly affects the course of your disability.

You have successfully changed your attitude about disclosure when talking about mental illness no longer evokes a sense of hesitancy or shame. It should lead to the same kind of matter of fact feelings as a discussion of your childhood home, your physical health, or your hair color. Its not bad or good; it just IS. Persons who have accomplished this kind of reframe say things like,

- "I'm more than a bag of symptoms."
- "I don't care what others think."
- "Take me as I am."

Can you handle indiscriminant disclosure?

Indiscriminant disclosure requires a hardy personality. Many more people are going to find out and

Table 5.10
Are You Able to Cope with Indiscriminant Disclosure?

Find a friend to role-play the following:

You are with several co-workers and say:

"I was hospitalized for schizophrenia about six times."

Your role-play partner says:

"Wow, and they let you out?"
"That's affirmative action for you. Anybody can get a job here."
"Do you ever feel out of control?"
"I'm asking for a transfer. I don't want to work around your kind."
"That's okay honey. I'll cover up your mistakes."
"Do you live in a hospital at night?"
"Would you flip out if you stopped taking your meds?"

These comments are based on the three stigmatizing attitudes about mental illness reviewed in Chapter 2.

After listening to these comments, rate yourself on the scales below.
Circle the number that best represents how you feel in response to these statements.

not at all		moderately		very
ashamed		**ashamed**		**ashamed**

1	2	3	4	5	6	7

not at all		moderately		very
nervous		**nervous**		**nervous**

1	2	3	4	5	6	7

not at all		moderately		very
sad		**sad**		**sad**

1	2	3	4	5	6	7

not at all		moderately		very
angry		**angry**		**angry**

1	2	3	4	5	6	7

react negatively to your mental illness than other decisions about disclosure. Hence, you need to be able to cope with the disapproval that results from bigoted reactions. One way to tell whether you are up to this is to role-play bigoted situations. Ask a friend to repeat a list of nasty or ignorant comments someone might say to you about your mental illness; a sample list of comments is summarized in Table 5.10. Then determine your reaction.

The goal of this exercise is not to practice effective replies. The best kind of response is probably to ignore the person. (Other suggestions for handling ignorance are discussed in Chapters 7, 8, and 9). Rather, the goal of this exercise is to monitor your reaction. Scores above a 4 on any scale in Table 5.10 may suggest that these kinds of insults will hurt you. You are reporting significant feelings of shame, anxiety, sadness or anger because of bigoted comments. You need to ask yourself whether you want to put up with this kind of grief. And remember, a comment from a friend in a role-play has far less sting than a remark from a co-worker in real life.

5. Broadcast Your Experience

Indiscriminant disclosure means no longer trying to hide your mental illness; but you are not likely to go out of your way to inform people about it. Broadcasting your experience means educating people about mental illness. It's similar to coming out of the closet in the gay community; the goal is to actively let people know your experience with mental illness. This kind of disclosure is much more than dropping your guard and throwing away any notion of secret. Your goal is to seek out many people to share your past history and current experiences with mental illness.

Broadcasting your experience has the same benefits as indiscriminant disclosure. You no longer need to worry about keeping a secret. You will also find people who may provide understanding, support, and assistance to you because of your message. However, people who choose to broadcast their experience seem to derive an additional benefit. Namely, it seems to foster their sense of power over the experience of mental illness and stigma. No longer must they cower because of feelings of inferiority.

> *"I'm equal to everyone else. I have nothing to hide."*

This kind of consciousness raising may help you to understand that your problems with mental illness are not solely a function of biological limitations. Society's reactions are equally to blame. Shouting this out relieves you of community oppression. In fact, many people who choose to broadcast their experience wish to surpass the limited goal of talking about their mental illness. They also express their dissatisfaction with the way they have been treated because they have a mental illness.

> *"I'm angry. If I so much as question my meds, my doctor thinks I'm acting out and talks like he is going to put me back in the hospital. I'm not able to be a partner in my treatment."*

This discontent is also aimed at society—anger at being viewed differently, losing opportunities, and having to keep secrets.

> *"I've done nothing wrong. I'm no criminal.*
> *Don't steal my chances from me because I*
> *have been hospitalized."*

Be prepared for anger and distancing

Broadcasting your experiences will yield hostile responses, just like indiscriminate disclosure, and more. Citizens hearing someone's story about mental illness frequently battle the message AND the messenger. Like the person choosing indiscriminate disclosure, broadcasters get hostile reactions to their messages.

> *"Why do I have to live next to a crazy guy*
> *like you? You're dangerous to my family.*
> *I'll be keeping an eye on you."*

Broadcasters also get angry responses to the message.

> *"I don't want to hear this stuff. You think*
> *I'm a bigot? I give money to charities to*
> *keep psych hospitals open. Why do you*
> *have to go stirring up trouble? Just live in*
> *your community quietly and don't go*
> *telling me all your troubles."*

Civil rights leaders have experienced similar reactions for decades. Challenging messages from racial groups about economic equality and political injustice upset the status quo. People in power don't want to hear this. In a similar manner, talking about your mental illness and your displeasure with society's reaction is disquieting. Citizens may rebel against the messenger with angry denials.

> *"You're making things out a lot worse than they are. Life in state hospitals isn't that bad."*

Once again, you need to make sure you're up for this kind of reaction. You may wish to complete the role-play in Table 5.10 to find out. Determine whether your emotional response is excessive.

Some persons who choose to broadcast their experience join advocacy groups for support and guidance. These groups are described more fully in Chapter 6. Contact information for specific groups is provided in the "Learn More About It" section of the book. The next section of the book also describes other ways to foster a sense of personal empowerment.

How Might People Respond to Your Disclosure?

Be certain of one thing: disclosure will impact the people around you. Whether you choose selective disclosure (where information is cautiously shared with a carefully chosen person) or broadcasting (where you announce your experiences to as many people as possible) those who discover the facts are likely to react strongly. You need to consider the varied ways in which people may respond and plan your reactions accordingly. Table 5.11 lists a variety of reactions to disclosure which are sorted into groups by two factors.

> Factor 1. *Emotional Response:* People may emotionally respond positively or negatively towards you.

> Factor 2. *Behavioral Reaction:* People may decide to seek you out to express their emotion or they may pull away and try to avoid you.

Table 5.11
How People Might Respond to Your Disclosure

BEHAVIORAL REACTION	EMOTIONAL RESPONSE	
	POSITIVE	**NEGATIVE**
Seek You Out	**Understanding** "It must be hard living with your illness and the secret." **Interpersonal Support** "I'm here for you if you need someone to talk to." **Assistance** "Can I give you a lift to the doctor?"	**Disrespect** "I don't want some dangerous loony like you around." **Denial** "I'm not giving you any special breaks because of your illness." **Retribution** "I'll get you fired. I don't have to work next to a crazy guy like you."
Pull Away	**Shared Experience** "I have those experiences too. But I don't want any one to know."	**Fear/Avoidance** "You're dangerous. I'm staying away." **Gossip** "Hey, did you hear about Joe? He was committed to the insane asylum." **Blame** "I have the same kind of problems as Gayle but I don't go around and blab about it."

Positive Experiences

Citizens hearing your disclosure can positively respond in a variety of ways. Three of these involve reaching out to you. They may express understanding of or empathize with your experiences.

> *"Dealing with mental illness must be very tough. I'm impressed with how well you handle it."*

Along with understanding they may provide *interpersonal support*. Support may include explicit commitments to be available to you. Interpersonal support might also include *assistance*.

> *"Let me know if I can provide you a lift to the drug store or if you'd like to come and hang out some time when you're feeling blue."*

Oddly, another positive experience might take the form of *pulling away* from you. Someone with similar problems with mental illness and stigma might let you know that they understand. However, they do not currently share your resolve to disclose and hence, wish to keep their experiences a secret. This might mean occasionally backing away on interactions so they are not discovered.

> *"I really am impressed with the guts you show for letting other guys in the shop know about your psych problems. I have them, too. But I'm worried how people will respond. So, I might back away if you're*

talking about a doctor's visit at the lunch table. I don't want anyone turning to me and asking questions."

Negative Experiences

Unfortunately, hearing your story of self-disclosure will lead to negative responses, too. Some of these responses occur when people seek you out to share their reactions. This includes *disrespect* ("People like you are all loony."), *denial* ("You're just looking for sympathy. You don't have any problems."), and *retribution* ("I'll make sure the other guys in the poker club hear about this. You're out pal."). Negative experiences also occur by pulling away. People may *fear* you ("You're dangerous, you have a mental illness.") and *avoid* you as a result. Even though they avoid you, you become the butt of *gossip* ("Did you hear about Sophie? She has to see a psychiatrist!"). People may *blame* you for your decision to disclose ("Why did you have to stir everyone up with talk about your mental illness?").

Like all other points we made about disclosure in this chapter, it has its costs and its benefits. Only you can decide whether disclosing to others is worth pursuing.

Two Rules for Deciding About Disclosure

We propose two rules (summarized in Table 5.12) to guide any final consideration of strategies for disclosing mental illness. The **first rule** suggests caution. To paraphrase a Supreme Court Judge, "It is impossible to quiet the sounded bell." Once you have disclosed, it is near impossible to retract the news. According to *Rule 1, Minimal Risks with Little Information*, disclosing and then recanting is much harder than being conservative and letting people know slowly.

> *"I told some people at the club about my manic-depression. They didn't respond as I hoped. And then that guy murdered two guards at the U.S. Capitol. Now, all my buddies are looking at me suspiciously."*

This woman would not be in her predicament if she had waited to tell. Rule 1 counsels overall caution in disclosing such private information.

Table 5.12
Two Rules for Deciding About Disclosure

Minimal Risks with Little Information

Rule 1 >	Those with no information, pose no risks. Hence, when not certain, don't tell.

Delayed Decision is Lost Opportunity

Rule 2 >	When putting off tough decisions until later, benefits are lost now. Hence, when looking for support, take a chance.

Rule 2, Delayed Decision is Lost Opportunity, suggests caution leads to unnecessary delay. There will always be hostile and ignorant people who will chastise you for talking about your mental illness. Don't let them keep you from humans who care and are supportive.

"To think, all this time I was afraid of telling my bible group that I was hospitalized for schizophrenia. They were amazingly supportive. I'm glad I finally got it out because now we're much closer."

Although these rules represent wise advice to guide this tough decision, they obviously contradict each other. That's because there is no clear answer to the question about disclosure. Only you can know for sure. You must weigh all the costs and benefits and decide for yourself what to do.

Chapter 6

Seven Ways to Foster Personal Empowerment

"There is no medicine like hope, no incentive so great, and no tonic so powerful as expectation of something tomorrow."

O.S. Marden

Persons who have a sense of power over their illness and, more importantly, a feeling of control over their lives, are not victimized by stigma. Even though they are aware that this kind of prejudice and discrimination continues to disrespect them as a group, empowered individuals are able to avoid the sting of others' ignorance. Moreover, they do not turn this kind of prejudice against themselves as self-stigma. Personal empowerment is the opposite of stigma victimization.

Self-stigma ⟵⟶ **Personal empowerment**

Hence, ways in which people can improve their personal sense of empowerment suggest a path to avoiding personal harm from stigma.

We review seven ways to foster empowerment in this chapter. First, however, we discuss what is meant by the term: what is personal empowerment? A Personal Empowerment Self-Assessment Scale is provided that helps interested readers determine their level of empowerment. In this way, readers can learn about empowerment by determining where they fall on different factors that represent control over one's life. We follow up presentation of the scale with a thorough discussion of empowerment in its various forms.

Personal Empowerment Self-Assessment Scale

One way to assess empowerment is to complete the Personal Empowerment Self-Assessment Scale in Table 6.1. Readers should answer the questions in the Scale to determine whether they beat themselves up with stigma or whether they have some sense of personal empowerment. Alternatively, readers might share this test with peers who have questions about their level of empowerment. The key for the test as well as the interpretation guidelines can be found at the bottom of the page. Complete the test fully before reviewing the key; also, don't forget the caution we provided in Chapter 4 about using the results of self-tests.

The Self-Assessment Scale provides two scores for persons who complete the test. They represent the two ways in which empowerment impact the person with mental illness; although a brief distinction is provided here, these different ways are discussed more thoroughly below. Empowerment can affect *one's self.*

Table 6.1
Personal Empowerment Self-Assessment Scale

Rate how much you agree with the following statements using this scale.

strongly disagree	disagree	neither agree nor disagree	agree	strongly agree
1	2	3	4	5

_____ 1. I am able to accomplish my personal goals.

_____ 2. I want to change my community's view of mental illness.

_____ 3. I have control over my treatment.

_____ 4. It is okay for me to get mad at people who stigmatize mental illness.

_____ 5. I am not a bad person because of mental illness.

_____ 6. We can beat stigma if we work together.

_____ 7. Things will work out in my future.

_____ 8. I'm going to make waves about stigma.

_____ 9. I am okay even if I have a mental illness.

_____ 10. I get mad at the way mental illness is portrayed on TV.

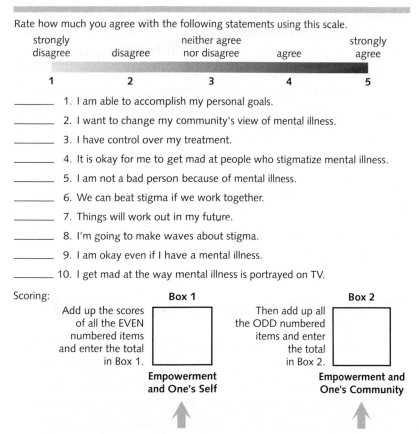

Scoring:

Box 1
Add up the scores of all the EVEN numbered items and enter the total in Box 1.
Empowerment and One's Self

Box 2
Then add up all the ODD numbered items and enter the total in Box 2.
Empowerment and One's Community

The total in Box 1 represents views about empowerment towards yourself: self-esteem, future optimism, and self-effectiveness. Scores in Box 1 that are **less than 8** suggest you do not have much empowerment towards yourself. In this case, you will benefit from many of the suggestions to improve empowerment listed in this chapter.

The total in Box 2 represents views about empowerment towards your community: righteous anger and willingness to take action. Scores in Box 2 that are **less than 8** suggest you are unsure about challenging your community and its stigmatizing ways. You will benefit from the empowerment strategies reviewed in this chapter as well as the anti-stigma approaches summarized in Chapters 7, 8, and 9.

This self-assessment was inspired by a measure developed by Sally Rogers,
Judy Chamberlin, and colleagues published in Psychiatric Services in 1997.

Persons who feel empowered have good self esteem, believe they are effective in life, and are optimistic about their future. Low scores on this scale (below 8) suggest the person does not feel empowered about him or herself. This person may benefit from the strategies that foster empowerment reviewed later in this chapter.

Alternatively, empowerment can affect a person's view of his or her *community*. Empowered persons may show righteous anger against prejudice and actually participate in civil actions that target stigma. Low scores on this scale (below 8) mean the person is intimidated by public stigma and does little to counter it. Personal empowerment strategies summarized in this chapter as well as anti-stigma approaches in Chapters 7, 8, and 9 may all be of help to this person.

What is Personal Empowerment?

As we stated earlier, personal empowerment is the opposite of self-stigma. Persons who feel positive about themselves and stand up to their community are not victimized by self-stigma. Hence, one way of defining empowerment is the absence of self-stigma. The reader may notice that much of the discussion on the next pages seems to be the polar opposite of the definitions of self-stigma provided in Chapter 4.

Unfortunately, this kind of definition suggests that personal empowerment represents the absence of pathology. Personal empowerment is much more than the *absence* of self-stigma, however. Personal empowerment is also a positive approach to one's life and his or her community. Consistent with the discussion in the Personal Empowerment Self-Assessment Scale, we describe empowerment in two *positive* ways: the affirmative way in which individuals view themselves and in which persons interact with their community.

Empowerment and One's Sense of Self

Persons who have a strong sense of personal empowerment have good self-esteem. They view themselves positively; self-statements include beliefs that they are dependable individuals.

> *"I am a good person. Sure, I might have a mental illness. But, I'm also a son, a brother, a husband, a friend, and a lover. I'm a student, a co-worker, a member of a church congregation. These things together add up to an important person in this world who has much to offer."*

This perspective exceeds the absence-of-disease view on self-esteem.

> *"Who I am has nothing to do with mental illness."*

The absence-of-disease view is almost defensive, where persons define themselves by denying their disease. Empowered people also deny negative self-statements about themselves. But, more importantly, empowered persons recognize their countless positive attributes rather than obsessing on their flaws. They can affirm why they are an important person in the world. Sure, they recognize the occasional errors that haunt us all.

181

But they acknowledge these mistakes and still value their role in the world.

Persons with a sense of personal power have confidence in their ability to be successful. Psychologists call this *self-efficacy*. They believe they can competently attain their goals and deal with problems in the future.

> *"I used to think that because I have a mental illness I couldn't handle real work. Why bother trying for a good job? I'm not up to an employer's demands. But now I realize that I have the same mix of strengths and weaknesses as everyone. I can call on these strengths to help me excel at my new job as a billing clerk."*

This kind of perspective helps persons gain control over their future. Rather then being victim to their disabilities, they are able to make decisions about how to attain personal goals.

Persons who are self-empowered are optimistic. Instead of being overwhelmed by their symptoms and a sometimes coercive treatment system, they believe they will be successful. Those readers who have not experienced the loss of hope fostered by a paternalistic treatment system may not realize how important regaining optimism and control over one's future can be.

> *"My doctors always meant well. But they robbed me of control over my life. They said I wouldn't get married, I can't live on my own, I'd never handle a job, forget about earning real money. I felt like a spec-*

tator watching my life go by. And it was a horrendous feeling.

"Now I have a different outlook. I can accomplish my goals. I don't need to wait for others. And the return of personal power has made me human again."

Self-empowerment does not mean hiding from one's disabilities. Persons with optimism and a sense of control over their life do not deny they have suffered psychiatric symptoms in the past. Nor do they think they will never experience them in the future. Instead, these persons replace being overwhelmed by symptoms with acceptance of their disability.

"Having a psychiatric disability is who I am just like being female, white or left-handed. There are disadvantages to these other qualities, too. My second grade teacher used to punish me when I picked up my pen with the wrong hand."

With acceptance also comes the realization that the person is more than just a diagnosis. Much more! Self-empowered persons accept their problems. But, they also recognize that who they are can be described beyond a set of symptoms. The total of one's sense of self includes the various roles and goals that make up life. Self-empowerment and positive esteem represent the appreciation of the breadth and depth of these goals and roles.

Empowerment and One's Community

Persons with a sense of personal empowerment are not intimidated by a frequently hostile society. Rather, they are confident that they can fight the ignorance of their community and beat stigma.

> *"Other groups have done it. The civil rights actions of the 50s and 60s turned around attitudes about race. We can do the same thing with mental illness."*

Persons who are empowered feel righteous anger. They feel it towards the disrespectful images of persons with mental illness on TV and in magazines, towards landlords and employers who won't hire them because they have been hospitalized, and towards mental health professionals who said they will never make it beyond the walls of an institution. These people have given up their sense of powerlessness in the face of an oppressive majority. In its place, they face the stigmatizing ways in which society responds to persons with mental illness.

Empowered persons are not overcome by anger. Instead, they are able to channel this anger into activities that diminish stigma and further opportunities. Empowered persons may affect change by becoming active in anti-stigma programs that protest hurtful images of mental illness, by joining mutual-help programs that foster empowerment among peers, or by earning the appropriate credentials and trying to change the mental health system from within as a provider.

Each of these ways that facilitate empowerment are more fully discussed below. The point here is that righteous anger can energize persons so they take control of their life rather than be victimized by stigma and discrimination.

Empowerment Does Not Mean Expertise

Because people have power over their lives does not mean they are expert in everything. Because persons with mental illness regain a sense of hope and self-esteem does not mean they no longer need the assistance of peers or the mental health system. This point can seem paradoxical for some pursuing personal empowerment.

> *"It used to mix me up. I thought that I didn't need the mental health system, that I could make all my own decisions. But then I got depressed again. I found my doctor's help to be invaluable. How could this be? I shouldn't need anyone if I'm truly empowered."*

It is the nature of the human condition that we all rely on each other, whether we are challenged by disability or not. Empowerment helps the person regain control over his or her life. But, it reminds people that this life is lived within a social world with others for whom we provide care *and* on whom we rely in times of need.

Seven Ways to Foster Empowerment

Empowerment can be construed narrowly in terms of control over the services that help people deal with their disabilities. It can also be understood more broadly in terms of command over all spheres of one's life; not just problems related to mental illness but succeeding at work, in relationships, during play, spiritually, and in as many other domains as possible. Table 6.2 lists seven strategies that facilitate empowerment. Each of these strategies is discussed more fully in the remainder of the chapter.

Table 6.2
The Seven Ways to Foster Empowerment

1   **From Noncompliance to Collaboration**   A change in perspective from expecting consumers to blindly comply with treatment to making care-plans that are user-friendly.

2   **Consumer Satisfaction and Other Input on Services**   At the absolute minimum, programs that empower participants need to be satisfactory to those participants. Moreover, these programs need to obtain input from consumers to assure that program design reflects their interests.

3   **Lodges and Clubhouses**   For more than three decades, the mental health system has supported treatment programs that were largely operated by persons with mental illness. Lodges are residential programs in this mold; clubhouses are social and work programs.

4   **Assertive Community Treatment and Supported Employment**   Instead of the consumer going to the professional, the best treatment occurs when the professional travels to the consumer, and all the places in which consumers need assistance. Provision of services in the person's home or community is the

Note that this write-up is somewhat different than most other chapters in the book. In other sections, we discussed what the person might *do* to deal with stigma, how they might personally beat its negative impact. While there is some discussion of individual activities that foster empowerment, the focus in this chapter is more on *expectations*. What should individuals expect from a service system that fosters their personal empowerment? These serve as benchmarks by which a person can judge an individual program. Does service system 'X' endorse the kind of philosophy and provide the kind of tools that foster a person's empowerment? Service system is broadly defined here to not only include professional services— from mental health centers, for example—but also include support and mutual help from peers.

hallmark of Assertive Community Treatment (or ACT). Services in real-world job sites is supported employment.

5   **Consumers as Providers**   Many persons with mental illness are deciding to return to school, obtain necessary credentials, and assume jobs in the mental health system as providers. In this way, they can change the system from the inside.

6   **Self-Help, Mutual Assistance, and Other Consumer Operated Services**   There is almost a fifty year history of programs developed by persons with mental illness to help peers. These programs provide places where people can provide and receive help from individuals with similar concerns.

7   **Participatory Action Research**   Much of the current research on psychiatric disability and rehabilitation reflects the perspective of the existing mental health system. Persons with mental illness must be equal partners in the research enterprise for future studies to represent the differing interests of consumers.

1. From Noncompliance to Collaboration

Many mental health providers must drastically re-conceive their viewpoint about the consumer's [1] relationship with treatment for empowerment to occur. The old notion: persons with mental illness should *comply* with all aspects of treatment. Professionals know best; anything that strayed from the prescribed treatment program represented unclear thinking due to the illness. Failure to comply was indicative of unconscious motivations to resist health. Mandatory treatments and a coercive system rested on these assumptions. Research evidence seemed to clearly support these conclusions. Depending on the study, anywhere between two-thirds and three-quarters of persons did not take their psychiatric medications as prescribed. More than half of all participants in rehabilitation and similar psychosocial programs do not complete the treatment plan as agreed. These data suggest resistance is rampant and significantly undermines treatment of serious psychiatric illness.

Considered another way, however, these data yield completely different conclusions. Rather than 66 to 75% of persons taking their medication incorrectly, perhaps two-thirds to three-quarters of all mental health providers are prescribing drugs poorly. They are prescribing medication wrong. Lack of compliance does not represent resistance by a person with psychosis as much as meager treatment by the mental health team.

---

[1] We use the term consumer in some parts of this chapter to remind us that empowerment is meaningful in terms of the person's consumption of mental health services.

Equally sobering statistics suggest that more than 70% of everyone who is prescribed any kind of medicine does not take it the way the doctor ordered. Clearly, it is not just a problem of persons with mental illness.

Rather than expecting persons to passively comply with care (be it psychiatric care, or general medical treatment), what is needed is more enlightened practice that calls for *collaboration* between providers and their clients. An equal partnership occurs when each party learns from the other: providers learn about the nature of specific symptoms and corresponding disabilities from the person challenged by these problems; consumers learn the range of treatments and services that address these problems.

> *"I've been struggling with my mental illness for 15 years now and its amazing how the relationship has changed with my doc. When we first met, he'd listen for about five minutes to my symptoms, then wrote down a script and sent me on my way. I wouldn't dare ask questions about what he was thinking.*
>
> *"I now have lots of questions. Should I be drinking alcohol? Should I be sleeping more? Taking pills less? And I also have lots of opinions. I told Dr. Mulhoney that I didn't like the side effects of the new pill he had me on and stopped it.*
>
> *"We're much more like partners now. And that wasn't easy for either of us. He had to learn that my view of the illness was just as important—no, more important because I live the symptoms everyday—as*

his. And I had to learn to speak up for myself, to tell him when things were working and when they weren't."

How do providers and consumers foster a collaborative working relationship? Almost a decade ago, we wrote a paper that outlined strategies for answering this question: they are summarized in Table 6.3. We listed these strategies next to corresponding barriers to collaboration, the hurdles to fully participating in treatment.

Ways to Overcome the Side Effects of Treatment

One reason why many persons do not regularly take medications is because of nasty side effects. Research has shown that medications for psychiatric illness can harm *every* organ system in the human body: lungs, heart, eyes, skin and hair, skeleton, muscles, digestion, reproduction, elimination, balance, attention, and thinking. No wonder persons who are prescribed medication frequently stop on their own. The side effects can be much worse than the symptoms they attempt to resolve. At an absolute minimum, it is essential that the psychiatrist and mental health team acknowledge the negative impact of these side effects for collaboration to be possible.

"My doctor told me just to ignore the side effects of the pill he was giving me. Here I was, on this new drug for my voices, so antsy I couldn't even sleep, and he's telling me to just forget about it. He didn't have a

Table 6.3

Barriers to Collaboration and Ways to Overcome Them

Barrier	Ways to Overcome Barrier
Treatment Techniques — Nasty side effects	> Use new generation of medications that reduce side effects. > Use low-dose medication strategies. > Educate consumer to side effects and teach self-tracking strategies.
Complex treatment plans	> Consumer should have central role in designing treatment plan. > Use simple language. > Clearly explain steps of treatment. > Begin simple, and slowly add more complex steps.
Long term treatment	> Regularly assess goals and relevance of treatments to these goals. > Provide treatment holidays. > Consider place-train options.
Treatment Delivery System — Clinics are depressing and dingy places	> Improve clinic decor and ambience. > Offer coffee and refreshments. > Require all staff (including clerks) to be courteous and respectful. > Move most services to the consumer's home or other convenient setting.
Long waits at clinics	> Maintain realistic schedules. > Send reminders to consumers.
Provider-consumer Relationships — Provider has poor interpersonal style and is disinterested in consumer feedback	> Educate providers about the importance of "collaborative" roles. > Educate providers about the need for consumer satisfaction. > Alert administrators about poor provider style. > Pair provider with mentor for remediation.
Family-consumer Characteristics — Possess little knowledge or unrealistic expectations about treatment	> Educate consumer and family member to treatment options. > Provide opportunities for consumers and family members to share concerns.

adapted from Corrigan, Liberman, & Engel (1990)

*clue what this all meant. I stopped seeing
him as soon as I got out of the hospital."*

Fortunately, the last decade or so has seen a significant revolution in the development of medications
that address the primary symptoms of the disorder and
do not cause as many side effects. Atypical antipsychotics like Risperdal and Zyprexa improve symptoms
like hallucinations, delusions, and agitation without
causing the movement disorders and dry mouth characteristic of traditional antipsychotic medication like
Thorazine, Haldol, and Mellaril. The new generation of
antidepressants like Prozac, Zoloft, and Paxil cause far
fewer and less dangerous side effects than the tri-cyclic
antidepressants and MAO inhibitors. Mental health
teams who are concerned about ways in which side
effects impede collaboration need to be fully informed
about these medications and willing to work with the
person to find the drug and dose that yields the best
impact on symptoms with the least side effects.
Sometimes, this effort might require educating the consumer about the main side effects of medication so he
or she can make fully informed decisions about them.

Side effects are not limited to psychiatric medication. Psychosocial services can also have unintended
results. For example, some programs that ask persons to
explore their past may unnecessarily upset them and
cause relapse. Other interventions might cause a break
among family members. Hence, service providers and
consumers alike need to be mindful of the side effects
of their interventions and be prepared to pull back
when the consumer lets them know treatment is hurting, not helping.

Sometimes people receiving mental health services have difficulty collaborating with treatment plans because they are unnecessarily complex.

> *"When I was first prescribed the medication, I was told to take it in the evening and morning unless I wasn't sleeping well. Then, I was told to skip the evening but make sure I got it twice as much the next morning. If this pattern made me edgy, I was supposed to skip the morning and try once at lunch and once at dinner. I was supposed to make sure I took the pill on a full stomach. But I was to watch what I ate. I was to be especially careful about taking too many fats and a certain monoamine, whatever that was. Oh, and I wasn't supposed to worry about side effects unless they became too severe, in which case I might skip the medication for one period only, unless my anxiety continued to increase... then I should never skip, unless I didn't sleep the night before."*

The practice of psychiatry (including medication management, psychiatric rehabilitation, peer support, and individual psychotherapy) can be very complex. Providers need to remember that to collaborate with the consumer, they must present their treatment proposals in a simple and straightforward manner. Physicians learn more than 13,000 new terms during medical school. They need to replace this jargon with simple and straight language. Instead of saying,

> *"Prolonged dosage of traditional antipsychotic medication at maximum points of*

193

> *the therapeutic range can lead to akathisia
> and dystonia."*

the doctor might say,

> *"Taking high doses of Thorazine can make
> you jumpy."*

Some providers might believe that a consumer's inability to understand the treatment plan is further evidence of his or her disability. "We wouldn't have to over-simplify our plans if they had their full cognitive faculties." However, confusion with treatment plans is not solely a problem of persons with mental illness. All patients—those seeking help with a heart problem as well as those wanting aide for social anxiety—may have difficulty understanding the various aspects of the illness and ways to fix it. In the past decade, all of health care has realized that the person with the illness is central to managing the symptoms. That is why so many doctors' offices now include models of internal organs and charts that show disease processes. In this way, the person can learn firsthand about what is wrong and how treatments will help. Similar education needs to be provided to the consumer of mental health services.

One way to help a person understand complex treatments is to divide those treatments into easy-to-understand steps. The mental health consumer is more likely to become involved in a rehabilitation plan that clearly maps out the steps to returning to work, such as,

1. Identifying your job interests and abilities
2. Identifying available jobs in the areas that correspond with these interests and abilities

3. Practicing job interviewing

4. Calling and arranging job interviews

The opposite would be a paternalistic message like,

> *"Trust me as your counselor. I'll guide you
> and let you know when you're ready to
> return to work."*

The job process is less overwhelming when one can clearly see all the steps it comprises and consider them one at a time.

Another problem with services for persons with serious mental illness is they seem to continue forever. The end is never in sight and attaining goals never seems possible. This problem can be diminished by making sure that consumer and provider regularly re-evaluate treatment goals and the service plan that helps the person achieve these goals. If a person wants to work, then he or she and the treatment team need to consider each month whether the medication and rehabilitation program are helping him or her return to this goal. Treatment holidays also help with the never-ending feeling to some services. Adults in regular jobs take vacations to recharge their batteries. In similar vein, participants in long psychosocial services programs might take a week or two away to gain new energy.

Recently, some experts in rehabilitation have proposed a different service model that may significantly change the long-term, snail's pace of psychosocial services. The traditional model of psychosocial intervention is *train-place*: train the person on all the skills they need to live independently or work in a regular job before placing them in their own apartment or on a competitive job. This approach may encourage the consumer and treatment team to move slowly and make sure the person has all the needed skills and resources before attempting a goal. *Place-train* models provide a more timely alternative: place the person on the job or in housing immediately and then provide the needed support and skills that help the person stay there. Research is still preliminary but suggests that the place-train option may be equally effective in helping people make their goals and keep them.

Improving the Treatment Delivery System

Sometimes a person needing help for mental illness is hesitant to collaborate with service providers because the places to which they go for care are dingy and depressing. Many community mental health centers and rehabilitation programs are in dark dirty buildings. A simple coat of paint and pleasing artwork can greatly improve the attractiveness of these settings. Moreover, long waits need to be replaced by closer scheduling. Most readers would stop seeing the dentist who made them wait for an hour or more. Receptionists at dental offices frequently call the night before to remind us of the next day's cleaning. Similar courtesies could be extended to consumers of mental health services to help them keep their appointments.

Some staff have the attitude that persons with mental illness are poor and undeserving of the best treatments. They can be rude and curt as a result. Supervisors should require courteous and respectful behavior from *all* staff: the receptionist answering the phone, the secretary scheduling the appointment, the nurse dispensing medication, and the doctor providing therapy.

Perhaps the best way to make sure services are provided in a good setting is to offer them in the person's home. Called *assertive community treatment* and discussed more fully below, this approach believes services should be provided in the setting most convenient to the consumer.

Enhancing Provider-Consumer Relationships

There are still many providers who were trained in the old school. They act as the expert who prescribes treatment while the consumer's job is to obediently comply. Unfortunately, these kinds of people frequently do not believe good interpersonal skills are essential for good service.

> *"I once actually had a doctor come in and start asking questions about my sex life without so much as a 'How do you do?' When I wanted to know who she was, she actually got miffed. And when I asked why she was prescribing Navane instead of the Zyprexa, which I benefited from in the past, she walked out on me!"*

These practitioners do not believe that partnership and collaboration are essential for good care.

Sometimes, simple education helps professionals like these. Informing these staff that consumer control over care is essential for success may change their ways.

197

They may benefit from discussion of the research literature that shows consumer satisfaction of services is a
significant predictor of how much that consumer benefits from care. Moreover, research also shows medical
and mental health malpractice suits decrease considerably when the provider develops a mutually respectful
relationship with the consumer. Some providers may
need skills training courses that teach them the appropriate interpersonal techniques to foster a good working
relationship. Sometimes, pairing these practitioners with
senior mentors who can model appropriate interactions
may help.

Others of this ilk may need some extra motivation to learn and use the kind of skills that promote a
collaborative relationship. Cranky doctors who are short
with their clients reflect poorly on the program and the
administrators who are responsible for running these
programs. Hence, it is up to the practitioner's supervisor
to motivate the individual to use appropriate skills.
Consumers who are not satisfied with the quality of
interaction with the group of providers at an agency
should let program supervisors know.

Addressing Some Consumer Misunderstandings About Treatment

Sometimes consumers have difficulty collaborating with the treatment team because they do not fully
understand the scope of the treatment plan.

"No one ever told me that when I first
started taking meds for my hallucinations

I'd have to continue for months or even years. I thought it was like penicillin. Take it for a couple of weeks until the voices go away."

Let us reiterate points made earlier in this section. This lack of understanding does not mean the consumer has unconscious motivations to resist good care. Nor does it reflect their psychiatric disability, cognitive deficits that prevent them from grasping these concepts. Rather, service providers need to remember that what they are doing can be complex, just like caring for a heart ailment or fixing a car. It is the providers' responsibility to educate persons they are serving about the full extent of interventions.

Family members are key partners in the service plans of many persons struggling with psychiatric disabilities. They, too, may have misconceptions about treatments. Hence, family members need to be incorporated into education programs to make sure they are fully informed about the scope and extent of care. In addition to education programs, multiple family groups that provide consumers and their family members the opportunity to exchange information and concerns can be an excellent way to foster collaboration with the treatment team.

Beyond Collaboration

Collaboration as a model may not go far enough for many empowered people. Collaboration assumes compromise among two equal parties. It assumes that the consumer and provider of services have equal roles in making treatment goals and deciding future actions. This assumption may be incorrect; it is the person whose life is the focus of services who is the center of the relationship, and hence they should be the authority over interventions.

From Noncompliance to Collaboration to Consumer-Driven Services

This model is more akin to the relationship between homeowner and craftsmen who are making repairs. Clearly, the plumber, electrician, and carpenter know best how to fix leaks, shorts, and squeaky doors. But the homeowner has final authority. It is the unwise electrician who fails to work with the landlord in returning the house to lights. The customer is always right!

Many readers will respond to this notion with concern. After all, the relationship between doctor and client should be more intimate and respected than that with Don the Plumber. As we acknowledged above, close-working relationships built on mutual respect and good social skills is the foundation on which services should be provided. Consumers need to strive for these kinds of interactions with those who provide them services. However, consumers must also realize that when this kind of respect and skill is not provided by the treatment team, they should look for another.

This makes sense as a theory; being selective in practice is much more difficult. On page 87 of the local Yellow Pages, there are more than 20 plumbers from which we could choose. On page 92, there are 7 psychiatrists. If one is not satisfactory, try the next. In reality this can be more difficult. First, changing psychiatrists and other mental health providers is more personally painful than dialing up a new plumber. The consumer has shared many intimate details and learned to trust the provider. Second, many consumers have financial constraints that prevent them from changing providers. Frequently, services are offered as part of government entitlement programs with little choice (like Medicaid, Medicare, and state office of mental health grants). For example, there is only one major community mental health center in the South Suburbs of Chicago. Consumers have few places to turn if services are poor at this center. What real freedom do consumers have to discard a treatment team with whom they do not mesh and find a second set of providers who they work with well?

Government agencies are beginning to share this concern. Officials realize that until consumers have personal control over the monies that pay for their treatment, providers will not be truly responsive to them. One model for this kind of funding is discussed more fully in a later section of this chapter on "Consumer Satisfaction: Buying Services that are Satisfactory."

Collaboration May Mean Giving Yourself Permission to...

Many persons with mental illness have years of learning compliance: how to obey doctor's orders. Moreover, many persons have parents and other family members who have been telling them to be "good patients." These consumers may be fearful of collaboration. They may think they are unable to be partners in the treatment process.

> *"I've been told what to do for so long, I'm scared of making decisions. What if I decide to move out on my own and I fail? What if I get a job and lose my Social Security? It's better to leave all the major decisions in the doctor's hands."*

These persons need to give themselves permission to regain control over their lives. One way to do this is to consider the costs and benefits to assuming this role. They also need to give themselves permission to occasionally fail in pursuit of working side by side with providers. This change in roles will be easier when they get support for becoming collaborative; support from family members, peers, and mental health providers themselves.

2. Consumer Satisfaction and Other Input on Services

One of the assumptions of empowerment and collaboration is that treatment teams will design interventions and programs that are pleasing to participants. Hence, assessing a person's satisfaction is a minimal requirement for establishing programs that empower consumers. One might think this to be a straightforward process.

> *"Mr. Smith, do you like the program you've been attending?"*

Assessing a consumer's satisfaction is more difficult in actuality. Hence, some rules for developing a useful satisfaction scale are discussed below. Unfortunately, concern with consumer empowerment frequently ends with the assessment phase. Programs collect data on satisfaction but fail to use it in subsequently improving services. A second important part of this process is to consider ways to use information from satisfaction evaluations to further improve the setting.

What goes into a Satisfaction Scale?

When evaluating a person's satisfaction, satisfaction scales should consider four categories or domains (summarized in Table 6.4): the service environment, providers, specific interventions, and preparation for autonomy. What is the quality of the *service environment*: are the rooms pleasant including the decor, lighting, furniture, and temperature; if food is provided, is it tasty and plentiful? How are the *service providers*? Are they knowledgeable and competent in their specific job? Are they approachable, respectful, and friendly? Can I interact with them informally? How useful are *specific interventions* themselves: do they provide me with the skills I need? do they help me better understand my goals? do they provide the resources and support needed for my goals? Is the service preparing me for *autonomy*: after finishing the program, am I better able to live independently; am I more hopeful about my future?

Table 6.4
Four Domains for Assessing Consumer Satisfaction with Services.

Domain and Definition	Example of Items that Assess These Domains

Service Environment

How satisfied were you with

Is the physical setting in which services are provided satisfactory?

> the rooms in which treatment was provided.
> the temperature in the rooms.
> the lighting in the rooms.
> the manner in which the rooms were decorated.

Providers

Are the persons providing service satisfactory?

> the providers' approachability.
> the providers' knowledge of mental illness.
> the level of respect with which providers talked to you.
> the amount of informal talk between you and the provider.

Specific Interventions

Are the tasks that comprise a service satisfactory?

> the clarity of treatment expectations.
> the manner in which time was structured.
> the amount of activities in treatment.
> the amount of fun in treatment.

Preparation for Autonomy

Does the service help persons achieve their independent goals?

> the relevance of services to your goals
> whether the service helped you to live on you own.
> whether the service has prepared you for a job.
> whether the service has helped you to better understand yourself.

Typically, consumers are presented with 30 to 40 questions like those in Table 6.4 to assess satisfaction with a specific program. They are then asked to rate each item on a seven point scale. For example,

How satisfied are you with the relevance of services to your goals?

highly dissatisfied		neither			highly satisfied	
1	2	3	4	5	6	7

Leon believed the program ignored his goals and therefore circled 1 on the scale for highly dissatisfied. Kelly was very pleased with the way the program was helping her consider whether she should live independently. She circled 7. Usually, about eight items are asked for each of the four domains. After completing the test, all the individual item scores are added up for each domain and yield a satisfaction report card like the ones in Table 6.5.

Table 6.5

A Satisfaction Report Card that Shows the Differences Among Halo, Devil, and Comparison Effects.

Satisfaction Report Card

	Halo Effect		Devil Effect		Comparison Effect
Service Environment	56	Service Environment	7	Service Environment	50
Providers	54	Providers	9	Providers	42
Interventions	55	Interventions	8	Interventions	9
Autonomy	56	Autonomy	7	Autonomy	9

Note. For this report card, each domain consisted of 8 items that were rated on a 7 point scale like the ones in the text. Hence, a score of 56 represents a rating of total satisfaction and a score of 7 represents total dissatisfaction.

Satisfaction of services and the individual programs that comprise them.

Many services are often made up of separate programs. Opportunities, for example, actually include a supported employment program, independent housing program, and program that addresses problems related to mental illness and substance abuse. Satisfaction for these kinds of services should be conducted for each service separately.

Consider the report card for a satisfaction assessment conducted on Opportunities in June (See Table 6.6). Consumers participating in this evaluation rated the three services differently. Participants of the supported employment program were relatively satisfied with the services environment, specific interventions, and preparation for autonomy. However, they expressed marked dissatisfaction with the providers. Participants in the independent housing program seemed to be pleased with the providers as well as specific interventions and preparation for autonomy. They were, however, unhappy with the environment. Persons in the program for mental illness and substance abuse were satisfied with the services environment. They expressed dis-

Table 6.6

Results of a Consumer Satisfaction Evaluation for Three Programs that Comprise the Opportunities Rehabilitation Service.

Date conducted *June, 2000*		No. of consumers participating *68*	
Supported Employment Program	**Independent Housing Program**	**Program for Mental Illness and Substance Abuse**	
Service Environment *51*	Service Environment *12*	Service Environment *50*	
Providers *10*	Providers *53*	Providers *21*	
Interventions *46*	Interventions *52*	Interventions *9*	
Autonomy *56*	Autonomy *40*	Autonomy *18*	

Note. A comparison rating approach was used in this evaluation. Each domain comprised 8 items that were rated on a 7-point scale. A score of 56 represents a rating of total satisfaction and a score of 7 represents total dissatisfaction.

pleasure with providers and preparations for autonomy. However, they were particularly unhappy with the specific interventions used in the program. In each case, the consumer evaluation report card suggested clear directions for improving services.

Having Input on Services

The full benefit of evaluating consumer satisfaction will only be realized when providers use the results from these evaluations to actually change services. The report cards in Table 6.6 are only worth the effort when Opportunities staff use the results to upgrade the providers in the Supported Employment Program, enhance the environment in the Independent Housing Program, and broaden the interventions in the Program for Mental Illness and Substance Abuse. Unfortunately, this kind of program improvement is frequently done without input from consumers. Instead, treatment providers take the findings and decide how to improve program aspects on their own. This kind of approach fails to promote empowerment.

The preferred way to handle findings from satisfaction evaluations would be to involve participants in focus groups where they discuss their concerns about aspects of the program and, more importantly, provide recommendations for ways which the program might improve. For example, consumers participating in the Supported Employment Program could meet in a focus group to discuss ways to upgrade providers so they are viewed more satisfactorily in the future. Table 6.7 lists several guidelines for conducting these focus groups.

Table 6.7
Guidelines for Conducting Consumer Focus Groups to Improve
Mental Health Service Programs.

- The best leaders of these groups are trained consumers.
  - Groups should comprise about six to eight consumers.
- Invite persons who are both satisfied and dissatisfied with the program.
  - The leader should prepare questions based on the evaluation and with input from providers.
- Don't settle for problems; also identify solutions.
  - Consider whether solutions are practical.
- Be cautious of the LOUD voice; be alert for the QUIET one.
  - Seek consensus.
- Have a scribe and equipment to list suggestions.
  - Make the group time limited.
- Develop a report which lists recommendations for change.
  - The report should include a follow-up date.

There are two essential roles to fill in these kinds of focus groups: the leader and participating members. The best leaders for these groups are consumers who are trained to facilitate these kinds of groups. Although traditional service providers may have skills for running discussion groups like these, members might be hesitant to speak freely because they believe the provider will side against them with the established program. Many consumers are able to lead these groups with an hour's training. We do not have the space here to consider the skills for a focus group leader; useful resources where these issues are discussed are listed in the *Learn More About It Section* at the end of this book.

Focus groups should comprise six to eight members. Groups with fewer do not have enough people to promote lively discussion. Conversely, individuals in large groups may believe their opinions are lost in the masses. Programs that have many consumers wishing to participate should set up more than one focus group with each one comprising separate leaders and six to eight members. Members should be clearly informed of the goals of the meeting; namely, to provide feedback on ways to improve aspects of the specified services program. Moreover, members should be given ample notice regarding the time and place of the meeting so they can set aside the necessary hours.

A good mix of persons with different opinions should be invited to the focus group. Include consumers at both ends of the scale—persons who are fully satisfied with the program and those who are highly critical—as well as individuals in the middle. In this way, a polite contrast of opinions is possible. Leaders should develop a series of questions to guide the discussion prior to the meeting. These questions should be based on the results of the consumer satisfaction evaluation. For example, results from the Opportunities report card on the Independent Housing Program shows participants are fairly satisfied with all components except the physical plant. Hence, the leader might want to generate a few questions that get the group thinking about the quality of the environment.

- What could be done to improve the physical aspects of housing?

- What might we do to redecorate that would help?

- How's the lighting?
- How's the temperature?
- What might we do to make it safer?
- Any point you'd want to add that I didn't touch on?

Note that the questions are mostly open-ended. Open-ended questions cannot be answered with a yes or no; instead they require some explanation. In this way, the depth and breadth of the problem can be understood. Moreover, open-ended questions do not lead participants. Consider how this closed-ended question might yield inaccurate information:

> *"Don't you agree that, although it can be too hot in our rooms in the summer, we are all able to put up with it?"*

Identifying problems is a necessary part of focus groups. You want consumers to list the parts of the program that currently do not work for them. However, the fruit of the focus group comes from solutions to the problem. Hence, leaders want group members to look beyond what is wrong with a program. This kind of limited focus is easy and can lead to a complaining session. No change results from a list of grievances. Real improvements come from solutions to these grievances. These solutions need to be in the form of "doing" statements: what can staff and consumers do to improve the quality of a program? In addition, group members need to ask whether solutions are practical.

> *"Sure, the best way to improve the housing program is to tear it down and build brand*

*new condos. But that's not going to hap-
pen. So how do we improve what we've
got?"*

There are two kinds of members with whom the leader
need be cautious. Some members have loud voices; not
necessarily speaking thunderously but speaking in an
authoritative manner. They presume to speak for everyone.

*"I know what all consumers think. All con-
sumers hate green paint because it reminds
them of the state hospital."*

No one speaks for all persons with mental illness.
Hence, this loud voice should not be set up as the only
source of ideas. Rather than trying to suppress this person, leaders need to make sure that there is consensus
about what the outspoken person has to say.

*"Who agrees with Frank that we should
not use green paint?"*

An equally important person to be aware of is
the quiet person, the group member who offers no opinion. This person may actually have no thoughts about a
topic. However, all the group members went out of their
way to participate in the group. More than likely they
have views about the topic but are somewhat shy, or
perhaps intimidated by more outspoken members.
Group leaders should actively seek out their opinions in
these cases.

Someone should be appointed secretary for the
group; his or her job is to write down ideas as they are
generated. A chalkboard or paper and easel are also

useful tools for the meeting. Suggestions can be listed on them as they are generated for all to consider. At the end of the meeting, a brief report listing suggestions should be produced based on this list. The report should end up with a follow-up date at which time administration can review with the focus group how the agency has progressed on the recommendations.

Designing skills training programs. One of the main stays of services for persons with serious mental illness is the skills training group. A peer support program might teach participants coping skills. An advocacy group might teach skills related to obtaining the full range of one's entitlements. A rehabilitation program might teach interpersonal skills. Typically, manuals and other support materials are developed so that these programs are presented as highly structured modules. Unfortunately, modules like these are rarely developed by the kinds of persons who are going to implement them. A common critique heard about social skills training groups, for example, is that they are all developed by a bunch of middle class white guys from the suburbs for persons with mental illness living in the poor center of the city.

A four-step process for giving consumers a central role in developing skills training programs is summarized in Table 6.8. The purpose of this strategy is to develop skills training groups that reflect the interests of the people who are expected to use these skills. Hence, if social skills are to be taught to groups that are largely African American, then African Americans should be involved in development of the skills training program. We used this four-step process when our group developed a street smarts module[2]: "How to live safely in a large urban area." We wanted to make sure that the final product represented the perspective of consumers living in poor sections of the City rather than suburbanites.

Table 6.8
Four-Step Process for Developing Skills Training Groups

1	**Identify Problems**	Survey a consumer group regarding list of problems related to specific skill area; e.g., What specific problems do you have living safely in the city (street smarts)?
2	**Validate Problem List**	Validate problem list on independent group. For example, "A group of your peers made this list of problems related to living safely in the city. Check off those items on the list which you agree are problems."
3	**Identify Solutions to Problems**	Survey consumers for solutions to list of validated problems. For example, "A group of peers listed these items as problems with living safely in the city. What are solutions to these problems? In other words, how have you learned to live safely and deal with each of these individual problems?"
4	**Validate Solution List**	Validate list of solutions on an independent group. "A group of your peers said these were solutions to problems related to living safely in the city. Put a check next to those items which you agree are good solutions."

During the first stage, we asked a group of about 20 persons who had mental illness to specify their concerns about living in the Chicago area. They generated a list of 75 distinct concerns; e.g., traveling on public transportation, being out at night, and avoiding gang trouble. We were then curious which, among these 75

---

[2] Information about our Street Smarts module can be obtained through Recovery Press, 7230 Arbor Drive, Tinley Park, IL 60477, 708 614-2496.

responses, a separate group of consumers would endorse as most important. This sort of consensus building helps us to focus on key issues in street smarts. Twenty-five consumers who did not participate in the original survey were handed a checklist that included the 75 responses and instructed to check off items on the list that were of direct concern to them. Based on this feedback, we cut the list down to about 25 problems and grouped them into core areas:

- How to avoid being a victim of crime;

- What to do if you are a victim of crime; and

- How to stop needlessly being arrested (e.g., for vagrancy).

The important part of training groups is actually teaching skills that help people accomplish their goals and avoid problems. Hence, in Step 3 of developing the Street Smarts module, we asked a group of about 20 consumers to complete an open-ended survey. They were instructed to list ways they would deal with the three core areas above, for example, "What do you do to avoid being a victim of crime?" The 20 participants provided 61 unique answers. We then asked 20 different consumers to complete a checklist of these 61 answers; circle the items that seem like good solutions to you. About five solutions emerged for each core area. For example, five learning points were agreed upon for ways to avoid being a victim of crime:

- have your home and car secured from burglars;

- stay away from dangerous places;

- do not flash money or other valuables;

- ride public transportation safely; and

- do not talk to strangers.

Specific skills for each of these solution areas were then generated.

The important point of this process was to develop a skills training module that reflected the interests of people who really use these skills—inner city dwellers. In a separate study, we compared the response of city dwellers to a group of suburban business people. Results showed the suburban folks to be more reactive in their approach to street smarts, for example, how to use self-defense strategies if they should get mugged. The city group had much more experience with crime. As a result, their solutions were much more proactive, strategies that help them avoid crime. Moreover, consumers living in the city were more ingenious in their suggestions. For example, one elderly lady gave this suggestion if mugged.

> *"Yell fire! City folk will lock their doors or run the other way if you yell, 'Help, I'm being mugged!' Being nosy like they are, they'll come out to see what's up if you yell, 'Help, fire!'"*

The point here is that subgroups of consumers may not view skills training issues the same. Hence, their perspective needs to be incorporated into development of training modules.

Buying Services that are Satisfactory

In the business world people are concerned about satisfaction by users because it is linked with profits and financial stability. Customers stop using businesses that are unsatisfactory. For example, a hot dog stand that continues to produce tasteless sandwiches in a dirty store with grouchy clerks will not stay open long. Business owners listen closely to the complaints of their consumers.

For the most part, this kind of relationship does not exist between satisfaction and the financial stability of mental health services. As discussed briefly above, these services are frequently funded by government programs: grants-in-aid from state offices of mental health or entitlement programs like Medicaid or Medicare which reimburse individual services with set fees. In this kind of situation, providers are going to be acutely concerned with the demands of government agents, frequently to the exclusion of consumers themselves.

Some government programs have experimented with vouchers as an alternative. In these systems, consumers receive vouchers that can be turned in for services (e.g., $1000 per month for rehabilitation services). They can then take this voucher to the provider *of their choice* and receive services. Consumers can decide to pull their funds from an agency providing unsatisfactory services. They might also pool funds with peers to start new services altogether. Nassau County in the State of New York experimented with this system in the early 1990s with some success. The Work Incentives Act of

1999 includes vouchers which consumers can use to pay for employment or psychosocial rehabilitation that best meets their needs. When legislation like this is passed, these laws will economically empower consumers to pursue services that best meet their needs.

3. Lodges and Clubhouses

Consumers have obtained further control of the mental health system and their world in two kinds of programs: lodges and clubhouses. In both settings, persons with mental illness have equal authority to the professional staff in operating the program. Lodges were started in the 1960s by George Fairweather as a residential and work community for persons who were recently transferred from long-term hospitals. Clubhouses spontaneously emerged in New York City as a meeting place for people recently discharged from the state hospital. Both of these models represent consumer dissatisfaction with the way mental health providers acted towards persons with mental illness. This dissatisfaction led to a philosophy that clearly echoes the importance of empowerment.

The Fairweather Lodge: Living and Working Together

George Fairweather was a psychologist working on an inpatient unit at a VA in Menlo Park, California in the early 60s. He noticed that many of the persons in the hospital handed over control of their daily lives to nurses and other staff even though they were capable of making most decisions for themselves. The controlling nature of hospitals had taught them to be timid and hold back rather than to assume responsibility for themselves. To counter this loss of control, Fairweather devised his Lodge program.

The lodge is made up of persons with psychiatric disabilities who live and work together. Typically, lodges form real-world businesses to maintain themselves; (e.g., janitorial services, bulk mailing, copy centers, or temp agencies). Sometimes, lodges hire people with expertise in areas needed to maintain the business. They may also seek professional help as "consultants" to lodge members. Assistants in those psychiatric and rehabilitation strategies need to help members manage their symptoms and disabilities. The lodge program is built on several principles that clearly reflect the spirit of personal empowerment. Several of these principles are summarized in Table 6.9. Fairweather and his later followers divided Lodge principles into two areas:

1. those that helped the consumer fill the role of lodge member (living and working with peers) and

2. those that help the lodge develop norms which make it a thriving community (or what Fairweather called a social subsystem).

Persons are more willing to embrace a role when they have a stake in it. In other words, living and working with others has to satisfy what the person wants and needs in his or her life now. This means the person needs to have autonomy in his or her role within the lodge. At the minimum, a person's role needs to be vol-

Table 6.9
Principles for Operating and Maintaining a Lodge

Roles played by members of the lodge

Members must have a **stake** in the system.

Persons must have **autonomy** in their roles as lodge members.

Interventions must promote **self-determination**.

The person's role in the lodge must be **voluntary**.

Members must have the opportunity to be **promoted** within the lodge.

All roles in the lodge must be **covered**.

Development of the **social subsystem** and its **norms**

Members are encouraged to do things **as a group**.

The subsystem should comprise a **limited** group of people.

The lodge and its members must abide by the norms cherished by the **larger society**.

The lodge must be **compatible** with the community in which it is implanted.

Nevertheless, the lodge needs to develop its **unique set of norms**.

The lodge should not depend on the **goodwill of the larger society**.

untary. People cannot be court ordered to a lodge or sent against their will. In addition, persons need the right to self-determination, namely, the opportunity to decide for one's self how they meet their responsibilities in the lodge community.

It is the nature of interaction that there be some hierarchy among social roles. Namely, some people need to be supervising others to make sure all needs of the lodge are met. For example, some member needs to be in charge of shopping and cooking. Others need to watch over the budget. Another principle of lodge programs is that all members have the opportunity to be promoted to leadership jobs thereby experiencing the benefits, as well as the demands, of different roles throughout the hierarchy. At the same time, all roles within the lodge must be filled. In this way, the community is assured that all tasks of the lodge are covered.

There is an interesting contradiction between the goals of autonomy and the demands of operating a residential and work community. How does the lodge balance each person's right to self-determination with the community's need to get all its work done? Won't some people end up with what might be perceived as less than desirable duties? The second set of principles in Table 6.9 discusses development of community norms which seek this balance. One of the major rules of the Fairweather Lodge is "Members are encouraged to do things as a group." Proponents of the lodge program believe that its strength lies in sharing both good times and tough decisions among all members. Group discussion is central to the empowerment and personal growth experienced in this setting. Unfortunately, a second principle of the lodge recognizes that this group must be limited in size. The community can only serve a small number of people and meet their work and home needs satisfactorily. This can be a sobering thought for some lodge members; their community is closed to many others like themselves also in need.

The success of the community occurs in a complicated balance between norms. On one hand, the norms of the program must correspond with those of the larger society in which the lodge finds itself. In part, this is necessary because these are the rules and laws which lodge members must follow when leaving the lodge either for short outings or permanently to resume one's position in society. Moreover, basing lodge rules on those in the larger society makes sense because these are the rules with which community members are likely to already be familiar. For example, "do not steal property" and "respect privacy" should be two familiar rules to Americans and, therefore, be incorporated into the norms of lodges in the United States.

The lodge also needs to develop norms that reflect the unique character of its community. For example, the prime rule—members are encouraged to do things as a group—is not reflected in Western society as a whole. We tend to be an individualistic nation that ignores making decisions with groups. However, proponents of the lodge program believe this kind of norm is essential for the special atmosphere needed to develop a community of living and working peers. In like manner, each community needs to consider as a group what other unique rules it will adopt to meet the individual needs of its members.

Although lodge programs reflect the norms of the larger society in which it is immersed, the program cannot depend on the goodwill of society. Communities that require financial assistance or professional guidance from people outside the lodge will soon find their unique set of rules and norms threatened by these outsiders.

> *"The local mental health center provided us with a psychiatrist who could meet with interested members about their meds. This worked great for about eight months. Then, the doc had to change her night from Tuesday to Wednesday, the time of our community meeting. We couldn't move community meeting to another night because Fred and Sylvia were working evenings and couldn't make it. So we*

*decided to cut our meeting time in half so
Doctor Browning would have time to meet
with members. But then we didn't have
enough time to make decisions about our
meals, budget, housekeeping, parties, and
countless other items we had to wrestle
with to keep our lodge thriving."*

Even what appears to be as harmless an offer as free
psychiatric care can undermine the efforts and rules of
the lodge. And because they were provided this service
for free, lodge members were not able to dictate when
they would receive these services. Hence, these kinds of
programs need to be independent of society's goodwill
to maintain its special character.

The Fountain House: A Clubhouse for Persons with Mental Illness

During the years after the end of World War II,
many people were released from Rockland State
Hospital outside of New York City with no community
connections. In order to survive, they met on the steps
of the New York Public Library to provide each other
resources and support. Soon, the group gained notoriety
and others also released from Rockland joined them in
this makeshift society called WANA (We Are Not
Alone). In 1948, the group bought a building through
the generous donations of a Jewish women's philan-
thropic group. The building had a fountain in the back
yard; hence its name, Fountain House. A picture of
Fountain House can be found in Figure 6.1. It was built
around a fundamental philosophy:

"Men and women with mental illness have the right to a life which includes access to meaningful, gainful employment; a decent place to live; a community of support; the opportunities for education and recreation offered by the communities in which they live; and the chance to be needed, wanted, and expected somewhere everyday" (International Center for Clubhouse Development).

The number of clubhouses has mushroomed around the United States since that time.

Figure 6.1
A picture of Fountain House in New York City, taken in 1997.

Several values characterize the clubhouse. In some ways, these principles overlap with the Lodge model. In other ways, they reflect the special charm of social clubhouses. Persons belonging to the clubhouse are *members* rather than clients or consumers. They have equal power with the professional staff hired to support clubhouse activities not only in daily operations but in decisions about budgetary issues, too. With membership comes responsibility. All members are expected to contribute to some aspect of the clubhouse's operations. Clubhouses are

223

designed so that each member is essential for efficient operation.

> *"It was unlike any other mental health program I belonged to. It was important to them that I be there. At first, I thought the expectations would overwhelm me. But the sense of responsibility and belonging-ness actually made me feel like a man again!"*

The fully collaborative nature of staff and consumer leads all members to being considered co-providers.

Clubhouses are open every day of the year. Unlike mental health centers that typically close for holidays, clubhouses are open for their members to celebrate occasions like this. Clubhouses also provide a wide variety of opportunities including housing, education, social support, recreation, and vocational training and placement. Services are never pressed upon members. Rather, they are used as the individual sees fit.

Clubhouses operate according to a work-ordered day with normal 9 to 5 working hours. Each day, members (consumers and staff alike) decide among a variety of work units that comprise the necessary tasks to keep the clubhouse running effectively. Work activities at Fountain House have included horticulture, thrift shop, snack bar and dining room, clerical, education, and research. Participation in this kind of activity reacquaints members with the demands of the work world as well as its many benefits.

4. Assertive Community Treatment and Supported Employment

Even though Lodge and Clubhouse programs have many values that promote empowerment, they still require the consumer to go outside their home "turf" to receive services. In the 60s and 70s, two professionals from Madison, Wisconsin, Leonard Stein and Mary Ann Test, turned the service world upside down. Instead of demanding that consumers go out of their way to the offices of providers, why not bring services to the consumer where he or she needs it: their home or anywhere else the consumer might deem necessary for resources and support. Called Assertive Community Treatment or ACT, Stein and Test believed the entire range of services—medications, psychotherapy, skills training, money management, and the rest—could be and should be provided in the person's home or community. A variation of this idea is supported employment where a job coach provides services alongside the consumer at his or her place of work.

Table 6.10 lists several ways in which ACT and supported employment facilitate empowerment. First and foremost, these programs are consumer-centered. Services are defined by the needs of the consumer, not the provider. Although this may seem obvious now, this value was revolutionary when first proposed. In the past, treatment plans reflected what was best for the consumer and the provider. Hence, a person may not be referred to an independent housing program if it was outside the case manager's district. A consumer may not begin competitive work until the agency has an available job coach. Consumer-centered services remind the provider that it is up to the agency to find the necessary resources and supports to help consumers achieve their goals on their timeline.

Table 6.10
Qualities of Assertive Community Treatment (ACT) and Supported Employment that Strengthen Empowerment

Consumer-Centered

Service goals are defined by the consumer, not the rules of the treatment program or expectancy of family and friends.

Strengths Model

Service planning reflects skills which the person has already mastered.

Cross-Sectional and Comprehensive

ACT and supported employment address the full range of services needed by the consumer.

Longitudinal Services

ACT and supported employment is provided as long as the person needs service. It is not time-limited.

Accessible and Available

Providers of ACT and supported employment meet consumers in places and at times convenient to the consumer.

Accountability

The individual services that comprise the treatment plan are top quality.

ACT and supported employment are also strengths-oriented. This view differs from the disease model that dominates traditional services. Proponents of the disease viewpoint believed that persons are defined by their symptoms and other weaknesses that need to be fixed through treatment. The strengths model recognizes that people are described by their skills and not their fallacies. Awareness of these skills is essential; these are the tools which persons use to accomplish their goals. A strengths-based approach is a much more empowering, and much less stigmatizing way to provide services. Rather than seeing people as nothing more than their symptoms, it reminds us that *everyone* is a complex being defined in large part by our accomplishments and skills.

As stated earlier, ACT and supported employment represented a radically different way of doing business. In being consumer-centered, providers of these services made interventions as convenient and efficient as possible. Hence, ACT is comprehensive and cross-sectional. Namely, it provides services across all domains of need: housing, finances, family, health care, spiritual matters, and recreation.

> *"Things are sure different now. About 15 years ago, I was working with four different programs in three different cities. The local mental health center provided medication and helped me with my symptoms. I went to the Oak Tree for sheltered workshop. I lived at the River Woods board and care center. And Mary Lou, from the township office, helped me with my social security and Medicaid. It was almost a full time job keeping all this straight."*

ACT represents one-stop shopping where a single team provides medication help, assists with managing the home, and coaches the person at work.

ACT and supported employment are also longitudinal. By this, we mean the service is provided by a single team as long as the person needs it. Mental health providers used to have the bad practice of ending services at times that were not convenient to the consumer.

"Joe will lose his case management services in two more months because his funding runs out then. Too bad he's not ready to be cut loose."

Sometimes services are provided indefinitely. ACT and supported employment continue as the person changes homes or moves in and out of institutions. Mental health systems of the past had the unwise practice of discontinuing community services for those individuals who had to be hospitalized because of short-term psychiatric emergencies. Unfortunately, these persons had to start over with a new team when released a few weeks later. The ACT and supported employment team providing services longitudinally continues to offer support and resources even while the person is hospitalized or involved in the criminal justice system.

Effective ACT and supported employment is accessible and available. This means services are provided in places that are convenient to the consumer, typically their home or place of work. Moreover, service is provided at times that make sense to the consumer. That means the provider does not ask the person to stay home from work so he can come to the apartment to discuss shopping. Instead, the provider comes in the evening when the person is home from work and has eaten dinner.

ACT and supported employment are also accountable. Most consumers of any kind would not put up with lousy results. Who would continue to hire the electrician who could not get the lights working? Unfortunately, mental health had a tradition of providing the same old service, whether it met needs or not. We remember community mental health programs where therapists used to read the front page of the Chicago Tribune as reality orientation; this had no value for participants but continued for several years because it was easy for providers. Accountability means services impact persons and their goals. Cast aside are the treatment groups and case management meetings that continue because they are convenient for the staff even though they do nothing for participants.

5. Mental Health Consumers-as-Providers

What better way to influence the system that provides services than for consumers to assume jobs as providers in these services? In this spirit, consumers have filled almost every conceivable position in the mental health system. They have become job coaches, consumers have worked on assertive community treatment teams, and they have run support groups. Consumers have also worked at all the professional levels that comprise the treatment team: psychiatrists, psychologists, social workers, and psychiatric nurses. For example, several well-known consumer advocates have cut their teeth as mental health professionals. Daniel Fisher is a psychiatrist; Fred Frese is a psychologist. Both gentlemen have more than 20-year histories struggling with the psychiatric disabilities that result from schizophrenia.

As outlined in Table 6.11, consumers filling mental health provider roles yield several significant benefits for both the individual consumer as well as persons with mental illness in general. At the broadest level, consumers-acting-as-providers challenge stigmatizing notions about persons with mental illness. Public understanding of "Who is a consumer?" broadens beyond the simple idea that they are psychiatric diagnoses. Consumers are also helpers! Despite their disabilities— or perhaps because of them—persons with mental illness are able to support peers with mental illness, providing them with knowledge about psychiatric symptoms, skills to deal with these symptoms, and resources to meet their goals. Showing these abilities challenges the public idea that persons with mental illness are incompetent.

> *"I always thought ex-mental patients were unable to live on their own or work. But then I met Harry Larkin and I thought, 'Wow! He's pretty impressive being able to hold down a job as a job coach.' I guess all those ideas about persons with mental illness being unfit weren't true."*

Table 6.11
Some Advantages of Consumers as Providers.

- **The public's understanding of "consumer" is expanded to include helpers.**
- **Consumers assume roles which traditional providers cannot or will not assume.**
- **The credentials that define "helper" are expanded significantly.**
- **Providing help to others yields tangible benefits for the helper.**

For more information on these qualities, read the book edited by Carol Mowbray, David Moxley, Colleen Jasper, and Lisa Howell (1997). *Consumers as Providers in Psychiatric Rehabilitation.* Columbia, MD: International Association of Psychosocial Rehabilitation Services.

Consumers assume roles which traditional providers frequently will not do or are not able to do well. Many jobs related to supported employment and assertive community treatment require long hours and travel into places that are less than desirable. Most people are not willing to meet these challenges unless they have experienced the same struggles.

> *"A lot of the job coaches I worked with were college grads using this as a stepping stone to better jobs. They didn't want to go to K-Mart at 1 AM to see how Sidney was doing on the night shift. But, I knew what Sidney was going through. My first job out of the hospital was working the overnight shift in a bread factory. It was tough because no one from the mental health center wanted to come over to 33rd and Ashland at that hour and coach me."*

There are some tasks that only consumers can provide. One of these is the "I've been there, too" kind of support. Persons in the throes of depression or anxiety receive immeasurable benefits by hearing from a peer who has been in the same situation, survived the challenge, and thrived to become a mental health provider.

Answers to "Who is a provider?" broaden greatly when consumers join the services team. In the past, a person had to get a diploma in psychiatry, social work, or some other discipline and complete a long and rigorous internship to be certified as a mental health provider. However, we have learned from other service approaches that graduating from the school of hard knocks can be equally useful for mental health providers. The alcohol and substance abuse field, for example, has been hiring ex-addicts for decades to round out the drug abuse system. In like manner, hiring persons with mental illness adds a person who is intimately knowledgeable about psychiatric disabilities to the mental health team.

There is one last aspect to consumers-becoming-providers which must be highlighted. Namely, providing help to others reaps significant benefits for the helper. This is the principle of mutual help which is discussed more fully later in this chapter. Suffice it to say here that offering support and resources to others is a great boost to the helper's self-esteem as well as reinforces his or her confidence and sense of self-determination.

Although consumer experiences are useful for filling the provider role, experiences alone are not enough to offer good care. Just like the traditional professional, consumers who are providers need to master the necessary skills that will help peers accomplish their goals. The State of Illinois now has a psychiatric rehabilitation certificate program to help consumers learn to become providers. The program is offered through more than 40 community colleges across the state and provides basic knowledge as well as hands-on experience. In the process, this program also dispels some stigma about mental illness; here is a program that teaches people to assume a role of responsibility in the mental health system and not just be a "good patient."

Although working in the mental health system is a good opportunity on many fronts, it is important to remember that being a mental health service provider is NOT for everyone. There are many challenges to providing services for persons with psychiatric disabilities.

Most persons without mental illness are not up to the demands of training as well as the stresses of helping others who struggle with psychiatric disabilities. In like manner, we should not assume that every consumer has the necessary temperament and interests to be a mental health provider. Not every consumer needs to try this to move ahead towards empowerment and self-determination.

Mental Health Consumers as Providers Mixes Up Treatment Roles

> *"I have to admit, the first time I heard Harry was a job coach, it was kind of strange. I had known him back in Elgin State Hospital. We were both admitted on the same day in the summer of '78. We'd bounce in an out of treatment together and even lived in the same halfway house for about a year. Now he was staff at the local mental health center. I didn't know if I was supposed to call him 'Mr. Larkin'. I also wasn't sure whether Harry knew what he was talking about. After all, he was really no different than me!"*

Roles get mixed up when consumers become providers. Peers who have a long history with the consumer (who is now a provider) do not know how to act with them. Traditional providers must reframe how to understand this person who was their consumer and is now a colleague. And consumers who are now providing

233

services have a tough balancing act. Each of the ways in which consumers-serving-as-providers mixes up relationships is considered below. People need to be aware of these conflicts so that they do not overwhelm consumer-as-provider initiatives.

The impact on peers who are receiving services. One of the assumptions behind consumers-as-providers is that these people will be able to build stronger relationships with peers because they have shared many of the problems as their clientele.

> *"As a consumer, it was easier for me to relate to Harry because he knows where I'm coming from. He's had the same kind of problems and doesn't dismiss some of my harebrained ideas for recovery."*

Other people, however, might be concerned whether people with mental illness can actually meet the demands of providing mental health services.

> *"They're crazy just like me. They don't know how to deal with my problems. I want a professional with a degree."*

In some ways, these people are buying into the same stigma about mental illness that poison public opinion, refusing to believe that a peer would be capable of providing quality care.

Ironically, others have the opposite belief when a consumer becomes a provider.

> *"They're not one of us anymore. They're staff now. They forgot what it's like to deal*

with all the pressures of the system. They **are** *the system!"*

These individuals, who are providing services, need to balance these views so they can build a good working relationship and provide the best services.

The impact on colleagues who are traditional providers. Traditional providers are affected by the same biases that poison the rest of the world. They do not expect persons with mental illness to be capable of this kind of job. Hence, finding consumers as one's colleagues can be disorienting for many traditional providers. It will likely be difficult for some providers to exchange the traditional helper role ("And what brings you in my office today?") to one of colleague ("What do you think we should do with the local public aid office?") and friend ("Did you see the Cubs lost again yesterday?").

Stigma and bias can have an even nastier effect on consumers-as-providers. Traditional staff may be reluctant to refer persons needing help to a consumer-provider. Moreover, they may be constantly scrutinizing the consumer-provider for the inevitable break; an act of reasonable anger could be viewed as evidence that the person is becoming "mentally ill" again.

More practical concerns can also affect traditional staff's relationship with consumer-providers. Some staff may be concerned that hiring persons with mental illness may put them out of a job. Others may resent the accommodations that some consumer-providers get to help them with their job.

235

> *"It's not fair. Harry gets off early once a*
> *month to go see his psychiatrist. I don't get*
> *that kind of personal time."*

This kind of fear and bitterness can jeopardize the consumer's chances at fitting into the job comfortably.

The impact on the mental health consumer who is now providing services. One can easily see from the two previous lists of role conflicts that consumers who become providers have a lot of baggage to deal with. Not only must they learn the vast amount of knowledge and skills needed to be a successful helper, they need to figure out how to deal with other people's attitudes about them. There are also legal and ethical standards that complicate consumers-becoming-providers. Called "dual roles," most states prohibit mental health professionals from having roles with consumers other than providing them treatment. Hence, a professional can not provide services to someone and: offer them a job, rent them an apartment, or see them socially. In this way, providers do not take advantage of a person for whom they are offering service.

Consumer-as-providers stretch the traditionally-rigid boundaries between the two groups. It tears down the distance between traditional staff and their clientele. Hence, one might think that consumer-providers would have closer and more intimate relationships with peers. Nevertheless, the potential for abusing that relationship is a reality. For example, can a consumer-provider date a peer that is now in her job program? Consumer-providers need to be vigilant to this potential when they take on their new role.

Finally, we should not forget that just because a consumer becomes a provider does not mean that he or she will never need mental health services again. What happens if a consumer-provider gets depressed and needs to see the doctor for adjustment of anti-depressant medication? What happens if a person becomes confused while out providing assertive community treatment? In these situations, consumers may need help from professionals in the agency in which they work to overcome the temporary setback. This can be a tough challenge for the consumer as well as for the colleague providing service. This can also be another strain on the ethical norm of dual roles.

Most consumer-providers agree that becoming a provider is rewarding but stressful. Hence, they frequently recommend that a support group for consumer-providers be established on the job. This kind of accommodation can provide the necessary resources to get through the various role confusions that happen when consumers become providers.

Despite all these hurdles, it is worth it. One of the reasons why consumers-becoming-providers causes so much confusion is because the concept is new to the mental health system! In some ways, consumers, professional staff, and consumer-providers experiencing these changes in roles are pioneers. We suspect that two or three decades from now consumers-as-providers will be as common as providing mental health services in one's community (instead of a hospital) is now. In the meantime, it is important to remember that consumers who become providers serve a vital role for the mental health system. An executive director of a psychosocial rehabilitation program in Nebraska summed up the issues well.

> *"I've worked in the field for more than 15 years and always thought I was open-minded. I always believed in empowerment and giving the person with mental illness a fair chance. But, hiring consumers and promoting them to supervisory positions was a real eye-opener. Consumers were no longer just THOSE people to whom I happened to give a little of my grace. They were my colleagues and co-workers: people just like me! The significance of those words—just like me—radically changed my view. It was no longer us and them. We were all us."*

6. Self-Help, Mutual Assistance, and Other Consumer-Operated Services

Consumer-operated services, which include self-help and mutual assistance programs, are perhaps the best kinds of programs that promote empowerment. As the name suggests, consumer-operated programs were developed <u>by</u> consumers <u>for</u> consumers. These kinds of services are not just another form of clinical care. Clinical treatment reflects a medical model: persons seek out services to resolve symptoms and replace deficits. There is a hierarchy between healer and person in clinical settings; healers have some special power which they use to help people resolve their problems. The relationship between healer and person is expected to end when symptoms remit.

Consumer-operated programs have been likened more to communities with life-long histories or grass-root information and support systems. Mental illness may be the common experience that draws persons to consumer-operated services. But, unlike traditional clinical treatment, this is not where the impact of consumer-operated services ends. These services provide a caring and sharing community where the person can find the necessary understanding and recognition that society at large is not able to give. Nor is there a hierarchy of roles in consumer-operated programs; all members are peers who benefit from interactions with equals. There are no limits placed on the amount of time a person can be involved in a program. Depending on personal needs, some members come and go from consumer-operated programs while others may stay connected for their life-time.

There is a fundamental distinction between self-help groups and mutual assistance programs. *Self-help* programs are developed by consumers to help them help themselves. As such, benefits from these groups result from learning coping skills and obtaining support from others. Self-help suggests an ethos of rugged individualism where the person takes coping ideas and support from others to make it on their own. *Mutual help* recognizes an important element provided by these groups: persons benefit from helping each other. This kind of assistance extends beyond sharing information about coping skills or ways to manage the mental health system. The experience of both giving and receiving help enhances the person's sense of place in the community and overall well-being.

> *"I had been taking from others for so long*
> *that I forgot I had something to give. I*
> *can't tell you how important it was for me*
> *to realize that my advice can be useful to*
> *others. Just last week for example, I helped*
> *Sammy with her babysitting problems. It*
> *was the best pill for depression I could*
> *have taken."*

Consumers have also distinguished between mutual help groups and mutual help organizations. *Groups* are somewhat limited in scope. Members attend regular meetings where individuals benefit from the process, support, and exchange of information. *Organizations* have a similar structure of meetings and processes. However, the mutual help organization is augmented by regular social events for members. Many mutual help organizations also provide residential, vocational, legal assistance, transportation, food assistance, and temporary housing services so members can address appropriate role functioning needs.

Three examples of mutual help programs in the United States are Recovery Inc., Emotions Anonymous, and GROW. The goals of Recovery Inc. are to control symptoms and tension through an approach similar to cognitive behavior therapy. Emotions Anonymous is based on the 12 Steps of A.A. GROW also developed out of a 12 Step tradition. As such, it includes spiritual maturity as an important part of its program. GROW incorporates some of the cognitive coping strategies from Recovery Inc. into its weekly meetings. GROW also organizes social activities between meetings in order to foster the supportive community and provide residential and vocational services. A more complete list of self-help, mutual assistance, and consumer-operated programs is provided in the *Learn More About It* section at the end of this book.

How Do Consumer-Operated Programs Help Participants?

Figure 6.2 summarizes a model that outlines the effects of mutual help organizations (or any consumer-operated service, for that matter) on their participants. According to this model, several *processes* inherent to mutual help organizations lead to a variety of consumer *outcomes* experienced as overall well-being. Intervening processes include a prolonged opportunity to obtain validation through the kind of self-comparisons that these supported settings provide.

> *"The other persons in this group are just like me. And they are all good people. So I must be worth something, too."*

Important processes also include a decreased sense of stigma and personal blame as the result of these comparisons, positive community that arises out of extended social support, and increased personal skills gained from others. Outcomes are manifest in a variety of ways including increased self-esteem, diminished anxiety and depression, and greater achievement of personal goals related to relationships, work, housing, recreation, and other domains of living.

Figure 6.2
A model that explains the impact of consumer-operated services.

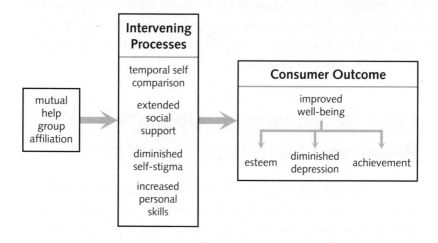

The federal government has recently recognized the importance of consumer-operated program. They have sponsored a four year, 20 million dollar study on consumer services begun in 1998. Participating programs can be found in Illinois, Iowa, Connecticut, Florida, Pennsylvania, California, Maine, and Tennessee.

Consumer Art Shows and Empowerment

Renowned consumer and mental health researcher, Kay Jamison, argued that there is a special relationship between expression through art and mental illness. Many people around the country have embraced this idea as an excellent form of consumer-operated service. For example, at their 1997 national conference in Albuquerque, the National Alliance for the Mentally Ill exhibited about 45 pieces of art from more than a dozen American cities. The show, curated by a Wyomingbased art group called Sistare, was entitled "Truth from Darkness: An Exhibition of Works by Artists with Mental Illness." Artistic merit was the sole criterion for selection. In May 1997, the National Mental Health Association opened "Inside Out," an art exhibit of works by persons with mental illness, for a three-month showing at the National Museum of Health and Medicine in Washington. The work at that exhibition came largely from a collection by the Miamibased National Art Exhibition for the Mentally Ill.

Faith in the substance of consumer art echoes throughout the movement. Another group bridging mental illness and art is Catskill, New Yorkbased National Artists for Mental Health. After their widely applauded 1997 conference in Westchester County, director Frank Marquit was expanding operations and arranging larger facilities for the group's second national meeting in 1998. The first conference punctuated natural healing techniques, maskmaking, and lectures on comedy. National Artists for Mental Health is developing a guide to organizing and curating an art show for people diagnosed with mental illness; Sistare is planning to publish a similar guide.

7. Participatory Action Research

A positive way in which providers and funding agencies know whether one kind of program is effective and another is not is through research. The purpose of research is to find out what kind of outcomes result from providing a specific intervention program (for example, Assertive Community Treatment) in a certain way (e.g., using a TEAM of providers instead of individual case managers) with a specific group of consumers (e.g., persons with mental illness recently released from prison). Research is meant to answer questions about programs:

- Does this program help the person manage disabilities that result from psychiatric symptoms?

- Are they able to live in an apartment instead of an institution?

- Can they find a job and keep it?

- Are they able to stay out of jail?

Traditionally, this kind of research is completed by academic experts, people with many years of education leading up to a doctorate in social science or medicine and working as professors in universities. We sometimes believe that social science requires many years of study in statistics and research methodology and can hence, only be completed by these kinds of experts.

Many consumers believe that this kind of scientist-as-expert view actually causes problems of its own and adds to stigma. They describe a "blame the victim" mentality that permeates much research. According to this mentality, traditional research shows how persons with serious mental illness *lack* skills, *lack* work histories, *lack* motivation, *lack* family ties, etc. It is these person-centered deficits that account for all the individual's problems and hence should be the focus of research and services. Others have argued with this notion. They believe that by focusing on individual limitations, research misses the cultural, economic, and environmental forces that lead to the difficulties associated with serious mental illness.

This point may be better understood if we consider how research in other disabilities—blindness for example—has developed overtime. As the result of forceful input from persons who are blind, researchers realized that teaching people how to live with their impairment is not enough. We also need to *change the environment* so that persons who are blind can get around more easily. Research in this area led to Braille in elevators, crosswalks that beep, and better use of seeing-eye dogs. This kind of research is only going to be accomplished when persons with disabilities are full partners.

Participatory Action Research (PAR) describes how researchers and consumers become *partners* in studying mental illness and appropriate treatment. PAR calls for a significant change in the roles of consumers and professionals; consumers actively investigate research hypotheses themselves and enlist trained researchers as consultants to their projects. The goal of PAR is to advance research that supports the fundamental assertions of consumer empowerment. Instead of asking typical research questions like: "How does the consumer fit into society?" PAR examines questions like: "What resources and accommodations must society make to take advantage of the consumer best?"

Participatory Action Research is no longer a pipe dream. Many federally-funded research efforts have incorporated the priorities of PAR into their guidelines. For example, several large scale projects funded by the U.S. Substance Abuse and Mental Health Services Administration (SAMHSA) require a consumer advisory panel to have an active partnership in planning and implementing its research projects. Consider how this plays out in the eight-state evaluation now underway on consumer-operated services mentioned earlier in this chapter. Four of the principal investigators in the study are public figures in the consumer movement. Another 30 persons with mental illness are key figures in the project. EVERY decision that governs the project is made through a sometimes tortuous exchange between the consumers on the project and the science investigators. But the result is a research project that represents the best interests and insights of consumer empowerment.

Final Thoughts

We end by returning to the core message of this chapter. Namely, one of the best ways to address stigma is to facilitate empowerment. This message promotes a very different approach than other parts of the book. Earlier chapters discussed what persons with mental illness should NOT DO so that self-stigma does not beat them. Later chapters will discuss what the public should NOT DO so stigma and discrimination fail to flourish. Much of this book talks about what needs to be taken away so the opportunities of persons with mental illness thrive.

In this chapter, we discuss what can be DONE. In this way, we do not discuss how things can be taken away from persons with mental illness and the public. Rather, we discuss what persons might actively DO to promote the individual's self-determination, autonomy, and choice, as well as the public's respect and affirmative action. This kind of positive activity is essential if stigma is to be abolished and replaced by mutual respect.

Chapter 7

Changing Society's Reaction to Stigma Through Contact

"It is because of the devotion or sacrifice of individuals that causes become of value."

Julian Huxley

The stigma of severe mental illness is **not** just a problem of persons with these disorders and their families. Nor is it merely a harsh reality of the world which you must learn to overcome. Stigma and discrimination are problems for all society. [1] Everyone must examine their beliefs and actions which undermine the opportunities of persons with mental illness.

---

[1] Because we use person-first language throughout this book (e.g., referring to persons with mental illness rather than "schizophrenic patients"), there may be some confusion sorting out who are people with psychiatric disabilities from the rest of the population. We resolve the problem in this and subsequent chapters by continuing to refer to persons with mental illness and defining the rest of the population as the general public or members of society.

You need not wait passively until the public changes its attitudes and behavior. Chapters 7 and 8 discuss three strategies for stopping stigma: *contact*, people who regularly interact with persons who struggle with mental illness will be less likely to stigmatize; *education*, members of society who know more about mental illness are less likely to endorse shameful myths about it; and *protest*, discriminatory behaviors may decrease when important segments of society clearly state "these actions are not acceptable." Before reviewing stigma-busting strategies, let us consider the effects of stereotype and discrimination *on society*. This discussion is important because it suggests what anti-stigma advocates like yourself might target for changing society's reaction to mental illness.

The Impact of Mental Illness Stigma on Society

We argued in Chapter 2 that stigma is a grave injustice for persons with mental illness and their families. Its harmful impact does not end there, however. Stigma also harms society and those in it. It promotes injustices that undermine some of the basic assumptions of a community. It robs society of an important resource: persons with mental illness who could be gainful members of the neighborhood. Stigma perpetuates the personal fears of all people about becoming mentally ill and losing control. Each of these influences needs to be understood before there can be any broad changes effect on societal stigma.

The Injustice of Stigma Infects a Community

Clearly, people who agree with stereotypes about mental illness and choose to act on those stereotypes harm persons with psychiatric disorders. By no means, however, does the damage end there. Any kind of prejudice undermines ethical assumptions of the entire culture. For example, people of many societies believe individuals should have a fair opportunity to prove themselves based on their actions and accomplishments. Stereotypes like those experienced by persons with mental illness challenge this fundamental belief. Stereotypes mean persons lose their chance to be successful because they belong to marked groups.

Stereotypes about mental illness are just one of many concrete examples of simple-minded thinking about groups of people. This kind of naive categorizing ignores the unique and interesting differences among people. Instead, it paints all members of a group the same.

> *"You know mentally ill people. They are all alike: weak, dangerous, unable to care for themselves."*

Once these groups are identified, they can be quickly segregated from the majority. Black persons are different than white. Women are different from men. People with mental illness are different from "normals." Some may argue that recognizing these distinctions is nothing more than reflecting physical characteristics. Persons who promote these arguments, however, forget that the advancement of distinctions and differences undermines the sharing of resources:

> *"There's not enough to go around to begin with. Why should I share it with that guy from another group?"*

This kind of categorizing and divisiveness leads to scapegoating. It provides easy targets when problems occur. Consider, for example, the reaction to Russell Weston, Jr. When he stormed the Capitol in 1998 and killed two policemen, several news stories quickly attributed it to his mental illness and a poor treatment system (See Table 7.1). Quick fixes were proposed in response;

> *"States should pass commitment laws that allow us to keep tighter control on these persons, especially when they are out of the hospital."*

Table 7.1
Stigma and Statements from the Media about Russell Weston, Jr.

"But let's be blunt: to have misgivings about working next to a psychotic who may or may not have skipped his medication is not quite the same as to object to having a co-worker who is black, Asian, female, or gay."

by Cathy Young
the Chicago Tribune
August 12, 1998

mental illness is moral weakness. Persons with mental illness, so the theory goes, failed to choose a healthy lifestyle:

> *"With a little effort, they could overcome*
> *their trials."*

Social psychologists refer to this kind of logic as an example of the "just world" hypothesis. Persons who experience significant life problems like mental illness must have a character flaw. A just world would never deal people such an unfair hand. Hence, persons with mental illness have earned the disrespect of their community.

Stigma maintains personal fears. "If I were weak, I would become mentally ill like that homeless guy talking to himself." This kind of ignorance limits people's understanding of mental illness. In addition, it distances the general public from its own brushes with anxiety

"'Look, the guy seemed like a garden-variety nut,' one government source said. 'In the United States of America, you're allowed to be a garden-variety nut.'"
by Michael Grunwald and Sandra Boodman
the Washington Post
July 28, 1998

"For those who watched on television across the nation, the events of July 24 in the Capitol were horrifying and sensational, but also impersonal and in a sense routine—murder in the cathedral of and depression. Instead of trying to understand how life events converged to cause emotional upset, persons steeped in stigmatizing beliefs deny their own woes so they aren't associated with "these weak mentally ill."

Can a Stigmatizing Society Change?

The impact of stigma is broad and deep, suggesting it is a formidable enemy that is not easily overcome. After all, stigmatizing views about mental illness have been evident in history since human events were first recorded. Nevertheless, there is both past experience as well as contemporary research that suggests we can overcome stigma and prejudice. Consider, for example, the oppression experienced by persons of color (Figure 7.1). The United States has a long and dishonorable history of stigma and discrimination against African

democracy, but also just another bit of slaughter by just another lunatic with a gun."

by Richard Cohen
the National Journal
August 1, 1998

"Other countries produce terrorists and murderous psychopaths, but experts say the United States clearly leads the world in the production of deranged people with paranoid delusions who commit public acts of violence. "

by Joe Sharkey
the New York Times • August 2, 1998

Americans, Latinos, Asian Americans, Native Americans, and other groups. Although the country still has significant hurdles to resolve concerns in this area, milestones show clear progress: fewer disrespectful images in the media, more persons of color in positions of power, and frequent legislation that prohibits racial discrimination. Similar progress has been found in the field of disabilities. Society's ignorance and discrimination of persons with physical handicaps has decreased significantly during the past decade.

Given this history of progress, campaigns targeting mental illness stigma are relatively recent innovations. Advocacy groups including the National Alliance for the Mentally Ill and the National Mental Health Association have begun stigma-busting efforts to stop movies and television shows that disrespect mental illness. There have also been affirmative programs that seek legal and other support for job and residential opportunities for persons with mental illness. (Legal and

"We protect the civil liberties of homicidal maniacs at the expense of our own, allowing violent psychotics to wander our streets while we erect metal detectors and steel barricades outside our public buildings."

by Linda Chavez
the Denver Post
July 29, 1998

"The only thing unbelievable about all this is that we have developed such a laissez faire attitude toward serious mental illness in this country. What other industrialized nation allows florid psychotics political actions are discussed more fully in Chapter 9.) Controlled research by psychologists and sociologists has shown similar improvement on stigma. These efforts are most successful when the targets of stigma-busting are clear.

Targets for Change

As discussed in Chapter 2, stigma has three different effects on the general public: it influences what we think, how we think, and how we act toward persons with mental illness. Each one of these needs to be targeted for society's stigma to stop. As we said earlier, there are three ways to change these targets: contact, education, and protest. Contact as a change strategy is reviewed in this chapter, education and protest in Chapter 8. Before reviewing these strategies, we consider the individual's role in society's change.

to wander the streets unsupervised, unmedicated, with no access to long-term hospitalization? None."

by Joann Richi
the Arizona Republic
August 4, 1998

Figure 7.1

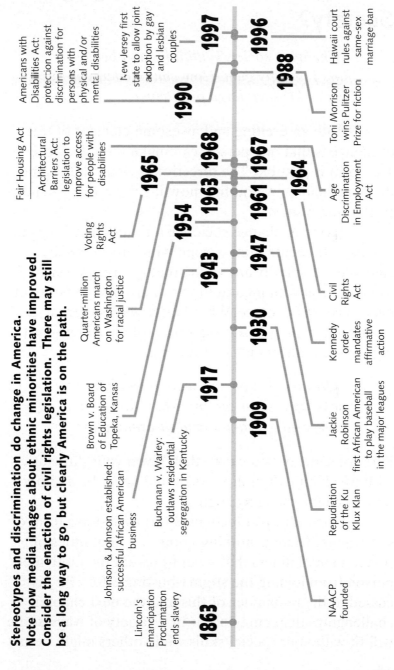

Stereotypes and discrimination do change in America. Note how media images about ethnic minorities have improved. Consider the enaction of civil rights legislation. There may still be a long way to go, but clearly America is on the path.

What is Your Role in Changing Society?

"Changing society's attitudes and behaviors is a hefty goal. How can one individual tackle such large problems?"

Both an exciting and awesome element of this challenge is that one person can make the difference. The spirit is possible. The direction is clear. In this and the next chapter, we outline how it's done: contact, education, and protest.

Trying to change society's attitudes also helps the person with mental illness cope with stigma. As discussed in Chapter 6, any effort that returns power back to the person with mental illness, helps him or her overcome a sense of shame. What better way is there to grab this power than by assuming some role in stigma-busting? Some readers may be thinking,

"How can I, a person with mental illness, possibly assume an important role in stopping society's stigma and discrimination?"

Perhaps some of you worry that, given your difficulties with psychiatric disability, you could never be an important voice for changing stigma.

Hopefully, you recognize this as another form of self-stigma. There is nothing about the disabilities of severe mental illness that would prevent the motivated person from joining the stigma-busting effort. As discussed in the remainder of this and the next chapter, challenging stigma may occur in a variety of ways; some will fit with your special skills while others might be better suited for peers. Persons who choose to join the struggle bring their unique talents to the cause.

Strategy I. Provide Contact with Persons with Mental Illness

Research conducted by our group at the University of Chicago has shown that one of the most effective ways to change public attitudes about mental illness is to foster interactions between the general public and persons with mental illness! Ignorant attitudes are easy to maintain when members of the public do not encounter persons who have overcome their psychiatric disabilities. Meeting persons with mental illness who are productive members of the community challenges stigmatizing attitudes.

> *"Wow, they don't all have horns. Hank said he has schizophrenia. But his life is a lot like mine."*

Individuals with mental illness like yourself have a central and essential role in changing attitudes about mental illness.

Tell Your Story of Struggle and Recovery

The place to begin is to find a place to tell your story about struggling with and meeting the challenges of mental illness. The National Alliance for the Mentally Ill has speaker's bureaus through their local affiliates; so do many of the other advocacy groups listed in our *Learn More About it Section* at the end of this book. These speaker's bureaus can hook you up with local churches, school groups, civic organizations, and others to speak about your experiences.

Telling your story works best when you are clearly on the group's agenda. You do not want to be added to a program as an afterthought. In a typical presentation of this kind, you might be given an hour's time. Thirty minutes could be used to present your story followed by 30 minutes for questions and answers as well as general discussion from the audience.

As examples, we have included stories developed and presented by two advocates in Table 7.2. Kyle Uphoff-Wasowski[2] struggled with manic-depression for more than eight years. She is now a wife and mother of two children living in the Western suburbs of Chicago. She is also a successful consultant to mental health organizations. Bob Lundin has had a similar struggle with a schizoaffective disorder. He is a freelance writer, publications director at the University of Chicago, and organizer of consumer art shows in the Midwest. Bob is also one of the authors of this book. Bob and Kyle have told their tales in public events throughout the Chicago area, Illinois, and the country. Their stories illustrate some of the common struggles and successes of persons challenged by mental illness. Yet, they also show that persons struggling with the same illness lead very differ-

---

[2] Throughout this book, we provide quotes and vignettes representing the experiences of people with mental illness which are sometimes fictional but always meaningful. Most of the time, we use pseudonyms, or provide no name at all. Kyle Uphoff-Wasowski and Bob Lundin wanted to use their real names to broadcast their "real" story of mental illness.

ent lives. This is perhaps one of the messages people learn through contact: persons with mental illness are unique human beings with different approaches to life... just like the rest of the population.

Elements of a good story.

Kyle and Bob's stories illustrate some of the essential elements of stigma-busting presentations that are likely to change public attitudes (these are summarized in Table 7.3). First, *your story needs to be personal.* It needs to reflect *your* experiences and impressions. This is accomplished by using first person words like "me", "I", and "my." Don't talk about your experience in the third person and steep it in formal language;

Table 7.2
The stories of Kyle Uphoff-Wasowski and Bob Lundin.

Kyle Uphoff-Wasowski's Story

Hi. My name is Kyle Uphoff-Wasowski and I'm here to tell you about a disease I have called bipolar disorder or manic-depression.

The disorder I have, when it's untreated, can cause severe mood swings. The actual disorder occurs in the brain and neuro-pathways. Illnesses like depression, manic-depression, and schizophrenia are referred to as neurobiological brain disorders.

I was diagnosed with manic-depression seven years ago now—shortly after the birth of my first child. I

> *"The experiences of persons like yours
> truly, the speaker, are comparable to those
> exigencies unfavorably put upon all alien-
> ated outgroups."*

Bring it home by *telling good stories illustrated with concrete experiences.* Note how Kyle and Bob did this; they are illustrating their stories with specific persons, places, and times. People learn much better by explicit example

have had one severe depression that was so devastating I began thinking about ending my life. This is not a depression that most people think of as depression. There should be a different word for what those of us with a mental illness experience. It is like a paralysis of the brain—nothing like what I used to call depression! I honestly felt physically disabled—as though I'd had a stroke or something. Just getting out of bed and brushing my teeth was an unbelievable challenge. There was no joy in anything!—even my newborn son who I loved more than life itself, and who through no fault of his own, was a constant reminder to me of how useless I was.

Before my illness struck I lived a life much like anyone else, I guess. I am one of five children in my family. We have loving and supportive parents and come from an upper middle class background. I was always active in school with sports and friends and was quite popular in high school. I was a cheerleader and a gymnast and hung out in the "popular crowd." I don't tell you any of this to impress you, but to impress upon you that my life was not abnormal from the get-go!

My own stereotypes of mental illness made it

("Sometimes I would get so depressed that I would lie in my bed and cry for three days or more.") not heady abstraction ("Depression is like a dark cloth causing utter sadness."). Listeners can clearly imagine being in bed for 72 hours; the dark cloth metaphor is vague and more difficult to make sense of.

At the same time, *don't avoid professional terms when they illustrate a point*. It may provide an opportunity to inform listeners about an important issue related

impossible for me to accept the diagnosis at first. I didn't fit the stereotypes, so how could I have a mental illness? I was not a loner as a child. I had loving, supportive parents and had not been sexually abused or traumatized as a child—nothing "twisted" happened to me at all. Therefore the doctors must be wrong!

I received a bachelors degree in Speech Pathology and Audiology from Western Michigan University where I met my husband Kevin. We married in 1984 and moved to New Jersey. I got my masters degree from New York University in Deafness Rehabilitation. I took a job in New York City and enjoyed every aspect of big city life! I worked for two years as a rehab counselor with people who were deaf— some deaf and mentally ill (what a twist of fate). Even when I was working with people who had mental illnesses I still had misconceptions and fears that I know now are ridiculous and unwarranted. I realize how much damage the media has done to the lives and reputations of people with mental illness. Much more damage than we could ever do ourselves!

When I was 28 years old I had my first child. My son, Luke, was born in Edison, New Jersey, and we lived to mental illness. Notice how Bob Lundin educates his audience about psychosis; "A psychosis is where you completely lose touch with reality and become very disoriented." This also communicates to the audience that persons with mental illness have an expertise about mental illness worth learning from.

Presentations need to be truthful; don't try to embellish them. You shouldn't tell your story in an overly positive light;

happily there for another seven months. We wanted to move back to the Midwest because that's where we were both raised, and our families were there. My husband got a transfer.

The stress of moving, having an infant, the physical change going on in my body (at the time, my son was gradually weaning from nursing) and the fact that I was pre-disposed to having a mental illness—all created the right environment for this illness to emerge.

Before the move to Illinois, I felt tremendous lethargy and was also losing weight as well as having trouble sleeping. I attributed all of these symptoms to what was happening in my life—not to a mental illness.

The unrecognized "blip" of depression that occurred in New Jersey was replaced by a full blown manic episode in Illinois. At first my husband and I thought it was wonderful! I went from having no energy and feeling low, to feeling great and unpacking the entire house we'd move into, painted rooms, and got the whole house organized in a day! Who would not love this??

I was very verbal and had tremendous insight about all kinds of things. My husband thought I was brilliant. Then my wonderful, insightful talks became hard

"Mental illness isn't that bad. I survived my three suicide attempts easily."

Listeners might get the idea that your depression was not really challenging or that you did not have a "real" mental illness. Nor should you try to paint too bad a picture;

"Being in a psych hospital is like living in a rat-infested slum."

to follow and somewhat bizarre. I had lost a lot of weight and was having trouble sleeping too. But having just had a baby I thought it was a good thing I was losing weight—and just figured I was having trouble sleeping because of stress. We still owned our home in New Jersey and we were unhappily paying the mortgage on both homes! My husband was concerned but kept telling himself I'd be O.K. Finally one day he came home from a business trip to find the house a mess (very uncharacteristic of me), and I was laughing and crying very inappropriately about things. Somehow as sick as I was, I always took good care of my son—he was not sitting in a dirty diaper somewhere in a corner!

By this time, my husband was quite frightened of my rapid mood swings, and called 911. The ambulance came and took me to the hospital and held me there against my will. It's interesting to note that my illness became much more severe the moment I was forced to stay in the hospital. I became delusional and paranoid and was convinced the whole staff was plotting some story about why I had to stay on the psychiatric ward when I really didn't need to be there—and they all knew it! I thought there was literally a key I had to find to get

Although it is true that losing the liberty to come and go from an inpatient ward is demoralizing, some people are likely to think you have a political agenda and are misrepresenting experiences when you use extreme examples like this. Moreover, when you stray from the facts you are likely to say something that is not truthful—"Were you really in restraints and not fed for an entire week?"—and lose your credibility. Be reassured that your story of struggles with mental illness is compelling enough to get most listeners' attention.

out of there and the only way I could get it was to get the information from the staff. When I got the "information" I would find the key. During this hospitalization I was put in isolation and in restraints, shot up with antipsychotic drugs, and put on suicide watch.

That first hospitalization was the most painful thing that's ever happened to me—to know your mind can go off like that with no warning and that you could think and do such goofy things is terribly frightening. There is so much shame involved with this illness. I went home from the hospital and fell into a severe depression that lasted 9 months. I lost all my self confidence and was so ashamed. My only focus was to make sure no one found out about my illness and try to look "normal" at all times. It was the beginning of hiding my big ugly secret.

For a long time my illness was kept under control, but I was the sickest I've ever been. I was sick in my heart and in my soul. I had no love for myself and wasn't able to feel the love pouring in from my husband and family. I'm certain that I was experiencing hell on earth!

So much of this illness has to do with stigma. In my experience most of the stigma was self-induced. I did

Table 7.3
Elements of Your Story about Mental Illness

> **Be personal. Talk about your experiences.**
> write from the heart
> not too formally

> **Be concrete and to the point.**

> **Use and define professional terms where needed.**

> **Be truthful.**
> don't hide facts
> don't over-embellish

> **Only discuss those things you are comfortable about.**

> **Keep it short and focused.**

> **Provide specific examples of your illness where needed.**
> no skeletons in the childhood closet
> the impact of disease onset
> struggling with some failures
> the impact on family
> slowly coming to grips and winning

> **Tackle the impact of stigma head-on.**
> the effect of other's judgements on you

> **Remember the moral of your story.**
> I work, live, play just like everyone

more damage to myself than anyone could have! I worried so much about what people would think if they knew and convinced myself I wouldn't be accepted. I lived in utter fear that people would find out. I worried my friends wouldn't want to hang out with me if they knew, or the neighbors wouldn't let their kids play with mine. I worried about what my family "really" thought of me. I even went so far as to think of what my mail

There may be some aspects of mental illness you are still struggling with and do not want to talk about publicly. *Don't feel you have to discuss everything.* Respect your own sense of privacy. If, for example, you feel uncertain or embarrassed about an unrealistic fear of riding in elevators, there is no need to air this problem with everyone. Only share those concerns you have resolved in your life. Don't get pushed into telling your story in public until you are ready. Talking to the public

carrier thought of me because I got mail from the National Alliance for the Mentally Ill and the Depressive and Manic-Depressive Association. I was consumed by fear of being found out, and loathed the self-knowledge. I hated the life I was dealt!

After a few years of being episode-free I convinced myself this was a fluke and I didn't need the medication and that I'd be fine without it. I went off my medication. Two weeks later I had my second episode and was hospitalized again. Same scenario; isolation room, restraints, shot up with anti-psychotic drugs, and put on suicide watch. The reality that I could no longer deny this illness was staggering. I slowly began to accept my illness.

I began to get better the more I grew to accept my illness! I did this through educating myself. I read all the books I could find about manic-depression. I also joined a support group which helped me see that people do recover. I found a new doctor who is very supportive and encouraging and has never made me feel that I'm in any way responsible for my illness. Nor has he made me feel my parents are!

The one thing I've done that has improved my

about mental illness can be an empowering activity, but it can also be risky. Don't expose yourself to these extra challenges unless you feel you will benefit from the experience.

Bob and Kyle's stories included several areas in which the speaker might want to provide specific examples. *Talk about your childhood and the absence of skeletons in the closet.* Bob, for example, talked about a pleasant up bringing in New York. Kyle noted that she

recovery the most is talk about my illness. What I have come to find out is that mental illnesses are extremely common and nothing to be ashamed of. In talking about my illness privately and publicly now for four years I feel totally liberated and healed.

I coordinate the Speakers Bureau at the National Alliance for the Mentally Ill and encourage other people with mental illness to speak out about their experience. We go out to colleges, high schools, church groups, etc. I have actually found that my illness is something I can derive tremendous reward from; that in fact without the illness I would never know the reward I now experience. I would not be someone who would be doing public speaking otherwise! I am consistently amazed and pleased by the number of people who come up to me after I speak and share their stories of mental illness — either their own or family member and friends.

I have, since my diagnosis, had a second child, my daughter, Madison. She is such a gift. Not only did I think I would never have any more children after my son was born, and I felt tremendous sadness and loss because of this, but I felt my life would never be the same and was irreparable. My daughter was born in the had loving parents and was not traumatized as a child. This kind of message challenges the notion that mental illness results from bad parents and stunted development.

Share your feelings about the sudden impact of mental illness. Bob illustrated this point well;

> *"Then, after high school, the summer before I went to college, I had my first psy-*

same hospital where I've had my hospitalizations and has helped change the way I see it. The hospital is a place of health and life!

My illness will never be gone, but I feel recovered. I feel I have triumphed over this illness personally, and I know I am doing a lot to help other people recover by sharing my experience and by being open about my illness. I know it would have made a difference to me if I had seen someone like me talk at my high school or college about their illness. I used to think mental illness was someone digging in garbage cans and mumbling to themselves. That was my whole vision of mental illness. Now I know people with mental illness are people like me.

*chiatric problem. One night in Atlanta,
with a friend of mine, I took some drugs
and they triggered a psychosis."*

This discussion elicits empathy from listeners. Everyone understands the terror of a successful life grinding to a halt because of the sudden intrusion of severe mental illness.

Bob Lundin's Story

Hi. My name is Bob Lundin and I live with a psychiatric illness. I have a mental illness called "schizoaffective disorder."

It's a mood and thought disorder. In other words, a schizoaffective disorder causes abnormal swings in my moods. In my life, I've had long, severe depressions. And I've had many episodes of manic behavior where the disorder has made my thinking excited, grandiose, irrational, and just hyper. On the other hand I've also had to deal with delusions and hallucinations. I've had this problem for nearly 20 years.

Of course, I can remember how things were before I became mentally ill. Life seemed a lot simpler then. I'd like to tell you a little about my life. As a kid I lived in upstate New York. My father was a college professor. He taught at a small college in Clinton, called Hamilton College. That's where I grew up.

I remember when our new house was built in 1963. It was a big white house. In the back was a hill that was just great for sledding and skiing. I used to sled with my sister, who's three years older than I am. Her name is

Talk about how the impact of your mental illness lasted beyond the relatively brief period of onset. Listeners need to hear that this is not just another short-lived emotional crisis. You were struggling with biological disorders that derailed life goals just like any major physical illness. Bob said,

"The illness was disastrous to my life. I had never been a quitter. I had never failed at

Sara. She isn't mentally ill at all. She works for a corporation in North Carolina, Bell and Howell.

My family moved down south when I was eight years old. After that, I grew up in a small college town in Tennessee called Sewanee. It was beautiful. It was located on a mountain known as the Cumberland Plateau—not far from the Appalachians. There were creeks, and coves, huge forests, and cliffs. It was like a paradise for me since I like to hike and camp and do other outdoor sports.

I went to a very small high school, called St. Andrew's School, just outside Sewanee. Many of the teachers were Episcopal monks. They were very friendly but very austere. I loved it there, though. I did very well in high school. I was a varsity athlete, I won many awards for academics, but I think my best ability was as the photographer for the school's yearbooks. We were proud of our yearbooks. They won awards across the state.

Then, after high school, the summer before I went to college, I had my first psychiatric problem. One night in Atlanta, with a friend of mine, I took some drugs and they triggered a psychosis. A psychosis is *anything I put my mind to. But things were very different."*

You might also *describe how your experiences with mental illness affected the family.* Speakers may relate how parents and siblings are frequently overwhelmed by mental illness. Family members may progress through a variety of reactions that include anger at the person for his or her mental illness ("Some members thought I was goldbricking," said Bob), sad-

where you completely lose touch with reality and become very disoriented. I was so disturbed that I tried to commit suicide. I wasn't depressed or anything. My disoriented thinking just told me to do it. I'm glad I failed. The doctor let me out of the hospital in three days and I went home. But I remember seeing a man in the hospital's psychiatric ward who had tried to slit his own throat. That image stayed with me for many years.

The next fall I entered a small college in Ohio called Kenyon College. It had a good academic program. My psychiatric problem stayed away. I finished college with good grades and a major in psychology. In 1976 and 1977, my junior year, I went to England to study at Exeter University.

Then after leaving college I was unsure which career I wanted to pursue. That's not too unusual, I think. So, I decided to get an MBA (Masters of Business Administration) at Vanderbilt University. I was unhappy. It was a lot of stress. After a year and a half I got really sick. The psychoses came back with a vengeance. This time I wasn't taking drugs. One night, during a lightning storm, I was very sick and I was sure the U.S. was being bombed by the Russians. So, I wanted to tell the ness at the interloping symptoms, and acceptance of the disability. This kind of message opens the door to a discussion of the stigma experienced by families.

The take-home message in Kyle's and Bob's stories comes next; this should be a climactic moment in your presentation. *Despite the challenges of mental illness, you have come to grips with your disabilities and are now achieving your life goals.* Kyle talks about the meaning of her achievements.

University's chancellor. By a fortunate accident I drove to the hospital instead.

Now the doctors feared I had a mental illness. But not for another year would a doctor diagnose me with manic-depression. It would be another 20 years I would be diagnosed with a schizoaffective disorder.

In the meantime the illness was disastrous to my life. I had never been a quitter. I had never failed at anything I put my mind to. But things were very different. I started having more delusions and attacks of anxiety. They were crippling. Sometimes the anxiety left me paralyzed and exhausted. The delusions reeked havoc on my judgement and ability to work. In two short years I had to quit graduate school, and I was fired from a very good job at the college. I would never get a good job from them again.

Most people never have to cope with terrible blows like this. But worse, in between the delusions, I had to cope with a series of severe depressions. A doctor prescribed lithium; I take it today. It's a drug that is commonly prescribed for mental illness, but it didn't help the depressions. I just had to live through them. But they never came back. It's funny that the best psychiatrist I

"I have, since my diagnosis, had a second child, my daughter Madison. She is such a gift... My daughter was born in the same hospital where I've had my hospitalizations and has helped change the way I see it now!"

Bob said,

"I remember when I started, I was so shy

saw didn't say, "I'm going to cure your depression." He said, "Hang on, it will eventually go away." And it did.

But that wasn't nearly the end of my problems. Next I had a series of mildly psychotic and manic episodes, which went on for years. I would think I had special powers, like ESP or expert judgement, or I'd be on a mission. God, I remember the missions. When the mania got bad, I would think I was a great person or a religious entity. Sometimes I would think a newscaster on the television would speak to me. All sorts of routine daily events would have special meaning or significance to me. They call these "delusions of reference."

Over a number of years I've seen many different doctors for this and finally, in 1991, one doctor in Evansville, Indiana seemed to get the medications right. He put me on a combination of mood stabilizers and anti-psychotics and since I've been very well controlled. But he didn't diagnose me with a schizoaffective disorder, that would happen later. I still have problems, but they're manageable.

Best of all, I started making friends, I took my own apartment, and I started working. Starting work after 10 years of mental illness isn't easy. My résumé was

> *that I took my photos to the local paper*
> *and slipped them under the front door at*
> *night. Then I saw them published.*
> *Eventually, I worked my way up the ladder*
> *until I started writing for the Chicago*
> *Tribune in DuPage County."*

This point directly challenges the myth that mental illness is insurmountable. Disabilities are overcome. Most persons with mental illness live fruitful lives.

full of holes. Most companies wouldn't look at me, so I took a job as a freelance journalist and newspaper photographer. You don't really need a résumé for these. You just show editors that you can do it.

I remember when I started, I was so shy that I took my photos to the local paper and slipped them under the front door at night. Then I saw them published. Eventually, I worked my way up the ladder until I started writing for the Chicago Tribune in DuPage County, Illinois. And now, for the past three years, I've been employed by the University of Chicago, first as a research project assistant, now as a managing editor. I really like the people there, I can be open about my mental illness, and the pay's a lot better.

There are still issues in my life which are problematic, but I'll never give up on my recovery. You can't give up. If you give up you'll waste away.

I'd like to say a few things about stigma. People often say that the worst part of living with mental illness is not the disease itself as much as the negative attitudes which people have toward the disease—the stigma. I remember after I tried to take my life after high school many of my friends learned about it. I guess it made great

The story cannot end here, however. *You need to also tell listeners how stigma worsened your experiences of mental illness.*

> Bob: "I remember after I tried to take my life after high school many of my friends learned about it. I guess it made great gossip. Some of my friends never looked at me the same way again."

gossip. Some of my friends never looked at me the same way again. Instead of feeling comfort and sympathy, I felt shame and distress. I denied my problem; I hid it.

But after college my illness was so bad that I could no longer deny it or hide it. Subsequently, I was socially isolated. I had health insurance taken away from me. I faced a life where employers could ask if you had a "nervous condition;" where members of the opposite sex would abruptly end a conversation if they got a hint of your disability; where even members of my own family accused me of "goldbricking" because I couldn't work.

To many I was not so much Bob Lundin as I am a mentally ill man, and all that means. Think of your own attitudes toward mental illness. The stigma isn't right. I hope this story will get you to think a little differently about mental illness.

Discussion Questions

How many people here have known someone with a mental illness [Show of hands]?

> Kyle added, "I lived in utter fear that people would find out. I worried my friends wouldn't want to hang out with me if they knew or the neighbors wouldn't let their kids play with mine."

You need to punch the audience with this point; a stigmatizing public only makes the tough course of mental illness that much worse.

These assertions lead to the moral of your story; *I work, live, and play just like you!* Persons with mental illness are capable and can accomplish. You look for no special favors. With appropriate support, all you need is the same opportunities granted all people.

How many mental illnesses, besides manic-depression, can you name?

What are some of the negative attitudes that go along with mental illness?

What are some of the positive attitudes of mental illness?

What can we do here to fight stigma?

Suggestions on how to tell your story.

Public speaking can be a daunting task, even when telling your own story. There are several values, listed in Table 7.4, that will help to improve the style of your presentation. First, you need to feel *confident about your presentation. This feeling is achieved by telling yourself that your story is important*; "My story challenges society's stigma."

You also should recognize that your presentation is *interesting*. Masters of public speaking say that relaying a personal story is one of the best ways to get an audience's attention. As one Toastmaster put it, "People like to hear human-interest accounts, blow-by-blow details about what happened in your life."

Also recognize that your story is *humble*. You are not trying to give the definitive statement about mental

Table 7.4
Some Values to Keep in Mind When Public Speaking

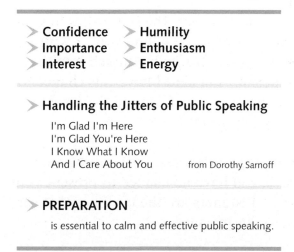

> **Confidence**   > **Humility**
> **Importance**   > **Enthusiasm**
> **Interest**   > **Energy**

> **Handling the Jitters of Public Speaking**

I'm Glad I'm Here
I'm Glad You're Here
I Know What I Know
And I Care About You   from Dorothy Sarnoff

> **PREPARATION**

is essential to calm and effective public speaking.

illness. Nor are you trying to bring down all stereotypes in a 30-minute presentation. Your goal is to provide listeners a brief glimpse into the life of a person with mental illness who does not act like stereotypes suggest. Remember the importance of *enthusiasm and energy*; they are infectious and tell an audience to carefully hang onto the words of your story. Enthusiasm shows the audience that you believe your message to be important and interesting. Enthusiasm is communicated through your energy. Never sit down when you present: stand up, walk around, and gesture when needed. Meet your audience head on and look them in the eye. Speak loudly and vary the emotional tone of your voice and facial expression.

Some speakers have difficulty because of the jitters or nervousness that accompanies public exposure. Dorothy Sarnoff, president of Speech Dynamics, recommended the four verse mantra in Table 7.4 to deal with this kind of performance anxiety. If you are feeling nervous, you should repeat this to yourself several times before starting to speak.

> *I'm glad I'm here.* The butterflies in your stomach might be telling you, "I wish I were home." But talk yourself into the opposite. "I'm glad I have this chance to see the audience. I can tell them something important."

> *I'm glad you're here.* Without the audience, you have no chance to present your story. Listeners are the currency that carries your message.

I know what I know. Remind yourself that you are not here as an expert on mental illness. You are making this presentation as an expert on *you.* No one else can tell your story as effectively.

And I care about you. That's why you're there. You care about your audience, want them to listen to your message, and learn from your story.

Perhaps the single most important public speaking consideration is preparation. Regardless of the amount of pre-speech planning and legwork, you need to feel prepared and ready to face your audience.

How Much Should I Prepare My Presentation Ahead of Time?

Table 7.5 includes a worksheet that will help you write out a biography that reflects the key parts of your story. Some of you may want to use this worksheet to carefully plan all details of your presentations. Others may wish to use it as a loose outline for an extemporaneous, off the cuff, speech. There are advantages and disadvantages to extensive preparation versus extemporaneous speech; these need to be considered so you can choose the style that works best for you.

By extensive preparation, we mean writing out the presentation entirely or preparing a thorough outline with specific examples of each point. Extensive preparation also includes dress rehearsals with a friend who will provide gentle feedback about strong points of the story as well as suggestions for changing your pre-sentation. Specific advantages to extensive preparation are many; these persons will tell a well-organized story, cover the essential elements, make fewer errors, and be better prepared for reactions from the audience. Some

Table 7.5
A Guide to Setting Up A Story About Your Experiences with Mental Illness

---

Hi, my name is _____

and I have a severe mental illness called _____ .

My childhood was not that unusual.	List some events in your youth that are typical of most people.

1. _____

2. _____

3. _____

4. _____

Make sure you stress that your mental illness was not due to bad upbringing.

My mental illness started when I was about ____ years old.	List some of the difficult things that happened to you when you first noticed your mental illness beginning.

1. _____

2. _____

3. _____

4. _____

Unfortunately, my mental illness did not go away quickly.	List some of the things you have struggled with the past several years due to your mental illness.

1. _____

2. _____

3. _____

4. _____

---

speakers might also decide to prepare visual aids to illustrate key points in the worksheet. For example, you might present photographic slides from your childhood illustrating the normalcy of your life.

On the downside, extensive preparation may lead to a stale presentation because of rote practice. Moreover, some speakers might find repeated consideration and critique of their stories to be anxiety producing. Sometimes, it is better to just do the speech and not spend a lot of time worrying about how it sounds.

Despite these problems, I have achieved several accomplishments.

List some of the things you have accomplished in terms of your work, relationships, and other personal goals.

1. _____

2. _____

3. _____

4. _____

5. _____

Despite my accomplishments, I have experienced some stigma and unfair responses to my illness.

List some of the unfair experiences and harsh reactions you have experienced from society.

1. _____

2. _____

3. _____

4. _____

5. _____

I want to end with these two key points.

> 1. I, like all persons with mental illness, live, work, and play just like you.

> 2. So please treat me the same.
>   Do not view me or respond to me based on any unfair stereotypes.

Finally, extensive planning requires several hours of preparation before the presentation, time which many busy people may not have.

There are several benefits to speaking off the cuff. Some experts are able to provide an engaging summary of their experiences with mental illness and stigma with nothing more than a half dozen notes. They believe this approach is fresh and allows the speaker to weave in talking points that address the specific interests of the audience. For example, Clarence noticed his audience was comprised of several homeless persons. So, he decided to talk more about his own experiences with living on the streets. There are disadvantages to an extemporaneous style, however. Many persons are unable to present an organized story without some upfront preparation of their ideas. Without this kind of careful organization, the audience may become confused about the purpose of the presentation; the effect on stigmatizing attitudes may be muted.

How does telling your story affect you?

Putting your experiences with mental illness into a cogent story and sharing it with others will benefit not only the audience, but you too. For some, it serves a therapeutic process. It helps you make sense of the challenges you have endured and take stock of your accomplishments. It may also outline areas in your life that need further attention.

Telling your story can also be empowering. Telling your story helps you to recognize that you are no longer a passive responder to mental illness nor to a society that puts down your disabilities. Instead, speaking publicly about your illness is evidence that you are a person that accepts your responsibilities to society (to become a productive member of society and a supportive neighbor) and demands the rights these responsibilities entail.

Table 7.6
The Story of Ron and Betty Chaggaris.

Hello, We are Ron and Betty Chaggaris. Our son, Chris, lives with a mental illness called schizoaffective disorder. He's 36 years old. Since the age of 17 he's suffered bravely from this devastating disease. But Ron and I, and his brother James who is a year younger, also have suffered with Chris. We've felt the pain that he's had; we've felt the stigma he's felt. Even though this terrible illness struck one of our children, it strikes us as well.

When Chris developed schizophrenia we lived outside of Chicago. Chris had always been a warm and loving son, despite his struggles since birth with a different brain difficulty: an organic brain dysfunction. Doctors believed that when he was born, his brain was robbed of oxygen for several minutes. This resulted in damage to the left and right frontal lobes. Chris was not able to talk until a relatively late age; then we suspected that something was wrong. But when he was a junior in high school, we did not expect that our wonderful and loving son would also be struck with mental illness.

I remember how it was before Chris became ill with a schizoaffective disorder. By then life had not been easy for him. He had difficulty with his short-term memory, and his ability to conceptualize caused him trouble,

Telling a Family Story

As we said in an earlier chapter, parents, siblings, spouses, children, and other family members are often victimized by the stigma of mental illness. They, too, benefit from sharing their stories publicly. Table 7.6 includes the story of Betty and Ron Chaggaris and their son, Chris.

In some ways, the story is outlined much like the presentations made by Kyle and Bob. Ron and Betty

beginning in elementary school, because of his inability to do mathematics and other conceptual subjects. Ironically, he did well at reading, and later at history. But mathematics remained a chronic problem.

As parents we worried greatly about our son. One teacher at the school he attended thought he was mentally retarded. Without even being tested, the school placed Chris in a special education class. Yet as parents we ultimately thought this to be a good move, since Chris would get special tutoring. Still, we were troubled

by it. We discovered we would have to pick up Chris from school at an earlier time in the afternoon which the other children would notice. Our son would be labeled a special education student and he would suffer all the stigma which this involved. Years later he would

present Chris as a "warm and loving son." Unfortunately, he was struck by a brain dysfunction that interfered
with his early schooling. The parents wrote eloquently
about Chris' challenges and his heroic effort to struggle.

A family member's story differs from those written by consumers in two ways. First, the pain experienced by persons with mental illness is equally terrify-
ing on family members. They must sit by helplessly and
watch their innocent child withstand these tortures.
Families feel alone and without support as they deal

begin his other struggle, and our struggle, with the stigma of mental illness.

In 4th grade, Chris returned to regular classes at
school. The school helped him in math by assigning him
a tutor; reading and history remained his strong points.
Sometimes his classmates were amazed when Chris
would read clearly in front of them. Still, Chris was
shunned by most of his peers, and he began to take on
characteristics of a loner. He was picked on and
ridiculed. But Chris remained stoic and meek. It was so
sad to see our son suffer like this. Despite all, Chris
remained very close to his family with whom he could
communicate well. We loved him very much.

In January 1981 we began to see changes in Chris
that troubled us and compounded his problems in high
school. His personal hygiene slipped. He wore dirty
cloths. He no longer looked neat. Before this Chris had
in fact been a "neat-nick." He was always clean and well-
groomed. Now he had a hard time getting up in the
morning, where before he was up and full of energy first
thing in the morning. His room started to become a
mess. "There's nothing wrong," he would say. Then a
couple of months later Chris came home crying. He

with these difficulties. Ron and Betty said, "The church was just not there for parents of a mentally ill child. It seemed the minister couldn't even talk about mental illness. We thought he wouldn't talk or preach about it because it might in some way stigmatize him."

The Chaggaris' story illustrates the second important point of the family story. The shame of mental illness stigmatizes family members too. "We felt a little ashamed and looked deep within ourselves thinking, 'What did we do wrong, where did we go wrong?' Even

remarked that things were looking strange; that his father was looking strange. He said his father's skin looked like it was falling off and that his dad's neck looked too long. I had no idea where this was coming from. Then in May, 1981 my son came home, crying, saying he needed help, that something was wrong.

Chris' first diagnosis was schizophrenia. He had been hearing voices for years but they were indefinite, like a bunch of noise. Now he heard definite voices. Ron and I didn't realize that 17 was a common age for schizophrenia to emerge. Chris was hospitalized. That was difficult on all of us, as was seeing his changes in mood. He had always been good with his family before this, especially with his grandmother. Now he was separated from us. He spent four months in a locked unit in Aurora, Illinois. The ward population was a combination of mentally ill people, people from broken homes, people addicted to drugs, and runaways. Chris was like a babe in the woods. He was not street-smart; he has never been street smart. The experience was an ordeal for him. The medical staff put him on a number of different medications.

After his stay there he came back home and we

though you're being told it's not your fault, these things happen. You think you have control—why didn't we take better care of the situation?"

The same principles for how to tell a personal story apply to how to tell a family story. Be honest, be concrete, and be personal. We provide a worksheet for preparing family stories (in Table 7.7) to help family members who might decide to take on this task in their community.

tried to get him back into high school so he could finish his degree. It was very difficult. Even though the high school was two blocks away, Chris would ask me to walk with him—which I did—and he'd sit on the corner looking at the school. The school authorities were very patient. They'd let him "work it out." He'd finally make a decision and would go into class. At school, occasionally Chris would lie down on the sidewalk and I'd get a call from the teacher that something was wrong. I'd say, just let him do it, it took all of his energy just to go back to class. We were so proud when we saw Chris go from attending school one hour a day to full-time and then graduate with his brother. We were so happy for him— and his brother!

But living with a loved one who has mental illness is difficult, to say the least. Ron and I talked about it and learned about it—that's about the only way to deal with it. We tried to find out about his illness but that wasn't easy. The National Alliance for the Mentally Ill (NAMI) did not, at that time, have a chapter in our county. We'd read newspapers to try and find out what was wrong with our son. Too often the doctors were silent. They'd say, "He's schizophrenic; we're going to put

Other Factors that Facilitate Contact

The effects of contact on stereotypes and stigma have been researched by a large number of social psychologists. These studies have identified several factors that enhance the effects of stories on public attitudes.

him on these meds." We were supposed to have to deal with it! In recent years, the new NAMI chapter near us has been our savior.

Sometimes the stigma hits us. We felt socially isolated after Chris' illness. We felt a little ashamed and looked deep within ourselves thinking "What did we do wrong, where did we go wrong?" Even though you're being told it's not your fault, these things happen. You think you have control—why didn't we take better care of the situation? You were able to bring your child out of other illnesses, why can't you bring him out of this illness? Maybe Chris' brain dysfunction led to his developing mental illness. Whether it did or did not, we have the obligation to care for this child. We're stoic and stubborn.

Our relationship with the church faltered. The church was just not there for parents of a mentally ill child. It seemed the minister couldn't even talk about mental illness. We thought he wouldn't talk or preach about it because it might in some way stigmatize him. Ironically, his wife had manic-depression. But she could not bring herself to talk about it for fear of losing her own job as a nursing supervisor.

Contacts should MILDLY disconfirm stereotypes. Stories have little effect on public attitudes when they greatly differ with stereotypes about mental illness or when they unintentionally reinforce the stigmatizing attitude; examples of these kinds of stories are provided in Table 7.8. Some listeners will question the honesty of stories that grossly diverge from stereotypes; "I just don't believe it happens that way."

I love my boys so much and I've had such joy from them. It hurts so much to see the pain Chris goes through with mental illness, and it's as if it will never go away. We know what it is to bring a child into the world and watch him suffer. Today, our goals, energy, time, and funds go into working with the mentally ill.

It is so wonderful to see people who have recovered and families who have gone through this ordeal successfully. But what happens to Chris when Ron and I are gone? We have to face it: if Chris is living at home, then what? It's the biggest thing we worry about. We're getting older.

That's why were so happy to see Chris get settled into a group home. It's the biggest thing he's accomplished since his illness. He used to go to the group home and call home 5 or 6 times a day. Now he's more independent. He used to come home every weekend. Now he has a dance every Friday night. This independence is the biggest thing he's done. Not a lot of people can see the changes he's made. We can. And we're proud parents.

Others will likely view the story as irrelevant to the issue of mental illness if it seems radically different from public expectations:

Table 7.7
A Guide to Setting Up A Story About Family Experiences with Mental Illness

---

Hi, my name is _____
and I have a son/daughter/brother/sister/relative/close friend who has a severe mental illness called _____ **.**

His/her childhood was not that unusual.	List some events in his/her youth that are typical of most people.

1. _____

2. _____

3. _____

Make sure you stress that this mental illness was not due to bad upbringing.

His/her mental illness started when he/she was about ____ years old.	List some of the difficult things that happened when you first noticed the mental illness beginning.

1. _____

2. _____

3. _____

Unfortunately, his/her mental illness did not go away quickly.	List some of the things he/she has struggled with the past several years due to mental illness.

1. _____

2. _____

3. _____

The mental illness was also very hard on the family.	List some of the things family members have struggled with during the past several years due to mental illness.

1. _____

2. _____

3. _____

"I don't care what he says; I don't believe that guy is really mentally ill. I still think all schizophrenics should be locked up."

As a result, people discount or ignore stories that grossly differ from their expectations about mental illness.

Despite these problems, he/she has achieved several accomplishments.

List some of the things he/she has accomplished in terms of work, relationships, and other goals.

1. _____

2. _____

3. _____

4. _____

Despite these accomplishments, he/she has experienced some stigma and unfair responses to his/her illness.

List some of the unfair experiences and harsh reactions he/she has experienced from society.

1. _____

2. _____

3. _____

4. _____

My family has also experienced some stigma and unfair responses as a result of this severe mental illness.

List some of the unfair experiences and harsh reactions family members have experienced.

1. _____

2. _____

3. _____

I want to end with three key points.

> 1. **Most persons with mental illness, including my son/daughter/brother/sister/relative/close friend live, work, and play just like you.**

> 2. **Give them a break. Do not view them or respond to them based on any unfair stereotypes.**

> 3. **And give the families a break too.**

295

Stories that reinforce or otherwise support stereotypes are equally problematic. People who hear a speaker say she is not capable of working will fail to change their belief that persons with mental illness can live independently. These kinds of presentations are likely to strengthen stigmatizing attitudes.

> *"See, I told you all mental patients needed a guardian. They just can't care for them-selves."*

The best kind of story mildly disconfirms stereo-types. Coming up with these kinds of stories requires a

Table 7.8

Stories that Grossly Disconfirm, Unintentionally Reinforce, or Mildly Challenge Stereotypes About Mental Illness.

| Example of Stereotype | Persons with mental illness are unable to care for themselves, work in competitive jobs, or live independently. |

A Story that **Grossly Differs** with the Stereotype	A Story that **Reinforces** the Stereotype	A Story that **Mildly Challenges** the Stereotype
I was first hospitalized with schizophrenia when I was 18. I then spent six years in and out of psychiatric hospitals. Then, on my 24th birthday, I decided to stop giving in to my illness. I put myself through law school, spent a few years in the DA's office, and then became a county court judge.	I have been hospitalized several times and still suffer frequent psychotic symptoms. I am not able to hold a real job nor am I capable of handling my own money. I cannot maintain a committed relationship with a loved one and need to live in a sheltered environment for the rest of my life.	I was first hospitalized while in Army boot camp. I dropped out and spent the next several years trying to learn to deal with my symptoms. I was able to get through community college with some support and now am a mechanic at a large auto dealership. Even though I have occasional flare-ups, I'm able to keep my marriage alive as well as be a good parent to my two kids.

delicate balance. On one hand, you need to acknowledge common concerns about mental illness. This is evident in the two examples of Table 7.8. Speakers agreed that they have a significant illness that periodically returns and requires regular treatment and support. This kind of admission qualifies you as a person who has struggled with severe mental illness and knows something about stereotypes. On the other hand, stories need to include a message that challenges the stigma. In Table 7.8, the speaker said he was able to hold down a responsible job and participate in a happy family life despite some recurring problems. You need to avoid the trap of overselling your accomplishments, even if they are true. Persons with mental illness who say they worked their way through Harvard Medical School may be discounted as not representative of the typical *"mental patient."*

Example of Stereotype	Persons with mental illness are dangerous and need to be locked up to protect the community.

A Story that **Grossly Differs** with the Stereotype	A Story that **Reinforces** the Stereotype	A Story that **Mildly Challenges** the Stereotype
I have paranoid schizophrenia which makes me suspicious of people. However, I never raise my voice or even get angry at people. I always handle differences with others in a responsible and direct manner.	I have schizophrenia and am incapable of controlling my anger. Sometimes I think I am going to explode. When people make me angry, I want to kill them. I need to be put away so I don't hurt others.	Sometimes I become manic and get angry at the world. One time I was on a street corner yelling at people for breathing my air. But, then I started taking lithium and my mood disorder is under better control. Sure, sometimes I get angry at people. But don't we all? I'm able to control my symptoms and myself.

This problem can be avoided by framing your accomplishment in terms of the moral that needs to be stressed in anti-stigma stories: *I work, live, and play, just like you*. Hence, your accomplishments are no different than the average person who is struggling with making a living, raising a family, and dealing with daily stressors. Daily stressors for you include some recurring symptoms of major mental illness.

The audience *should interact with contacts*. Telling your story is a good beginning to challenge public stereotypes. Contact has an even greater effect when the audience interacts with the speaker and engages in an exchange of ideas. One way to do this is to provide a question and answer period after your story. Note that Bob Lundin listed several questions after his autobiography in Table 7.2. Some of these were quite personal, hoping to draw in listeners:

> *"How many people here have known someone with a mental illness?"*

Others are related to the central point of the presentation:

> *"What are some of the negative attitudes that go along with mental illness?"*

In addition, you should encourage listeners to ask about your experiences.

> *"Bob, do you really mean to say that you can hold down a job like 'normal' folks? This sounds too good to be true. Are you really mentally ill like I see on TV?"*

Some of these questions can be alarming. But you need to remember that many people attending your group are going to be skeptical about your message. That's good. These are people you especially want to reach. Skepticism means their stereotypes about mental illness are being challenged. Unfortunately, this skepticism may come out in the form of jarring questions. Your task is to try to provide a polite and direct answer.

> *"That's a good question. Yes, I can work like others. In fact, I've held my current job for more than a year and have risen to quite a responsible role. Do I have a mental illness like those people on TV? Well, I'm not sure what you're referring to on TV. But I had a bona fide severe mental illness that caused numerous hospitalizations, doctors, and medicines for more than 20 years. It's something that I continue to struggle with, just like a person with diabetes."*

Bob was not defensive in his reply. In fact, he acknowledged that this was a good question. He then proceeded to answer each concern directly.

Interactions should not be limited to intellectual topics. People also need the opportunity to mingle with you in a less structured setting; a social hour after the presentation provides a good opportunity. In this way, they will see that you are a genuine person with the same strengths and foibles as others. Your story was not just a well-prepared act.

Finally, interacting with the public on a common *task* is an excellent way to challenge stigmas. One activity we have found to be useful is for the speaker and audience to agree that stigma is a problem in their community and join together in developing some stigma-busting project. This might entail identifying local examples of images that are disrespectful to mental illness—for example, the neighborhood ice cream store has an ad campaign that says, "You must be crazy not to buy our chocolate soda."—and brainstorming some way to encourage the store to change their slogan. The section on Protest in the next chapter more thoroughly discusses stigma-busting efforts like these. The point here is that personal stereotypes are challenged when people interact with you on tasks like these and see firsthand that you have the same social skills and limitations as the average person.

Institutions should support contact. You are likely to have greater impact when presenting to established groups rather than trying to assemble a bunch of people together for this one issue. Established groups have an organized membership, regular meetings, and a common place to rendezvous. The purpose of churches, synagogues, and mosques make them especially appropriate groups to contact; their mission is to promote a moral view of society that should include an open-mindedness to groups like persons with mental illness. Several civic, service, and social groups are also excellent venues for presenting your story on mental illness. Rotary International, for example, inaugurated "Erasing the Stigma" (see Figure 7.2), a campaign to educate business leaders about the truths and misconceptions of severe mental illness. The League of Woman voters also has a rich history of inviting disenfranchised groups to its meeting. In some ways, however, seeking out groups like Rotary and the League is like speaking to the converted. You may also wish to contact other groups in your area.

Figure 7.2
A brochure from the Erasing the Stigma campaign of Rotary International.

A private-public partnership
which is changing
the way the world views mental illness

ERASING THE
STIGMA
OF MENTAL ILLNESS

Sponsored by: Mission Valley East Rotary Club and
The Thomas C. Ackerman Foundation

Administered by: Serving Hands International,
a public non-profit 501(c)(3) corporation
Federal I.D. No. 95-3797996

Adult education provides another place where you may seek out people to tell your story to. Growing numbers of adults are returning to community colleges either to improve career opportunities or participate in stimulating courses about areas of interest. Frequently, instructors in service-related disciplines—nursing, social work, psychology, pastoral ministry, education, and recreational therapy—would find the story of a person with mental illness to be an interesting addition to their curriculum. You may also wish to contact children. Schools and service groups (like the Scouts) would benefit from your story and provide you a stage to present it from.

Your presentation is further enhanced when authorities of these institutions publicly support you and your story. For example, your impact on a church group would be even greater if the pastor welcomed you in front of the congregation and encouraged participants to listen carefully to your message. Similarly, school principals and civic group presidents should endorse the presenter in front of the audience.

Sometimes, group leaders may not be aware of the importance of their public endorsement. You may wish to talk with them before your presentation and encourage them to provide an introduction that supports your message. The leader's introduction should include the following parts:

- you are a person who has successfully met the challenge of mental illness;

- you have come to discuss with the group the fact that mental illness, like most disabilities, can be overcome;

- one unnecessary burden you wish to inform the audience about is society's stigma; and

- everyone in the audience can assume an important role in changing stigma by listening to your speech and supporting your strategies.

Find opportunities for frequent, "real world" contact. Going to various church and civic groups as an invited speaker, and interacting with members after the presentation, are excellent ways to introduce the public to ideas that contradict stereotypes about mental illness. This beginning can be expanded further when you find opportunities to *regularly interact with the public. One way to do this is to become a member of the group and participate in activities. Joining* *alongside* members of the public in *"everyday, normal"* activities communicates a key message in a subtle way: I'm just like you.

For this kind of interaction to have significant impact, you need to interact with fellow group members as *equal* members. This means you should become a member of and regularly attend church and civic groups. Of course, you need to consider what kind of groups in your community coincide with your values and fit into your schedule. You will have greatest impact on peers in the group when you assume equal status. Equal status is earned when you meet all the responsibilities of membership; for example, attend meetings, volunteer for tasks, and assume authority roles. This goal is not achieved quickly. It takes everyone several months or years to be fully accepted into a new group. But this kind of acceptance is perhaps the best evidence that stereotypes are beginning to be torn down in your community.

Responses from the Audience

Audiences frequently have strong reactions to stories about mental illness. You are presenting an emotionally poignant story that challenges some long held viewpoints. Their responses vary from polite acceptance to angry denial. The response you hope for is *"sign me up."* These are individuals who recognize their stigmatizing attitudes and vow to stop them. In addition, they hope to amend past mistakes by joining the stigma-busting effort.

Sometimes, these people respond with a *"me too."* The "me too" listeners may be struggling with a psychiatric disability and have experienced firsthand the injustice about which you spoke. They may be family members who suffer stigma because of the trials of their loved ones. "Me too" respondents may be persons who are challenged by other physical disabilities or are members of society's other "outgroups" (like ethnic minorities or gay and lesbian groups). Regardless of the source of stigma, these individuals understand the injustice about which you speak, and want to stand up and support your message in the meeting.

Perhaps the most difficult group to deal with is the *I don't believe it* crowd. These are the folks who ask tough questions about your experiences; their approach may take several forms. They may say they don't believe someone who is functioning as well as you could really have a mental illness. Or they may discount your accomplishments altogether; "getting out of the hospital and overcoming ten years of psychosis is no big deal." Or they may think you are an odd ball who does not represent real "mental patients." They might say you are whining and need to toughen up; "Aw c'mon. Public opinion isn't that bad against mental patients."

Having someone stand up after your presentation and challenge your message can be frightening. However, consider these persons—individuals who publicly question your message—as the success stories in the crowd. They represent the important group of listeners who once believed the stereotypes about mental illness. You and your story challenged their belief and changed the way they viewed the world. Now they are trying to set the world back the way they knew it by questioning you. Remember though, that every question that challenges you yields a response that threatens their stigmatizing attitudes.

Audience Member: You tell a great story and obviously have done okay for yourself. But you're not really mentally ill. Not like mental patients we see in the newspaper.

Speaker: What would you consider being really mentally ill?

AM: Well like you lose touch with reality, or hear voices, or, I know, get locked up in state hospitals for a while.

S: But that's me. I have an illness called schizophrenia. At times in my life I have heard voices. I have had delusions where I thought the radio was talking to me. I have been hospitalized for up to 3 months at a stretch.

AM: But mental patients don't get jobs.

S: Yes sir. We do get jobs, frequently good ones. We may still need some help but many of us are able to hold on to them and make an income.

One of the more difficult responses to your presentations are listeners who *politely accept* your message. They seem to offer no arguments nor do they seem to want to join the stigma-busting campaign. It is hard to determine whether the polite acceptors have heard the message and challenged their stereotypes or ignored its meaning and experienced no real change in attitudes. Polite acceptors may need repeated exposure to persons with mental illness in order to experience any real change in opinion.

Chapter 8

Changing Society's Reaction Through Education & Protest

"Justice delayed is justice denied."
William Gladstone

The general public may need more factual information about severe mental illness to challenge its stereotypes. Education programs help people identify the myths of mental illness and facts that challenge these myths. Many stigmas fall away in the face of this kind of evidence. Persons with mental illness and family members are excellent resources for conducting this kind of education program. This can be done while telling one's story, defining terms that might be foreign to listeners in the process. Alternatively, you might provide basic facts about mental illness to an audience in a separate lecture. An education program like this would require learning key points about severe mental illness; the first half of this chapter provides a brief overview of this material.

Having this kind of knowledge provides you with more credibility in the eyes of listeners in the audience;

"Gee, it seems this guy really knows something about the facts of mental illness. He's not just talking about his limited experience."

But, learning the basic facts about mental illness is a lot of work. Some readers may wish to pair up with a psychologist, psychiatrist, or other mental health professional who knows a lot about mental illness and is sympathetic to the overall goals of stigma-busting. (More than likely, a local office of the National Alliance for the Mentally Ill or the National Mental Health Association can supply you with a list of professionals who would work with you for no fee.) Readers can act as the overall facilitator of the presentation and let the mental health professional review basic facts.

Strategy II. How Education Helps the Listener

The goal of education sessions is NOT for the listener to learn the extensive literature on mental illness. This kind of effort takes professionals many years to master. Rather, your goal is to provide listeners with some simple facts so many of the public myths about mental illness crumple. Understanding and treating severe mental illness is a complex business. There are, however, a few key points which provide a clearer picture of mental illness. This information is summarized as handy fact sheets in Table 8.1; you might decide to photocopy the fact sheets and hand them out when you do your educational presentation. The fact sheets are divided into sections that address two central questions for understanding severe mental illness.

- What is the experience of severe mental illness like?

- Given this experience, what are effective ways to diagnose and treat severe mental illness?

The Experience of Severe Mental Illness

A variety of issues need to be understood to comprehend the impact of severe mental illness. First among these, is an appreciation of the definitive characteristics of a disorder that make it a severe mental illness, rather than a short-lived, and relatively nondisabling, disorder.

Defining severe mental illness: Three factors define severe mental illness.

- **1. Diagnoses.** Mental health professionals consider three diagnoses as commonly associated with severe mental illness: schizophrenia, major depressive disorder, and manic-depression. Note, however, that some other diagnoses also are severe because of the breadth and length of disability; these include severe anxiety disorders like agoraphobia (a broad fear that often prevents people from leaving their house) and borderline personality disorder. Moreover, some people with the characteristic diagnoses of schizophrenia, major depressive disorder, and manic-depression have no lasting disabilities and therefore might not be considered as having a severe mental illness.

Table 8.1
Severe Mental Illness Fact Sheet

FACTS ABOUT THE EXPERIENCE OF THE DISEASE

Defining Characteristics Of Severe Mental Illness

Diagnoses: Psychiatric diagnoses commonly associated with severe mental illness include schizophrenia, major depressive disorder, and manic-depression.

Exclusionary Diagnoses: Diagnoses like mental retardation, autism, substance abuse, and Alzheimer's Disease are usually not what is meant by severe mental illness. Some persons may, however, have dual-diagnoses that include one of the severe mental illnesses plus substance abuse or mental retardation.

Breadth of Disability: Persons with severe mental illness suffer problems in many life domains including work, relationships, housing, physical and emotional wellness, income, education, recreation, and spirituality.

Length of Disability: Persons with severe mental illness struggle with their disabilities for many years.

There are several diagnoses that are typically excluded from severe mental illness including mental retardation, autism, substance abuse, and Alzheimer's Disease. Note, however, that some persons are challenged by dual diagnoses. These are persons who have a severe mental illness AND some other diagnosis like mental retardation or substance abuse. Special

Prevalence Of Diagnoses

Schizophrenia: about 1 in 100 people develop schizophrenia.

Manic-Depression: as high as 3 in every 200 people develop manic-depression.

Major Depression: as many as 25% of all women and 12% of all men have a major depressive episode in their lives.

Examples Of Key Symptoms

Psychotic Symptoms: Hallucinations (hear voices), delusions (believe you are Jesus Christ), thought disorder (not talking clearly), significant agitation.

Negative Symptoms: A state of profound disinterest in the world.

Depressive Symptoms: Deep sadness, loss of enjoyment, inability to sleep well, significant change in appetite and energy, suicidal wishes, feelings of worthlessness.

treatment considerations are needed to serve persons with dual diagnoses.

● **2. Breadth of Disability.** Having a diagnosis is not enough. Persons with severe mental illness suffer problems in many life domains including work, relationships, housing, physical and emotional wellness, income, education, recreation, and spirituality. It is these disabilities, and

Manic Symptoms: Feeling invulnerable, grandiose ideas (I am so smart I invented the computer), flight of ideas (ideas racing through your head), not sleeping for days, intense energy.

Anxiety Symptoms: Profound worry, unreasonable fears, pounding heart, shortness of breath, chills or hot flashes.

Development And Course Of Mental Illnesses

Acquiring the Disorder: Persons are usually born with the potential for severe mental illness. These disorders are NOT caused by bad parenting.

Childhood: Unlike developmental disorders, persons usually do not show obvious signs of severe mental illness in childhood.

Onset of the Disorder: Major symptoms usually start between 16 and 40 years. Onset can be slow or abrupt.

The Illness Over Time: Many persons move among stages where symptoms: are quite pronounced (acute stage), they are fairly well-controlled (residual stage), and they are gone altogether (remission).

not the psychiatric symptoms per se, that make a mental illness severe.

● **3. Length of Disability.** Finally, severe mental illnesses are part of a person's adult life for a significant portion of that life. They do not occur for a few months and then go away. Persons with severe mental illness struggle with their disabilities for many years.

Long-Term Outcome or Prognosis: Most persons are able to learn to cope with their disabilities and achieve their life goals.

The Biology Of Severe Mental Illnesses

Nerve Cells: Severe mental illnesses are likely caused by the inability of nerve cells (neurons) to communicate with each other effectively.

FACTS ABOUT ASSESSMENT AND TREATMENT

Diagnosing The Disorder

The DSM-IV: The Diagnostic and Statistical Manual of Mental Disorders is the text used by professionals for diagnosis.

How Diagnoses are Made: There is no single test or easy way to diagnose. It is based on a careful assessment of symptoms, onset, course, and disability.

Prevalence of diagnoses. Severe mental illnesses are not rare disorders that effect a minority of the population. Depending on how prevalence is determined, as high as 10% of the population may have a major mental illness in their lifetime. About 1% of the population meets the diagnostic criteria for schizophrenia. About 1.5% would fit into the manic-depression category. And perhaps 25% of women and 12% of men meet the criteria for major depression. Keep in mind that although these people may be diagnosed with schizophrenia, manic-depression, or major depression, their mental illness may not be severe because the

Medication

The Goals of Medication: Medications reduce symptoms and protect the person from relapse.

Antipsychotic Medications: Often prescribed for schizophrenia and manic-depression, these medications have been shown to be particularly effective in reducing agitation, inappropriate affect, and hallucinations.

Antidepressant Medications: These drugs are effective in treating the sadness of major depression and other severe mental illnesses.

Mood Stabilizers: These drugs include lithium and typically are prescribed to treat the euphoria and agitation of mania.

Beware of Side Effects: Most of the medications prescribed for severe mental illnesses have nasty side effects including dry mouth, drowsiness, trembling hands and legs, and restlessness.

breadth and length of their disabilities may be fairly muted. Nevertheless, severe mental illness is clearly a fairly common experience and not the rare event some people might expect.

Examples of key symptoms. Several clusters of symptoms are common to the various disorders. Persons with schizophrenia characteristically experience psychotic symptoms, especially during acute phases of the illness or when symptoms flare up. Persons with manic-depression and major depression may also experience psychotic symptoms. Classic psychotic symptoms

Rehabilitation And Support

Goal Assessment and Motivation: Rehabilitation needs to reflect the person's goals, no one else's. This kind of assessment examines the person's life plan, strengths, limitations, and motivation to pursue various life directions.

Community Support: Many persons are able to achieve a variety of vocational and independent living skills when they have the regular support of a counselor. This kind of support occurs in the person's home or place of work, as often as the person needs it, and should be relatively limitless.

Skills Training: Skills training teaches persons the social, coping, and self-care skills they may need to achieve their goals and meet the unforeseen demands of daily living.

Cognitive Rehabilitation: Some persons are better able to cope with life when they learn ways to think about the world.

include hallucinations (hearing voices, seeing images, or feeling things crawling on the skin), delusions (untrue beliefs about yourself and the world like thoughts that you are Jesus Christ or that you caused the Vietnam War), thought disorder (inability to think clearly such that your speech does not make sense; e.g., "I'm the creator of the dog that jumped over the verbal carrot."), and significant agitation (uncontrolled crying, anger, laughter, or nervousness).

Psychotic symptoms are often known as the *positive symptoms* of schizophrenia; so called "positive" because they are the obvious evidence of the disorder. Many persons with schizophrenia also suffer negative

Family Education and Support: Families who learn about the course of severe mental illness (and are taught skills to cope with the illness and receive the support of others) are better able to deal with the illness and help the family member challenged by it.

Mutual Help: Also known as self-help, persons benefit when they interact with others who have mental illness.

Two Easy-to-Read Resources Where You Might Learn More About Mental Illness:

Kim T. Mueser and Susan Gingerich. 1994. Coping with Schizophrenia: A Guide for Families. Oakland, CA: New Harbinger Publications.

Richard Keefe and Philip Harvey. 1994. Understanding Schizophrenia. New York: Free Press.

symptoms. Persons with negative symptoms have a pro-found disinterest in the world. They show almost no investment in anyone else, rarely initiate activities with others, and tend to have almost no emotional expression. Frank showed these symptoms. First his father and then his mother died in unrelated accidents within a month of each other. Despite these sudden losses, Frank showed no anger, sadness, or grief at his mother's funeral.

As might be expected, persons with major depression show a cluster of depressive symptoms. There are three types of symptoms in this cluster. First, people experience profound sadness in the absence of any clear source of grief. Second, they suffer loss of enjoyment in things they used to appreciate;

> *"I used to like to watch TV but when I get depressed, I can't bring myself to flop down in front of my favorite shows."*

The third type is known as vegetative symptoms; per-sons who are depressed frequently experience severe fluctuations in sleep, (too much or too little), appetite (too much or too little), and energy (too tired or too restless). Depressive symptoms also include a sense of worthlessness and thoughts about committing suicide.

Persons with manic-depression fluctuate between depressive and manic symptoms. The manic symptoms distinguish this disorder from other severe mental ill-nesses. Mania is characterized by a sudden cheerfulness or euphoria, a sense of being invulnerable or on top of the world. Persons experiencing this kind of euphoria frequently have grandiose delusions, beliefs that they are famous or have accomplished great feats.

> *"I once beat Muhammad Ali for the World*
> *Heavyweight Championship. But they took*
> *it away from me because I was too young."*

Alternatively, some persons might feel a sudden anger at the world marked by suddenly snapping, or otherwise attacking, strangers.

A surge of energy accompanies the manic episode. Persons might go days without sleeping and decide to start several projects all at once.

> *"I was so energized, I started to write a*
> *book, began to paint the living room, and*
> *took apart the carburetor in the Mustang."*

Unfortunately, the manic person is fairly confused and unable to accomplish any of these activities well.

Anxiety-related symptoms are the last cluster experienced by persons with severe mental illness. Anxiety has both cognitive and physical components. The cognitive components include intense worry and obsession about things;

> *"If I don't graduate from school, I'll end*
> *up a bum on the street. Oh, what'll I do?"*

Sometimes this includes worries about things they are intensely afraid of. These are also known as phobias; for example, an intense fear riding in elevators or driving on highways. The cognitive component is frequently accompanied by physical reactions: shortness of breath, pounding heart, sweaty hands, and butterflies in the stomach.

Development and onset of mental illnesses. Most persons with severe mental illness are born with some subtle vulnerability for the disease. Think of this vulnerability as a silent time bomb. It is not usually obvious in the child. The disorder seems to appear when the person is stressed as an adult. This vulnerability probably is inherited genetically from the parents. One's parents do not have to show any mental illness to hand down the genes for schizophrenia or manic-depression. There is also some evidence that severe mental illnesses may be acquired during pregnancy. There is research from Scandinavia, for example, that found a small group of mothers who developed the flu during pregnancy gave birth to a child who later developed schizophrenia.

There is no evidence that bad parenting causes severe mental illness. While research clearly suggests that severe traumas like physical or sexual abuse will scar most children and lead to significant problems when they become adults, the reverse is not true. Namely, not all adults with significant psychiatric disorders were traumatized as children. Life problems due to the severe mental illnesses were originally caused by genetics or pregnancy-related problems.

As stated earlier, adults with severe mental illnesses have relatively benign and calm childhoods. They do not usually suffer common childhood psychiatric disorders like attention deficit hyperactivity disorder or childhood schizophrenia. Rather, they suffer very subtle signs of the future mental illness, especially as the child ages into adolescence. Teens who later develop schizophrenia are frequently remembered as being somewhat odd. Nothing stood out during high school as a mental illness but the person may have had a lot of fringe experiences that suggest severe mental illness; "I think aliens are watching the earth." or "I can work miracles and stop all wars."

Typically, the onset of severe mental illness occurs in late adolescence or early adulthood. Schizophrenia, on average, tends to start at an earlier age—during young adulthood—than major depression or manic-depression. Some persons experience a very rapid onset of severe mental illness; in the course of a few weeks psychotic, depressive, or manic symptoms seem to overwhelm the person. Others have what is known as a slow and insidious onset. These people experience subtle indicators of psychosis, depression, or mania for several months or years. Subtle psychotic indicators may include perceptual illusions rather than hallucinations. One example of a perceptual illusion is called a "corner of your eye" experience; "Was that my third grade teacher I just saw out of the corner of my eye?" This is not a full-blown perceptual hallucination but rather more of a simple misperception. These subtle indicators eventually lead to the onset of a full-blown severe mental illness. Generally, persons who have a sudden onset of symptoms tend to have a better outcome than persons with the slow, insidious beginning.

Once the illness begins, persons are not psychotic and depressed continuously. They move into and out of three distinct phases of the illness over time. During acute phases, the person's symptoms are relatively pronounced; for example, psychotic symptoms may be especially noticeable or the sadness and worthlessness of depression may be obvious. During the residual phase, symptoms are muted and relatively well-controlled by treatment. For example, a person with major depression may get blue several times a week but is able to work and assume his role in the family. The extreme form of sadness marked by frequent crying is mostly gone. During remission, symptoms are absent and problems related to psychiatric disability are gone. For example, a person with schizophrenia no longer experiences psychoses and is able to meet his or her independent living and vocational goals.

The long-term outcome of persons with severe mental illness also varies. Since the beginning of the 20th century, psychiatrists and other mental health professionals believed that persons with severe mental illness, especially schizophrenia, had a horrible long-term outcome. Persons with schizophrenia were thought to end up completely disabled and unable to care for themselves. However, research conducted during the past fifty years shows that many persons with mental illness learn to cope with their psychiatric symptoms and are able to meet their life goals.

The biology of severe mental illnesses.

Given that severe mental illnesses are fundamentally biological diseases, researchers have struggled to understand how they occur in the brain. Although considerably more investigation is needed, researchers seem to agree on several trends. First, severe mental illness does not seem to be caused by damage which occurs in a specific part of the brain. The brain is divided into a number of easily observed sections; for example, the cerebrum, hypothalamus, cerebellum, and reticular activating system. Research has failed to show obvious harm to any of these as the root cause of severe mental illness. Rather, severe mental illness seems to occur because of problems with the nerve cells or neurons that make up these sections; these nerve cells can only be seen with a microscope. Severe mental illness seems to occur because of ways in which nerve cells transmit messages with each other in the brain. Nerve cells discharge chemicals called neurotransmitters into the space between neurons when communicating with each other. These neurotransmitters have names like dopamine or serotonin; either poor discharge or reuptake of these chemicals is likely the immediate cause of severe mental illness.

Assessment and Treatment of Severe Mental Illness

Understanding the causes, course, and prognosis of severe mental illness is essential for treating it. The first step in treatment is assessing the disorder and all its ramifications.

Psychiatric diagnosis. Psychiatrists and other mental health professionals use the Fourth Edition of the *Diagnostic and Statistical Manual of Mental Disorders* (more commonly known as DSM-IV) as a way to guide their diagnosis of mental illness. Psychiatric diagnosis is a complex process which requires knowledge of current symptoms (What symptoms have you experienced in the past two weeks?); past symptoms (What symptoms have you experienced during your lifetime?); and lifelong history (What has been the course of your disorder? How have your symptoms waxed and waned?). Several paper and pencil tests have been developed which might help professionals collect this kind of information. Unfortunately, there is no single blood test or x-ray that permits absolute diagnosis.

Remember that coming up with a DSM-IV diagnosis is not enough to describe the impact of severe mental illness. The breadth of disabilities needs to also be identified. How do the mental illness and psychiatric symptoms disrupt goals related to work, relationships, housing, physical and emotional wellness, income, education, recreation, and spirituality?

Psychiatric Medication. There are many medications which a psychiatrist might prescribe after a DSM-IV diagnosis is made. These medications serve two purposes: first, they directly remedy the psychiatric symptoms that trouble the person. Second, medications seem to protect the person from relapse; a person who no longer is psychotic may want to continue to take medication to keep the symptoms from returning, just like a person with diabetes takes insulin every day to keep those symptoms from coming back. Medications are typically known by two names: the chemical name and the brand name provided by the drug company. Brand names tend to be better known by consumers and family members and hence, are used in the next few pages.

> **1. Antipsychotic Medications:** These medications have been shown to be particularly effective in reducing many of the symptoms of psychosis including agitation, inappropriate affect, and hallucinations. Psychiatrists distinguish two groups of antipsychotic medication. There are the traditional antipsychotics like Thorazine, Stellazine, Haldol, Prolixin, and Mellaril. Many of these drugs have been available for 40 years. Unfortunately, persons taking these drugs frequently experience severe side effects. Dissatisfaction with the num-

ber of side effects led to development of a new generation of atypical antipsychotics: Clozaril, Risperdal, and Zyprexa.

2. Antidepressant Medications: These drugs are effective in managing the sadness and crying spells experienced by persons with major depression and other severe mental illnesses. Psychiatrists first developed a group of drugs called monoamine oxidase inhibitors. Unfortunately, these drugs required that persons watch their diets closely (for example, no foods that are aged like wine or cheese) so they do not suffer problems with their blood pressure. Psychiatrists then developed a second group of drugs called tricyclics with names like Elavil, Asendin, Pamelor, and Norpramin. These drugs frequently made the person sleepy and had some other side effects leading to the most current group of anti-depressants: Paxil, Prozac, and Zoloft.

3. Mood Stabilizers: Lithium and Depakote are the best examples of this kind of drug which treats the euphoria, agitation, and overactive behavior of mania.

Almost all psychiatric medications cause side effects; in fact, these medications have been known to harm *every* organ system in the human body. Some notable side effects include dry mouth, drowsiness, trembling hands and legs, restlessness, and increased likelihood to sunburn. Some persons who take high doses of the traditional antipsychotics for a long time may acquire *tardive dyskinesia*, a disorder marked by involuntary movements of the lips, tongue, hands, and feet.

There are a variety of ways to treat side effects including changing the dose of psychiatric medication, changing the type of medication, or prescribing a medication that treats the side effects. Two drugs frequently prescribed for side effects are Cogentin and Artane.

Rehabilitation and support. Research clearly shows that a combination of medication and rehabilitation strategies is needed to provide comprehensive services to the person with severe mental illness. Medication provides the first line of treatment for many of the psychiatric symptoms and some of the disabilities; rehabilitation and support provide the necessary care for the remainder of the disabilities that plague persons with severe mental illness. Six broad categories of service are provided by comprehensive rehabilitation programs.

1. Goal Assessment and Motivation:

Rehabilitation begins with an assessment of the person's life goals and ways in which symptoms and disabilities impede these goals. Sometimes, people are reluctant to pursue life goals because of the troubles they may entail. For example, even though a person wants to work, he or she may be hesitant because in the past he or she was humiliated by coworkers. Careful assessment needs to examine the advantages and disadvantages of specific goals so persons can determine whether they are motivated to pursue the goal.

2. Community Support: One of the most fundamental services rehabilitation counselors can provide is support. Many persons are able to achieve a variety of vocational and independent living skills when they receive regular support. This kind of support occurs in the person's home or place of work, as often as the person needs it, and is relatively limitless.

3. Skills Training: Some persons are not able to achieve their goals because they have not learned the skills needed to accomplish them. Skills training teaches persons the social and self-care skills they may need to accomplish these goals. Skills training sessions also teach persons the coping and problem solving skills necessary to meet the unforeseen demands and stresses of daily living.

4. Cognitive Rehabilitation: Severe mental illnesses have a harmful impact on the way in which persons think about the world and process information. Cognitive rehabilitation and therapy teaches people ways to make better sense of this information.

5. Family Education and Support: Perhaps the most valuable resource for many persons with mental illness is their family. Parents and siblings who learn about the course of severe mental illness, are taught skills to cope with the illness, and receive the support of others. They are better able to deal with a loved one's disabilities with these tools.

6. Mutual Help: Another valuable resource is peers who suffer mental illness. Many persons decide to join self-help groups. These groups provide opportunities to learn from others with the same problems. Moreover, these groups help persons to feel better about themselves because they can be of help to peers; "Hey, I must be a valuable person if I can provide ideas to other group members about how to handle stress at work."

Myths and Contrary Facts About Mental Illness

Education on the experiences of severe mental illness and effective treatments for them may change some stigmatizing attitudes. An even more forceful way to provide facts about mental illness is to contrast them with the common myths that are the foundation of stigmatizing attitudes. Research suggests that members of the public are more willing to give up these attitudes when they realize the myths are false. Myths can be falsified by challenging them with corresponding facts about mental illness. Much of this evidence is outlined in the fact sheets of Table 8.1. In Chapter 4, we reviewed eight myths that are particularly troublesome for mental illness; this information is essential to education programs against stigma and hence is repeated in Table 8.2. A point by point contrast of myth and facts can be a powerful addition to an education program.

The myth of personal responsibility. There is one additional myth that has a powerful effect on the public's misconceptions; persons with mental illness are responsible for their symptoms and disabilities. As the result of bad life choices, personal weakness, or just not caring, they cause their mental illness and are responsi-

Table 8.2
Eight Myths and Corresponding Realities About Mental Illness

> **Once crazy, always crazy.**

1 People don't get over it. Long-term follow-up research suggests that many, many persons with the worst types of schizophrenia and other severe mental illness are able to live productive lives.

> **All persons with mental illness are similar.**

2 Persons with mental illness are as diverse a group of people as any other. Saying all persons with mental illness are alike is similar to saying all Latinos are the same. Not true!

> **Severe mental illnesses are rare, just like lepers.**

3 Actually severe mental illnesses like schizophrenia, manic-depression, and major depression may account for up to 8 to 10% of the population. That means 640,000 people in a metropolitan area the size of Chicago; or enough folks to fill Omaha, Nebraska and Des Moines, Iowa combined.

> **The mentally ill are dangerous, one step away from a maniacal killing spree.**

4 Very, very few people with mental illness ever murder someone. In fact, persons with mental illness are usually no more likely to be violent than the rest of the population.

> **The mentally ill can never survive outside the hospital.**

5 The vast majority of persons with mental illness live personally successful lives in their community.

> **The mentally ill will never benefit from psychotherapy.**

6 Carefully controlled research has shown that support and rehabilitation has significant impact on the lives of persons with mental illness.

> **The mentally ill are unable to do anything but the lowest level jobs.**

7 Persons with mental illness perform at all levels of work, just like the rest of the population.

> **Bad parents and bad upbringing cause severe mental illness**

8 Schizophrenia and the other severe mental illnesses are biological diseases. They are caused by genetic or other embryological factors.

ble for its consequences. We ended Chapter 2 by reviewing this perspective as a way to integrate what we know about stereotypes, prejudice, and discrimination. Namely, the average person's belief that a person is accountable for his or her mental illness leads to a loss of sympathy ("I don't pity someone who caused their own problems.") and an unwillingness to help ("I'm going to save my support for someone who truly deserves it."). This kind of attitude also leads to blame for problems ("That person caused his mental illness. He's just weak."), anger in response to blame ("I'm sick of these people who can't pull themselves up by their bootstraps."), and a call for punishment to meet one's anger ("Let's lock them up in hospitals until they can make it on their own.").

Studies conducted by researchers at the University of Chicago suggest that challenging the responsibility myth through education has significant effects on both attitudes and behaviors. Simply inform- ing people that mental illness is a biological disorder over which the person has little control can significantly improve attitudes AND behaviors towards persons with mental illness. One way to do this is to compare mental illness to better known diseases like diabetes or cancer.

> *"You don't blame someone for taking*
> *insulin because they are diabetic!"*

NAMI has supported a similar campaign:

Open Your Mind:
Mental Illness is a Brain Disorder.

On bumper stickers, letterhead, flyers, and pamphlets, this brief slogan broadly educates the public about men- tal illness. It's not a choice for which persons are responsible. It is the unfortunate result of heredity; the person is no more to blame than the individual plagued with cancer!

Education and Values Self-Confrontation

Education programs may have an even greater impact when combined with a technique called "values self-confrontation." Sitting quietly and listening to personal stories about mental illness may fail to stir listeners, fail to force them to think differently about their stigmatizing attitudes. Participants might believe that the person's story doesn't apply to them; "Other people might be narrow-minded, but not me." Values self-confrontation forces people to look at their own attitudes. In this technique, program participants confront their stigmatizing attitudes about a group. Research suggests that persons are likely to change their attitudes when they find out that, rather than being open-minded, they really stigmatize a group.

> *"Wow, I always thought I had a fair and unprejudiced attitude towards the mentally ill. But it looks like I have some bigoted views about them."*

The exercise takes about 15 minutes to complete and is usually introduced at the beginning of education programs. After a brief introduction to open the education program, the speaker hands out the first worksheet (part 1) in Table 8.3 (you can make copies of the table and hand them out) with the instructions,

"Your attitudes about persons with mental illness are strongly affected by your values. In particular, values about freedom and opportunity have a significant impact on the ways you approach persons with mental illness. Hence, the place to begin is to determine your views about basic attitudes in a free society. Please answer the four questions on the top of the Values and Mental Illness Worksheet, Part 1; circle the number that corresponds with how important you feel each value is."

Give participants about five minutes to do the top half of the worksheet before continuing with instructions.

"Now I would like you to determine your total score. Add up the numbers representing your importance ratings for each item. You can do this on the bottom of the Worksheet. Then mark that number on the left side of the Freedom in Society Scale. Draw a line across the scale at that point and blacken the area below the line. It should look like the reading on a thermometer. This score represents your view about freedom and opportunity in your society."

This exercise provides a baseline rating of the participant's view of freedom. Given the importance of this value in Western societies, most participants come up with a total score well above 12. Next, hand out the second worksheet (Values and Mental Illness Worksheet, Part 2).

Table 8.3
Values and Mental Illness Worksheet, Part 1

Name _____ Date _____

Your beliefs about persons with mental illness are greatly affected by your values about society. How important do you believe the following values are for a free society like the United States? Circle the best response for each of the four items.

		not important		important		very important
1.	Equal Opportunity for All	1	2	3	4	5
2.	A Chance to Pursue Your Dreams	1	2	3	4	5
3.	Fair Opportunity Regardless of Race, Creed or Disability	1	2	3	4	5
4.	Respect And Admiration For Your Accomplishments	1	2	3	4	5

Now determine your total score by adding up each of the four numbers you circled. Your total score should fall between 5 and 20.

number from Item 1 _____

number from Item 2 _____

number from Item 3 _____

number from Item 4 _____

Total Score _____

Finally, enter your total score on the Freedom in Society Scale to the right. To do this, write down your total score on the left side of the scale. Then draw a line across this scale at your score. Finally, blacken in the scale below that line.

FREEDOM IN SOCIETY

20 — 16 — 12 — 8 — 4 — 0

For example: Hector got a 10 on the scale. He marked the right side between 8 and 12. He then drew a line across the scale at this point. Lastly, Hector blackened in the scale below the line.

FREEDOM IN SOCIETY

20 — 16 — 12 — *10* — 8 — 4 — 0

Values and Mental Illness Worksheet, Part 2

How important to a free society do you believe the following opportunities are for **persons with severe mental illness**?

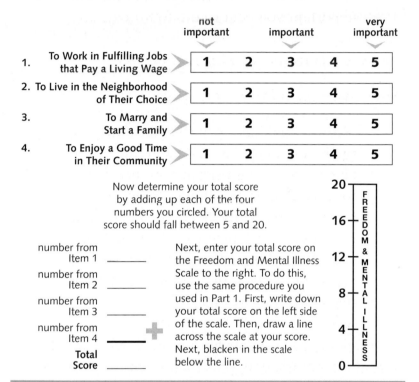

		not important		important		very important
1.	To Work in Fulfilling Jobs that Pay a Living Wage	1	2	3	4	5
2.	To Live in the Neighborhood of Their Choice	1	2	3	4	5
3.	To Marry and Start a Family	1	2	3	4	5
4.	To Enjoy a Good Time in Their Community	1	2	3	4	5

Now determine your total score by adding up each of the four numbers you circled. Your total score should fall between 5 and 20.

number from Item 1 _____

number from Item 2 _____

number from Item 3 _____

number from Item 4 _____

Total Score _____

Next, enter your total score on the Freedom and Mental Illness Scale to the right. To do this, use the same procedure you used in Part 1. First, write down your total score on the left side of the scale. Then, draw a line across the scale at your score. Next, blacken in the scale below the line.

For example: For example, Hector got a 6 on the scale. He marked the right side between 4 and 8. He then drew a line across the scale at this point. Lastly, Hector blackened in the scale below the line.

Finally, compare your score on the FREEDOM IN SOCIETY SCALE to the FREEDOM AND MENTAL ILLNESS SCALE. Which one is taller?

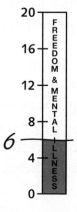

333

"On the first Worksheet, you reported
your values for freedom in society. Now
I'd like you to consider your views about
opportunity for persons with mental illness. Like before, I'd like you to rate how
important you believe the four items are
on the top of the sheet. Circle the number
that corresponds with your answer."

After giving them five minutes say,

"Now I would like you to determine your
total score in this area. Add up the numbers representing your importance ratings
for each item in the allotted space at the
bottom of the Worksheet. Then mark that
number on the left side of the Freedom
and Mental Illness Scale. Draw a line
across the scale at that point and blacken
the area below the line."

At this point, participants have a rough measure of their
overall view of freedom plus their open-mindedness to
opportunities for persons with mental illness. Finally,
you want participants to compare their perspectives.

"Now I want you to compare your perspective on freedom in society and freedom for persons with mental illness. An
easy way to do this is by holding up the
two Worksheets to the light and compare
the blackened part of the scales. Make

sure that the horizontal line 0 on the bottom of each scale overlap.

"If you have equal respect for freedom in society and opportunities for mental illness, then the two scales should line up evenly. However, some people have a much higher Freedom in Society Scale; for example, their Freedom in Society Scale is two fingers taller than their Freedom and Mental Illness Scale. These people need to reconcile the difference. How is it that you could be fairly supportive of freedom for society in general, but willing to limit the opportunities of people with mental illness?"

Many participants will show big differences between their views about freedom and their hesitancy to provide opportunities to persons with mental illness. The values self-confrontation exercise clearly illustrates this point. The education program speaker should inform people who show big differences across scales that these differences may exist because they believe myths about mental illness. Hence, reviewing these myths, and discussing more basics facts about them, may help them change their attitudes.

Some speakers repeat the values self-confrontation exercise at the end of the education program. Hand out a new set of worksheets and find out whether the two scales are now much closer.

Three Special Groups to Target for Education Programs

The education programs described in this chapter will help most people change their stigmatizing attitudes. Three groups, in particular, should be the focus of education efforts.

School children. Prejudice is not the sin of adults alone; children do it too. Childhood prejudice is evident at a fairly young age. Four-year-old children have been known to recognize differences across groups and belittle the outlier.

> *"Look at that person with dark skin. He's different from me. I don't want him around." Or, more specific to mental illness, "Look at the person who acts different from me. He's bad."*

Schools are natural places to start education for children. Many students are familiar with videotapes and training programs that attack racial stereotypes. These methods might also be used to help children develop a more enlightened perspective about mental illness. Persons with mental illness might pair up with teachers at local schools and review the mental illness fact sheet with their students (Table 8.1). They could also use this time to tell their story to the class. High-school age children might benefit from the values self-confrontation exercise.

The National Mental Health Association (NMHA) has used a puppet show for elementary and middle school children. They have five different scripts, each for various types of mental illness. The NMHA lends the puppets to its affiliates who then put on 20-minute live shows using all five of the two-foot tall characters.

Stigmatizing attitudes are learned from parents. Mothers and fathers who talk about their dislike of "crazies running wild in society" will produce children with the same attitudes. Research suggests parental attitudes are especially influential when children are about ten to thirteen years old. Hence, parents of children in this age range should be included in education efforts. They could be invited to special assemblies on mental illness and stigma. These programs are successful when they have the official support of the school board and the principal is present to host the show. School homework could also include anti-stigma exercises which might be completed with parents.

Mental health professionals. The stigma of mental illness is not just a problem of the uninformed public. Survey research has shown that many mental health professionals agree with these myths. All too many practicing psychiatrists, psychologists, nurses, and social workers have been known to endorse such attitudes as: persons with mental illness are all alike, don't get better, and need to be hospitalized. This is particularly troublesome given that the community turns to mental health professionals for information about psychiatric disability and for policies about how to act towards them. Hence, leaders in the mental health field have called for programs to educate future mental health professionals.

Special training programs have been developed for psychology interns, psychiatry residents, and social work students at such institutions as the University of Maryland, the University of Nebraska, Boston

University, UCLA, and the University of Chicago. For example, colleagues at the University of Chicago Center for Psychiatric Rehabilitation have completed a four-course curriculum to train paraprofessionals through community colleges. The curriculum focuses on rehabilitation services for persons with severe mental illness. Central to this curriculum are attitudes which foster empowerment and undermine any stigmatizing foundation which new students may bring to their training. You may wish to find out whether professional training schools in your area provide similar training. Faculty in these programs do not assume that traditional course work prepares students for a career in services to persons with mental illness. These special training programs provide in-depth review of the material in the Severe Mental Illness Fact Sheet. They also hire persons with mental illness and family members to come to class and tell their stories about mental illness and recovery. For example, the University of Chicago curriculum combines community college instructors with consumers of rehabilitation services who tell their stories.

Training like this should not stop when the graduate diploma is earned. In-service programs must continually address issues of stigma in professionals. Persons with mental illness are important speakers at these programs. These in-services might occur at professional conferences or they may occur as part of regular training at the treatment center. For example, most clinical programs that serve persons with mental illness have weekly or monthly professional seminars. Persons with mental illness might call the director of training at the agency and ask to be put on the schedule to tell their stories about mental illness and stigma. Stigma is not likely to seep into staff minds when they regularly hear stories like yours.

Opinion leaders. Contact and education strategies seek to change the average person's attitudes about mental illness. Perhaps an even more effective way to change attitudes is to target the opinion of leaders in the community. These are persons who influence the attitudes of large numbers of people. Leaders have a "bully pulpit" from which they are expected to change local opinion. Hence, if the leader's views change through contact and education, attitudes of their community follow.

Table 8.4 lists several groups of specific opinion leaders you may wish to target in education programs. Americans elect government officials at the local, county, state, and federal level to make decisions about many issues that affect daily living. In this capacity, mayors, governors, legislators, and the President himself seem to be ready-made champions for changing stigma about mental illness. Education programs tend to be more effective when conducted at the grassroots level; that is, among people who politicians view as their voters. Towards this end, you may wish to join the efforts of your local branch of the National Mental Health Association or National Alliance for the Mentally Ill. These groups sponsor an array of formal and informal meetings with politicians, using these forums to educate officials about mental illness and stigma. Meetings like these are especially effective during election times. The presence of persons with mental illness is essential for politicians to hear stories of recovery and empowerment.

Unfortunately, many elected officials are not up to the leadership task. Rather than fostering a vision for their constituency—in a manner like Franklin Roosevelt and John Kennedy—many politicians base their opinion on the desires of the majority. Instead of leading, they follow. Hence, you want to be vigilant for and support legislators and administrators who are willing to be heroes in the battle against stigma. National politicians who currently champion mental health issues include senators Pete Domenici (R-NM), Paul Wellstone (D-MN), Edward Kennedy (D-MA), and Harry Reid (D-NV) plus representatives Marge Roukema (R-NJ), Fortney Pete Stark (D-CA), Lynn Rivers (D-MI), Rose DeLauro (D-CT), Peter DeFazio (D-OR), and Nita Lowey (D-NY). The former Vice-President's wife,

Table 8.4

Opinion Leaders and Their Communities. These are great targets for education because they have a "bully pulpit" to which a significant following looks for guidance.

Opinion Leaders	Their Following
Elected officials and politicians	Their constituency
Religious leaders and clergy	Their congregation
Business leaders	Employees, co-workers, and other entrepreneurs
Reporters and entertainers	The media-consuming public
Teachers and youth group leaders	Their class and group members

Tipper Gore, and former First Lady, Rosalyn Carter, are also eloquent voices for people with mental illness.

Religious leaders may be better suited for influencing the masses. Congregations regularly turn to them for moral guidance, and the injustice of psychiatric stigma is clearly a moral issue. Hence, education programs for the clergy provide an excellent opportunity for changing societal attitudes. Religious leaders, in turn, develop programs for members to consider their prejudicial ways and to include persons with disabilities in their congregations. The Archdiocese of Chicago, for example, started "Open Doors, Open Minds" to identify and overcome barriers that prevent persons with disabilities from joining its mission. This program has developed a special "Faith and Fellowship" to encourage persons with mental illness to have active roles in their congregations.

Another source of opinion leaders is the business world. Employers, work colleagues, and entrepreneurs look to business leaders for their vision of society. Hence, business leaders are an important target for education and contact. A variety of civic groups cater to business persons. Many of these groups adopt public action efforts as part of their mission. Rotary International's "Erasing the Stigma" (ETS) campaign is one example of business leaders seeking to sway public opinion on mental illness. This program seeks to educate members about one particular myth: persons with mental illness are unable to get back to work. What's especially impressive about the ETS Campaign is not only education, but an actual commitment to hire persons with mental illness.

> "Once the business and community leaders understand the facts about mental illness, we inform them of qualified individuals who have completed psychiatric rehabilitation and are ready to return to the work force." (From the ETS brochure).

One final group of opinion leaders is especially relevant for children. Teachers and youth group leaders (like Boy and Girl Scouts, 4-H and debate clubs) mold the opinions of children as they develop. Hence, education programs targeting teachers and youth leaders are also important.

Strategy III. Protest Discriminatory Practices

Sometimes, education does not yield a fast or strong enough impact on stigma; despite efforts to educate one's community, large segments continue to express concern about persons with mental illness being dangerous. Other times, opinion leaders or media outlets continue to misrepresent mental illness. For example, elected officials play on community fears and attribute neighborhood problems to "those mentally ill homeless." Or, a movie producer distributes another psycho killer film. These kinds of efforts actually spread stigma and disaffection with mental illness. Still other times, change is observed in attitudes but not behavior; many people report they are more open-minded about mental illness but still refuse to hire persons with psychiatric disabilities or rent them apartments. Protest is needed in cases like these.

The targets of protest are fundamentally different from education and contact in several ways.

● The stigma targeted by protest is public: talk radio hosts are trashing mental illness, greeting cards are making mental illness the butt of jokes, or advertisers are selling products using disrespectful images. Education and contact programs target relatively private attitudes: what people think about mental illness.

● The targets of protest, by nature of being public, have a broader and more offensive impact: persons with mental illness are insulted by talk show hosts, children learn disrespectful messages from the greeting cards, and the public continues to believe myths because of advertising. Private thoughts don't affect anyone but the person thinking the thoughts and the handful of people they share their attitudes with.

● Public stigma leads to unfair behaviors. Landlords buy into these attitudes and fail to lease property to persons with mental illness. Employers don't want to interview individuals with a history of psychiatric disability. Legislators believe stigma and fail to support government programs that provide persons with mental illness a fair chance. Health care providers withhold treatment because of misguided attitudes.

Specific examples of protest targets. Table 8.5 lists several examples of groups that should be targeted for protest. Common to these examples are companies that generate products or services that perpetuate myths about mental illness. Newspapers and magazines frequently do this by only running headlines that focus on sensational aspects of mental illness. Compare the number of stories on John Hinckley's mental illness

("Man Who Shot Reagan was Wacko") versus reports on the amazing advances in practice related to schizophrenia ("Clozapine Brings Significant Cures"). Television and radio newscasters are equally guilty of

Table 8.5

Specific Examples of Groups that should be Targeted for Protest

Group	Example of Service or Product that Promotes Stigma
Newspapers and magazines	Sensational headlines about "Crazed Killers."
Television shows	Video magazines that focus on the "dangerous mentally ill." Situation comedies that disrespectfully portray mental illness.
Movie production companies	Studios that produce homicidal maniac films.
Radio stations	News stories that focus on dangerousness and mental illness. Talk show hosts that use disrespectful language.
Greeting card companies	Companies that produce cards which joke about mental illness.
Advertising companies	Marketers who sell products using disrespectful images; (e.g., a peanut distributor packaging their product in a bag that looks like a straight jacket with the slogan "Certifiably Nuts.").
Businesses	Companies that use advertising like the above.
Legislators and public commentators	Individuals who try to push their agenda on misconceptions of mental illness; (e.g., "There should be more gun control because mentally ill will get weapons and shoot people.").
Employers	Businesses who won't hire people if they have a history of mental illness.
Landlords	Real estate offices and property owners who won't lease homes to persons with mental illness.

focusing on the violence related to mental illness. Movie studios have created an entire genre that stretches this truth: slasher films that suggest all persons with mental illness are only one stressor away from killing someone.

Many groups make fun of persons with mental illness and should be targeted for change. Advertisers and greeting cards freely use words like wacko and crazy to highlight their products. TV shows and movies frequently feature a silly and crazy guy to generate some laughs.

Some politicians and commentators use mental illness to advance a personal agenda;

> *"We need to have gun control because too many psychos are packing pistols."*

Some employers won't hire persons with mental illness. Some landlords won't lease properties to persons with psychiatric disability. While these last two groups are important targets of protest, there are laws which prevent this kind of discrimination which you also should consider. Ways to use these laws are discussed in Chapter 9.

How protest works. As outlined in Table 8.6, protest has two components. First, protest carries a moral message.

> *"Your advertisement showing psychosis is wrong. Mental illness is not funny."*

The message is meant to be direct and clear. The general public and the community must accept blame for prejudice and stop it. This kind of message appeals to the community's sense of integrity and honor.

Table 8.6
The Fundamental Components of Protest

| A moral message that stigma and discrimination are wrong! | A negative consequence for public stigma and discrimination. |

Secondly, protest entails a negative consequence to stigma. Disrespectful representations of mental illness or discrimination against persons with psychiatric disability are met by a reaction which discourages such future practices. In some ways, protest is meant to punish public stigma and discrimination. Protest hinders this kind of behavior in two ways. First, protest holds up stigma to public scrutiny and disapproval.

> *"Did you realize that Smith Press[1] published a book called* Beware of the Psycho Killer? *This book is grossly disrespectful. Shame on them."*

Second, this kind of public condemnation can lead to financial repercussions.

> *"Do you want to buy books from a publishing house that sells things like that?"*

Businesses are likely to respond to this kind of economic incentive.

---

[1] Smith Press is fictional. We in no way intended it to reflect any existing business or enterprise.

What Might You Specifically Do to Protest

There are a variety of ways in which you might protest public stigma or discrimination (See Table 8.7). Some of these can be done by you alone. Others are more effective when conducted by a group of people. One letter may get someone's attention. But 1000 letters demand a response. Almost all of the mental health advocacy groups listed throughout this book (and summarized in the *Learn More About It* section) are supporting a stigma-busting campaign. You may wish to join one of these stigma-busting campaigns to increase your voice.

Strategies vary in the amount of discomfort experienced by the persons being protested against. Some are relatively mild because they are nothing more than a private communication between stigmatizing group and mental health advocates. Others represent more public expressions of dissatisfaction, trying to seek public condemnation for the company's behavior. Still others are direct assaults on the profits of the company. You should carefully consider the pros and cons of using painful versus mild forms of protest.

Relatively painful approaches are likely to be experienced as an attack by the company. You need to make sure that the public is not going to view this kind of assault as an overreaction. More mild and private approaches, like letter writing, are less likely to be seen as an attack. These kinds of approaches are especially useful if you wish to build and maintain a working relationship with a group in the future. For example, you may not wish to boycott a greeting card manufacturer

Table 8.7
The Progressive Ladder of Protest

Causes Much Discomfort

Product or Service Boycotts

Marches and Sit-Ins

Public Denunciation

Phone Chains

Letter Writing

Causes Little Discomfort

because they have distributed one stigmatizing card. Instead, the company may be very responsive to a letter writing campaign pointing out the disrespectful message. This kind of gentle approach might then lead to an alliance which will continue to promote positive images in the future.

Many advocacy groups typically start with relatively benign protests (letter writing) and escalate if companies or individuals are unresponsive or further disrespectful.

Writing campaigns. Frequently, members of the entertainment industry, news media, and other groups stigmatize mental illness without considering its implications. Receipt of several letters expressing your concerns is often sufficient to derail such practices. You may wish to gather a group of people to write letters when you find a stigmatizing example worth complaining about. Alternatively, you may wish to join a stigma-buster group that regularly identifies and responds to negative images of mental illness. An example of a letter from this kind of campaign is provided in Table 8.8

Note that stigma-busting letters need to be specific. Don't write to a company expressing general con-

Table 8.8
Example of a Stigma-Busting Letter

September 1, 1998

Patrick Corrigan
1122 Green Street
Smalltown, IL 60430

Mary Jones
Chief Executive Officer
Smith Press, Inc
1234 Main Street
Anywhere, NJ 01234

Dear Ms. Jones:

Recently I was shopping at Brown's Department Store in Smalltown, Illinois when I found the enclosed birthday card in the
racks. It says, "If you think I'm nuts about you, wait until you see
the wacko at the crazy house. Happy birthday." This card is pat-
ently offensive to persons with mental illness. Words like "nuts,"
"wacko," and "crazy house" are disrespectful and perpetuate
false perceptions about mental illness.

For your information, about eight to ten percent of Americans
have severe mental illnesses like major depression, schizophrenia, or manic-depression. With appropriate care, most are able to
live independently, work jobs, and build a family. Unfortunately,
one problem they experience is stigma and discrimination. Society has a lot of ignorance about mental illness.

Please help us stop this stigma and ignorance. I would appreciate
your company discontinuing this greeting card, and others like it,
that disrespect persons with mental illness. Thank you for your
consideration. I look forward to your reply.

Respectfully,

Patrick Corrigan

cerns about prejudice. Begin the letter by identifying a specific product or service you find stigmatizing (I found the enclosed birthday card in the racks. It says, "If you think I'm nuts about you, wait until you see the wacko at the crazy house."). Let them know where you encountered the product or service, naming the vendor as well as the city and state in which it occurred (I was shopping at Brown's Department Store in Smalltown, Illinois.). The issue may be a problem of the local vendor and not the company; providing the location allows the company to check it out.

State clearly why the product or service is offensive (words like "nuts," "wacko," and "crazy house" are disrespectful and perpetuate false perceptions about mental illness.). Unfortunately, too many people still don't realize that terms like "crazy" and "psycho" are disrespectful. Take the opportunity to briefly educate the person about mental illness. Provide a few facts from the severe mental illness fact sheet (For your information, about eight to ten percent of Americans have severe mental illnesses like major depression, schizophrenia, or manic-depression. With appropriate care, most are able to live independently, work at jobs, and build a family.). Also educate the correspondent to the impact of stigma (Unfortunately, two problems they experience are stigma and discrimination. Society has a lot of ignorance about mental illness.).

Letters should be sent to the person in charge. Company presidents and CEOs are acutely sensitive to the image of their company and often willing to respond unilaterally to repair this kind of problem. Middle managers may be more concerned about covering up the issue. Send it to the president or CEO by name. This kind of personal approach is likely to get a reaction. The president or CEO's name and mailing address can be easily obtained by calling the company.

Make sure the letter calls for a way to rectify the situation (Please help us stop this stigma and ignorance. I would appreciate your company discontinuing this greeting card, and others like it, that disrespect persons with mental illness.). Ask the company to remove the product. While you're at it, ask them to remove similar products of which you are not aware. End the letter with a request for the CEO to reply and let you know how he or she responded to your letter. Sign the letter and provide your mailing address. Don't send a letter anonymously; companies will ignore letters like these.

Two other qualities to note about the sample letter. First, be brief. Never send a letter that is longer than one page. Company presidents are very busy and unlikely to consider requests that are lost in several pages of explanation. Second, be polite. Don't accuse the company or otherwise attack them. This kind of language shows the same kind of respect you are demanding from the company in return.

Sometimes more is needed than simply discontinuing a product. For example, a local newspaper that published a misleading article about homelessness that led to municipal policies against housing programs needed to print a retraction. In this case, your letter should include a request for a prominently placed retraction; (i.e., a statement that the newspaper has made an error). You may even suggest language which they might include in their correction.

"In a recent article, we suggested that all persons with mental illness are homeless because they cannot care for themselves.

We suggested that more hospitals be opened and that money stop being spent on housing programs in our community. We were wrong. Recent information provided us by a local advocacy group suggests most persons with severe mental illness become useful members of the community with appropriate support. This information is based on research sponsored by the National Institute of Mental Health. We have reconsidered our position and now support community-based housing for persons with severe mental illness."

One last point about letter writing. When a group is sponsoring a letter writing campaign, make sure each writer varies his or her content in some way to represent his or her own opinion. Companies that receive 30 letters that are all alike will be less influenced than companies which receive the same number of letters that reflect the unique interests of each writer.

Letter writing campaigns are effective. Take, for example, newspaper and poster ads for a film titled *Crazy People*. The original ad included a picture of a cracked egg with hands and arms and the caption, "Warning: Crazy people are coming." Paramount Pictures changed marketing strategies after receiving numerous letters and meetings with several advocacy groups. The new ad had pictures of the film's stars, Dudley Moore and Daryl Hanna, with a revised header, "You wanna laugh tonight?"

Phone calls. If writing letters does not work, another way to get a target's attention is to phone it. Phone calls are more conspicuous and demand a response. You should develop a script which you and several advocates might use to call up the company. The script should include all the parts of a stigma-busting letter. Once again, make sure individual scripts are amended so they reflect the specific style and interest of the caller.

Phone calls should be directed to one person in the company. CEOs and presidents are probably not the best person to contact. They frequently have several levels of secretary and receptionist insulating them from the public; you're not likely to get them on the phone. Many companies have a consumer affairs office; the director of the office might be an appropriate person to call. Alternatively, the marketing department is typically concerned about community response to a product. The head of this office might also be a good target.

Make sure you have a specific name and number in mind when you and members of your group call. You may wish to do some preparatory work before beginning the phone chain by calling the company's central switchboard to identify the name and number you will all call.

Public denunciation. Letter writing and phone calling are relatively private efforts to get the company to respond to your concerns. If these are ineffective, you may wish to go public. Let the community know you disapprove and rally them to express similar dissatisfaction. One way to do this is to write a letter to the editor of your local newspaper. This is something you can do on your own when you are unhappy about the way a company is stigmatizing mental illness. The letter to the editor should contain all the elements of the letter in Table 8.8.

A stigma-busting group seeking a broader impact might send out a press release; an example of a press release is provided in Table 8.9. Editors and producers of daily newspapers or local television stations usually require that news stories arrive at their desks in the form of a press release. Press releases can be written without much trouble so long as you remember to include: (1) the organization's return address, (2) a contact person with his or her phone number, and (3) the gist of your story.

Note the press release in Table 8.9. After the address and other contact information, the words <<PRESS RELEASE>> are written across the page followed by the words "For Immediate Release." Sometimes a title for the story is written here. Then, begin the body of your press release with a dateline as shown in the first paragraph.

It's important to include in the body of the press release the names of the principal players in the story, in this case Bill Dekirk and Sally Evert-Dekirk and Citizens for Accurate Reporting on Schizophrenia (CARS). In the topic sentence of the first paragraph, briefly give the content of the story. Use later paragraphs to add background and quotes. It is customary to center three pound signs, "###," to indicate end of copy.

Make sure your facts are straight, names correctly spelled, and the story thoroughly proofread for spelling and grammar. Then send it by mail or fax to your targeted media outlets. Usually you can find addresses in the Yellow Pages. In fact, it is often a wise tactic to call the newspaper, TV station, or radio station and secure the name of a news editor or reporter beforehand who covers the health beat or your community news. Send your release directly to that person. Call

Table 8.9
Example of a Press Release

Citizens for Accurate Reporting on Schizophrenia
Box 123
Anytown, New York, 10023

For additional information:
Bill Dekirk, President
Tel: 1-800-555-1234
Sally Evert-Dekirk, Vice President
Tel: 1-800-555-2345

<< P R E S S   R E L E A S E >>

For Immediate Release

Mental Illness Advocates to Protest Newspaper Offices

(ANYTOWN, NEW YORK, Sept. 4) On Monday, Sept. 10, at 12:00 noon Citizens for Accurate Reporting on Schizophrenia (CARS) is planning to picket outside the offices of the Anytown Reporter to protest the newspaper's insensitive and misleading series of editorials about the homeless in Anytown.

In two recent opinion pieces, the paper implied that the homeless were lackadaisical and immoral, and their failure to work was due to weaknesses in their character based upon poor family upbringing.

CARS believes that many homeless persons are disabled with untreated mental illness worsened by the unavailability of community mental health services to care for them.

CARS is a grassroots organization that was founded last year by Anytown residents, Bill Dekirk and Sally Evert-Dekirk, whose daughter has schizophrenia. They were offended at inaccurate reporting on schizophrenia in their local media outlets.

the editor or reporter and ask him or her if they've received your press release.

The press release is meant to be an informative bite of the whole story. If your story is to be covered, a reporter will likely call you at the number listed on the release. Reporters will want to talk to you at length and might arrange a time for you to be photographed for the story. If a TV station becomes interested, they may want to send a crew to your home or meet you at some other place. In any case, when the media goes to report your story, you will have to be prepared for interviews and photos.

Marches and sit-ins. One way of garnering media attention is to stage a march or sit-in. Both forms of non-violent protest create a controversial distraction which directs public attention toward a political issue. Both require good organization and a committed group of protesters. Many of us remember marches and sit-ins from the 60s and 70s for civil rights and against the war in Vietnam. They were tremendously successful in shaping public attitudes about racial equality and the War. On the other hand, these actions raised the ire of segments of the population; resistance against participants of a march or sit-in supporting mental illness should be expected. Moreover, countless marches and sit-ins have not earned media attention and have gone down in the annals of obscurity. Good organization will minimize this.

Remember, you have a right to freedom of assembly which cannot be interfered with by municipal, state, or federal authorities except in reasonable cases. Municipalities may properly require that you obtain parade permits for large gatherings, but they cannot determine which groups do or do not get permits. They cannot discriminate except where public safety is concerned. However, sit-ins on private property—for instance, at a theater showing an objectionable film—may result in trespassing charges, and the theater might seek to have you removed. If you have permission to sit in a public area, you can make your point without unduly angering property owners who have a right to do their commerce without being impeded. In most instances, it is wise to notify the police of your activity

Table 8.10
Slogans for Signs and Placards

Mental Illness Strikes Your Friends & Neighbors!

I Don't Need Handouts. I Need Respect!

HOMELESSNESS EQUALS NEGLECT!

1 in 12 Have Mental Illness!

Mental Illness Does Not Equal Violence!

I'm Not "Crazy" You're Not a Fool!

Don't Be Cheap With Mental Health Funding!

Treatment For Serious Mental Illness Works!

Increase Funding For Mental Health!

STOMP OUT STIGMA!

so they won't be surprised by your presence. Examples of useful slogans for pickets are summarized in Table 8.10.

Boycotts. There is another pro-active way to put forward the agenda of the mental health user. Simply stop buying, selling, or using products or services of companies that behave poorly towards persons with mental illness. Boycotts have yielded some remarkable successes. For example, thirty years ago a boycott against segregation on busses, led by Martin Luther King, was a great success. A boycott against McDonalds for its use of ecologically damaging Styrofoam hamburger containers had an equal impact.

It is not only possible to boycott a product such as an offending movie or a firm that uses hurtful advertising, also consider boycotting the advertiser or media source in which ads appeared. In that way both the company and its media outlets know that you are angry and that their behavior was stigmatic. Your protest might generate a news story.

Like a successful march or sit-in, boycotts require widespread organization and communication. Unlike marches or sit-ins which can be colorful mini-events, a successful boycott generally requires a large number of participants. However, participation can be comparatively anonymous, such as refusing to pick up an item in the grocery store. On the other hand, participation in marches and sit-ins is more direct and may require bolder commitment on the part of a protester.

Some specific tips for effective boycotts: don't boycott a single product that a company produces, boycott all their wares. In this way your protest reverberates throughout the company, not only in one division.

Above all, let the offending company know that you are engaged in a boycott. Notify its president, media relations department, and board of directors of your intent to economically stymie them until they respond positively to your requests. In addition, fax a notice of your protest, in the form of a press release, to local, regional, and national news outlets. Inform the public and rally your constituency through meetings, newsletters, and phone calls.

Don't forget to reappraise your boycott after a predecided amount of time. Collect information on the success of your effort. Determine if the company has changed its offending behavior. Share this information with your allies and the media.

Beware of Protest Effect on Attitudes

Al-though protest may have a major impact on the behavior of some media sources, there is reason to believe it has no effects on attitudes. In fact, there is some evidence to suggest people who are the object of protest may actually become more stubborn in their attitudes about mental illness. This effect is caused "attitudinal rebound" and may occur for two reasons.

1. Suppression rebound. In essence, protest efforts are telling people NOT to think about negative statements about mental illness. "Shame on you for viewing persons with mental illness as homicidal maniacs like Freddy Krueger. That view is wrong. Stop thinking like that."

359

This kind of moral appeal was thought to hopefully suppress negative attitudes which in turn, will stop the public from discriminating against persons with mental illness.

Unfortunately, the human cognitive apparatus does not work in such a straightforward manner. As the white bear experiment in Table 8.11 illustrates, persons who try to keep an idea out of their head (like white bears) have to spend energy trying to keep it out of memory.

> *"I won't think of white bears. I won't think of white bears. I won't think of white bears."*

In the process of trying to suppress the thought, participants spend more time thinking about bears than if they were not told to suppress the image.

Consider what this means for mental illness. If people are told to stop thinking bad things about mental illness, they are likely to spend more time rolling these ideas over in their mind. Rather than squashing out attitudes like "Persons with mentally ill are dangerous," the attitudes may be reinforced.

2. Don't tell me what to think.

Psychologists have coined the term "social reactance" to explain why people, when told NOT to do something ("Don't open that door."), go ahead and do it anyway ("Don't tell me what to do. I'm going to open the door if I want."). People react to perceptions that some authority is restricting their social freedom. The phenomena of social reactance also applies to how we think. People are more likely to think about something when told not to.

Table 8.11
Suppression Rebound and White Bears.

Try this little experiment.

Find three friends.

Cut out and hand the first friend this card.

> # DON'T THINK ABOUT WHITE BEARS FOR THE NEXT SEVERAL MINUTES.

The other two friends receive no message, Next, ask them to sit quietly for five minutes. When five minutes have elapsed, ask the first friend how much time he or she spent thinking about white bears. Ask the other two friends how much time they spent thinking about white bears. I bet the first friend spent a lot more time thinking about white bears even though he or she was instructed not to.

Now cut out and hand the second friend this card.

> # DON'T THINK ABOUT PERSONS WITH MENTAL ILLNESS.

Hand the third friend this card.

> # DON'T THINK PERSONS WITH MENTAL ILLNESS ARE DANGEROUS.

The first friend gets no card this time. Ask them to sit quietly for five minutes. At the end of the time, ask each person,

How much of the five minutes did you think about persons with mental illness?

How much of that time did you think persons with mental illness were dangerous or violent?

EVEN THOUGH YOU ASK PERSONS NOT TO THINK BAD ABOUT MENTAL ILLNESS, THEY DO.

361

Social reactance has implications for protests that tell people not to think stigmatizing attitudes about mental illness; "Don't think all mentally ill need to be hospitalized." If social reactance occurs, some people are likely to respond, "I'm going to think what I want to think about mental illness." Rebound occurs as a result; persons are thinking more negative things about mental illness.

Protest reconsidered. Although protest may have some negative effects on attitudes, don't throw this strategy out yet. It still is essential for getting the general public to stop stigmatizing behaviors against persons with mental illness. When combined with education and contact programs, it will likely also lead to changes in attitudes and perceptions.

Protest and Social Reward

Protesters punish media groups that stigmatize mental illness. In like fashion, we should reinforce the media and business community when it does a good job. A short letter or a telephone call to an editor or reporter that has written a sensitive and fair story on an issue is likely to lead to another positive article in the future. Therefore, call the persons responsible and tell them that they did a great job when you see a good article or hear a positive segment on the radio.

There are already several positive examples like this. The popular media has produced films and television shows that disseminate stigma-countering information. For example, NAMI worked with CBS to produce *The Marie Balter Story*, a movie about the struggle and successes of a woman who had been institutionalized for more than a decade. CBS and Hallmark Cards aired a 1986 film, *Promise,* where James Woods and James Garner depicted the real life interactions of a man with schizophrenia and his brother. These media efforts are especially promising because they efficiently educate large numbers of people about mental illness stigma.

Chapter 9

Legal and Political Remedies to Stigma and Discrimination

"The law is reason free from passion."
Aristotle

The effects of stigma far exceed the loss of esteem and personal hurt felt by individuals with mental illness. They are also legal matters. Not hiring someone or not renting them an apartment because they are somehow different challenges the very foundation of our Western sense of justice. Unfortunately, American history has many examples where groups were harshly treated because of their differences. Consider the horrid experiences of African and Native Americans. Civil rights advocates have spent the past century struggling for laws that guarantee the rights and privileges we assumed were self-evident. Laws which clearly uphold the rights of persons with disabilities have only been guaranteed in the past decade.

Application of these laws to persons with psychiatric disabilities has occurred in just the past couple of years. This chapter focuses on legislation in two areas of particular concern to persons with psychiatric disabilities: employment and housing.

Sometimes, citizens believe laws are the stuff of attorneys, politicians, and rich folks. We need a lot of money to hire a lawyer who can fight our legal battles for us in court. Fortunately, this need not be the case! Persons with psychiatric disabilities are using laws like the Americans with Disabilities Act (for employment issues) and the Fair Housing Act (for housing) to make sure they are not treated unfairly. We review these laws here so the reader is better informed about full protections as well as resources which the person can use to benefit from these protections.

This information is a beginning. We provide general guidelines in this chapter to help readers understand their rights under the American legal system. Like most laws, these guidelines can be interpreted in many ways; judges and lawyers base their entire career on just this kind of activity. Their thoughts on the various intricacies of the law fill volumes and volumes.

Our guidelines are meant as a beginning. Persons who are concerned about their rights after reading this chapter should seek further counsel from an expert. This does not mean you have to pay money for a lawyer. The *Learn More About It* section at the back of this book lists several advocacy groups and other organizations which provide a range of activities from general advice to representing a person in a lawsuit. In addition, readers should consult the local United States Offices of the Equal Employment Opportunity Commission (EEOC) or Fair Housing and Equal Opportunity (FHEO)[1] to find out more about information discussed here.

The Americans with Disabilities Act and Work Discrimination

On July 26, 1990, President George Bush signed the Americans with Disabilities Act (also known as the ADA) into law, thereby opening significant opportunities for people with disabilities. The ADA outlawed discrimination against people with disabilities in nearly every domain of public life: employment, transportation, communication, and recreation. Its impact on employment was quickly felt; during the first 15 months of the ADA's existence, 17,355 discrimination charges relevant to work were filed with the U.S. Equal Employment Opportunity Commission (EEOC), a branch of the U.S. Department of Justice. Ten percent of these discrimination cases—1,710—were related to mental illness. Persons with psychiatric disability soon realized the relevance of the legislation for their place in the work world, using the ADA to address unfair employment practices.

Title I of the ADA specifically forbids employment discrimination because of disability; this wording from the ADA is copied in Table 9.1. Despite the legalese, the ADA provides persons with disabilities equal opportunity to work. The subsequent pages of

---

[1] One unfortunate byproduct of reading about legal matters is the alphabet soup which designates legislation (ADA, FHA) and government offices (EEOC, FHEO). We try our best in this chapter to keep these acronyms to a minimum so as not to confuse the reader.

Title I listed key points which readers must understand so they can use the legislation to their betterment. Some of these points are reviewed here.

Table 9.1
Requirements of the ADA in Terms of Employment

> **Requirements of the ADA**

"No covered entity shall discriminate against a qualified individual with a disability because of the disability of such individual in regard to job application procedures, the hiring, advancement, or discharges of employees, employee compensation, job training, and other terms, conditions, and privileges of employment."

(Volume 42 of the US Code, page 12112).

What is a Psychiatric Disability Under the ADA?

The ADA statement on employment begins with

> "No covered entity[2] shall discriminate against a qualified individual with a disability..."

The EEOC has given much thought about who is "a qualified individual with a disability." This is an important question because the answer suggests who is protected by the ADA and who is not. There are two essential components to what the ADA means by disability.

(a) a physical or mental impairment

---

[2] A "covered entity" is any American employer that meets certain broadly-defined hiring qualifications (for example, hires more than 15 employees).

(b) that substantially limits one or more of
the major life activities of an individual.

Mental impairment is defined in terms of a psychiatric
diagnosis using the *Diagnostic and Statistical Manual of
Mental Disorders, Fourth Edition* (DSM- IV); diagnoses
covered by the ADA may include schizophrenia, major
depression, bipolar disorder (manic-depression), personality disorders, anxiety disorders such as panic disorder,
obsessive-compulsive disorder, and post-traumatic stress
disorder. Not all conditions in the DSM-IV qualify as
impairments. Most interesting of these exclusions are
disorders related to substance abuse. Although the
ADA may cover DSM-IV conditions related to alcohol
and other drugs, individuals are usually excluded from
protection when the person is involved in the criminal
use of drugs.

A diagnosis of serious or persistent mental disorder is not enough for disability under the ADA. As a
result of this disorder, the person must have *substantial
limitations* in one of the major life activities. Major life
activities include learning, concentrating, interacting
with others, caring for oneself, speaking, performing
manual tasks, working, and sleeping. Limitations in
these areas must be broad and last a relatively long time
to be considered substantial. *Breadth* and *length* of the
limitation is judged by comparison with life activities of
"the average person." For example, given that the average person sleeps about eight hours, sleep disorders
related to depression where the person gets no more
than a few hours of fitful sleep each night is *broad*; toss-
ing and turning before falling to sleep for 8 hours is not.
Insomnia that lasts for months is sufficiently *long*.
Occasional insomnia lasting a few days is not.

Substantial limitations in sleep are only judged when the person shows both criteria. Let's consider some different forms of substantial limitation.

- *Emil is substantially limited in his abilities to concentrate and learn new tasks. He is frequently distracted by discussions of his office mates. As a result, he can't concentrate on his computer work. Moreover, he has had great difficulty learning a new word processing program.*

- *Katherine's ability to interact with others is substantially limited. She is very shy and has few skills to initiate conversations. She avoids the lunch room during breaks and is afraid to talk to customers in the store aisles. Although her supervisor has asked how he might be supportive, Katherine has been afraid to identify anything that might help.*

- *Kim's ability to care for herself is substantially limited. She rarely bathes or changes her clothes unless her parents tell her to. Co-workers have complained about body odor and have refused to share a work station with her.*

Limitations of a mental disorder on life activities is judged in the absence of treatment when the disorder is most troublesome. For example, although Shirley's sleep disorder is quite severe, such that she catches no more than an hour's sleep when depressed, insomnia is significantly corrected when she takes anti-depressant medication. Her disability, however, is judged at its worst—without medication—for purposes of determining whether depression causes substantial limitations.

Disclosure of Disability

In the majority of instances, employers may not ask you about your history with mental disabilities (or, for that matter, even other physical disabilities) as part of the application process.[3] Employment applications cannot have questions about whether you have ever had a mental illness or been treated for such a disorder. Nor are personnel interviewers allowed to ask questions about any aspect of your treatment history. Interviews may not include tests or other pencil-and-paper instruments to screen out people with disabilities. In addition, employers must ignore issues regarding your psychiatric disability should they come up. Employers cannot disqualify a person for a job if the applicant mentions he or she has previously been hospitalized for a mental illness. Similarly, employers who inadvertently find out information about a person's psychiatric history—for example, a co-worker reports he met the applicant when they were both inpatients at the state hospital—may not reject the person based on this information.

Employers can require job applicants to complete a medical examination after employment has been offered if the employer typically asks all prospective employees to complete this exam. Questions and tests

---

[3] The need for reasonable accommodation, discussed more fully below, provides one of the exceptions to the employer asking you about your psychiatric history.

on the medical exam are supposed to focus on functions related to the job; for example, examiners are not allowed to ask about sexually transmitted diseases if the job has no functions which would be diminished by a history of these illnesses. Questions during the exam may focus on psychiatric disability if relevant to completion of the task. However, employers may not use the results of the examination to subsequently rescind a job offer.

The ADA Does Not Promote Affirmative Action

> *"I applied for a job and told them I have a psychiatric disability. But the employer gave the job to someone else who was better qualified. Doesn't this violate the ADA?"*

Employers do not have to hire persons with disabilities according to the ADA. The legislation does not establish *affirmative actions* or quotas through which persons with disabilities can expect an advantage during the hiring process. Readers may remember that affirmative action was a government effort to promote opportunities for persons of color and women by setting hiring quotas. For example, some government contracts may require companies to be owned by women or minorities. The ADA does not promote this kind of affirmative action. Employers are under no pressure to increase the number of persons with disabilities among their workers as long as there are better qualified people for the job.

Instead of affirmative action, the ADA attempts to level the playing field in the application process. Individuals who can complete the *essential functions* of the job, with or without *reasonable accommodation*, are qualified for the job. Reasonable accommodation is discussed thoroughly below. Essential functions are an important part of the ADA considered here. Essential functions are those parts of the job necessary to complete it competently. The law gives the employer discretion on how essential functions are defined. There are no external standards by which essential functions are defined; for example, there is no dictionary of functions that define the essential work of a carpenter, store clerk, or cab driver. Typically, employers are expected to list these functions in a job description which might be posted in a newspaper advertisement (in a shortened form) but most likely is also filed with the company's personnel office.

> *"Waitresses at the Green Leaf Restaurant*
> *are expected to seat customers, take orders*
> *in a timely manner, serve food while it's*
> *still warm, add up the bill, bus tables, and*
> *be courteous at all times."*

The ADA says this list of essential functions must be applied equally to all job applicants. For example, an employer cannot add cash register skills for a waitress job to discourage one applicant with mental illness, but then omit this function in consideration of another person without an obvious psychiatric disability.

373

Reasonable Accommodation on the Job

The ADA requires employers to "accommodate" or otherwise change a job so that persons with disabilities can complete all essential functions; the goal is to remove barriers that would prevent persons from doing the job because of their disabilities. Accommodations can conceivably apply to any aspect of the job: specific tasks (e.g., how a typist word processes the boss' correspondence), work environment (how the work area is constructed), schedule (when the employee reports for work), dress policy (whether any special clothes can be worn), and co-workers (whether any changes can be made to fraternization rules). A long list of accommodations is discussed more fully in the next section.

The ADA says these accommodations need to be *reasonable*; they are not to cause undue hardship on the employer. Employers are only likely to follow through with a job change if the change does not overwhelm their resources. Undue hardship, according to the law, means "an action requiring significant difficulty or expense." Specific accommodations are considered to be "significant" depending on the nature and cost of the accommodation, the overall financial resources of the facility, and the number of persons employed by the company. Generally, the government expects large corporations to be better able to make reasonable accommodations than small, "mom and pop" operations. This does not mean small companies can ignore the requirement for such accommodations, only that they may not be expected to make such large changes.

Despite the attempt to define what is meant by undue hardship, the definition is vague and can be interpreted in different ways by employers and job applicants. Advocacy groups and business organizations have been struggling with this idea in the courts for the past ten years and probably will continue to do so for another decade. However, a brief review of some of the accommodations listed in the next section shows the government, and now the business world, is prepared to make some sizeable changes in work practices to accommodate persons with psychiatric disabilities.

Examples of reasonable accommodations.
The ADA specifically states that reasonable accommodations are determined on a person-by-person basis. Hence, it is up to the employer and the person with psychiatric disability to work out the kind of job changes that will help that person become a successful employee. Because this activity is governed by **law**, persons with disabilities and employers might approach it like a court battle; two adversaries fighting out for the best advantage. This kind of approach will probably lead to failure. Instead, both parties need to keep the overall goal in sight: hiring a person who will become a competent worker. It is in the employer's interest and the interest of the person who is hired to work together to find the best accommodations. *Collaboration,* not court battles, is the sign that reasonable and effective accommodations are being put in place.

> *"At first, Mr. Harkson thought my requests for reasonable accommodations were just a way to get a lighter load on the job. He said he was afraid of getting sued and so he was going to make some changes. But he didn't*

375

*like it. Frankly, his attitude pissed me off.
After all, I only wanted the kind of accommodations which the ADA guarantees.*

    *"Then we met with a job counselor,
Ms. Henry. She pointed out that the purpose of reasonable accommodations was to
make sure I was successful on the job. Mr.
Harkson liked the sound of this. And his
view about the ADA seemed to change in
the process. Instead of begrudging my
requests for help, he actually sat down with
me and brainstormed the best ways to do
my job."*

Table 9.2 lists some reasonable accommodations
that have been provided to persons with psychiatric dis-

Table 9.2

Examples of Reasonable Accommodations Made to Persons with
Psychiatric Disabilities

JOB RESTRUCTURING

Reallocating marginal job functions.

Example: As part of Sally's secretarial job, she was
supposed to shred confidential documents. This was
not an essential function, and the machine scared
her. Therefore, this duty was given to someone else.

SICK TIME

**Permit the use of accrued paid leave or unpaid leave
for treatment.**

Example: Sarah needs three weeks off to recover
from a relapse. She has accrued two weeks of paid
leave so the employer will need to provide another
week of unpaid leave.

ability. They are grouped into seven categories: job restructuring, sick time, modified or part-time schedules, modified work place, modified policies, supervision, and reassignment. Table 9.2 also provides examples of each category. We discuss overall implications of those categorics here.

Job restructuring frequently requires shifting work responsibilities. The ADA says employers should be open to moving workers around to fill *nonessential* parts of a job. For example, Sally had personal difficulties working with the shredder which was needed at the firm to dispose of confidential documents. Since it was not an essential part of her secretarial job, she asked to be relieved of it. This kind of reallocation means the employer must find someone else to do the job;

MODIFIED OR PART-TIME SCHEDULE

Change the work schedule.

Example: Harold wants to change his start time from 8AM to 9AM. His medicine makes it hard for him to wake on time. He will still work his full 8 hours.

Example: Shirl wants to change her full-time job as a stenographer to half time, at least for the next six months. She is not able to handle the demands of a full-time job because of recurring panic attacks. Of course, she would only get paid for four hours of work each day.

MODIFIED WORK PLACE

Provide room dividers or other soundproofing and visual barriers to decrease distractions.

Example: Office partitions were put around Marty's desk so he was not distracted by the sales room.

Margaret was assigned shredding duties at the firm. One way to offset what could appear to be an unfair distribution of work would be to trade these kinds of nonessential functions. In this case, Sally was given some of Margaret's photocopy work.

Some persons may need *sick time* to suitably take advantage of the full range of treatments for their disabilities. Sick time may be either paid leave (sick or personal days that are accrued according to normal company policy) or unpaid leave. Some people who need extended periods away from work may combine both paid and unpaid leave to receive services. Typically, employers are not permitted to penalize or terminate their workers for using paid *and* unpaid leave for services related to their disabilities. In fact, employers need to hold open the person's job so he or she has a position to return to.

Move a person away from noisy machinery or high traffic areas that may be distracting.

Example: Delores' office was moved to the back, away from the reception area, so she was not distracted by visitors.

Permit an individual to wear headphones that block out distractions.

Example: Molly wears headphones so she is not bothered by phones ringing throughout the day.

Work at home.

Example: Emily completes much of the computer work for her job at home. In this way, she does not have to deal with the social anxiety of working with other employees.

Some changes in the work environment are suitable accommodations. Adjusting work *schedules* may be useful. Many persons with psychiatric illness have sleep problems that result directly from the illness or as the result of medications prescribed to treat the illness. These persons may work more effectively if their start time is delayed to later in the morning; of course, the person is still expected to work his or her full eight hours. Other persons might benefit from *part-time* hours. This accommodation may require the employer to break up a full-time job into two part-time positions.

Some disabilities are better served by simple *changes in the physical environment.* Many persons with serious mental illnesses like schizophrenia have difficulty concentrating on the job. Strategies like room dividers, moving away from high traffic areas, or permitting headphones can help people control distractions.

MODIFIED POLICIES

Change work policies that govern personnel.

Example: Bert is permitted to take detailed notes during sales meetings even though other staff are not.

Example: Daniel has a soft drink at his work station for the dry mouth that results from his medication.

Example: Stanley wants to have the radio on in his office. The soft music relaxes him.

SUPERVISION

Supervisors adjust feedback style including changes in communication and extra training materials.

Example: Helene receives daily 10-minute feedback from her supervisor.

Some persons might also be able to accomplish the essential functions of their jobs at home. Many office jobs can now be accomplished by computer and phone modem; people could easily set up work stations in a spare bedroom to complete many of their duties.

Sometimes, *changes in work policies* are useful accommodations. Policies are needed in work settings to guide employees on matters related to typical work behavior.

- Don't take notes during sales meetings. We do not want this information to get out to competitors.

- Don't bring beverages to your desk. They might spill and damage the computers.

- No radio playing. It could distract your colleagues.

Sometimes, exceptions to these rules might help a person with psychiatric disabilities meet the essential functions of a job.

Example: Juanita was given illustrated instructions on how to run the packing machine.

Provide a job coach to offer counseling and support on the job.

Example: Phil is visited on the job by a coach from the local rehabilitation center. The job coach provides support and counseling on work-related issues.

REASSIGNMENT

Provide a job reassignment to another position whose essential functions more closely parallel the

- Bert is able to pay better attention by taking notes during sales meetings. Of course, he's responsible for making sure these notes are locked up.

- Daniel has dry mouth from the anti-psychotic medication he takes each morning. Keeping a can of pop next to his work station helps. He has it in a special holder so it does not spill.

- Stanley is greatly soothed by listening to the religious radio station. He has a private office and keeps the volume very low so it does not disturb others.

Supervisors are an essential part of success for any employee. Hence, they can be an important source of reasonable accommodations. Supervisors may need to examine the frequency and manner with which they provide feedback. They may also need to provide more or different kind of instruction related to the new job.

skills of the employee with disabilities.

Example: Brunetta was moved from clerk typist to telephone reception because she found these tasks easier.

Don't forget: all these accommodations can be arranged if they do not cause **undue hardship** to the employer.

One kind of supervision that is a useful accommodation for many persons with psychiatric disability is the job coach. Some qualities of good job coaching are summarized in Table 9.3.

Table 9.3
Qualities of Good Job Coaching

> **Job coaches:**

- provide their services on the job.
- represent the interests of the person with disabilities.
- provide support and counsel.
- mediate between boss and employer.
- provide services as long as needed.

The purpose of job coaching is to provide the guidance and support which persons need to competently participate in their job. The best way for a coach to determine how new employees are doing on the job is to visit the person on the job. Hence, most job coaches provide their services where the person works. This means the employer needs to open his or her doors to daily visits from the coach. Some persons report that a visit from their coach on the job is embarrassing. It further adds to the stigma they already experience from co-workers. In these cases, job coaches may wish to meet the new worker in other settings that are convenient to the person; for example, at the coffee shop down the block from the factory about a half hour before the shift starts.

Job coaches are "hands on" people. They may get between the employee and supervisor on small issues regarding how to improve the person's work. They may actually pitch in for periods of time to help the person through a tough period.

> *"I had a stock job at a super market for about a year when my symptoms came*

back. I was able to get to work every morn-
ing but I was really dazed by the new
drugs. Luckily, Dave—he's my job coach—
was seeing me at work. A couple of times,
he actually uncrated some canned fruit and
helped me get it on the shelves. He was a
crutch, but without him, I might not have
gotten through that period."

Job coaching can be an expensive endeavor requiring the services of an outside professional. Who pays for the job coach? Many states have funds from their Office of Vocational Rehabilitation which provides funds for job coaching. Typically, the state contracts with a private mental health agency to provide these services to a specific individual with disabilities. In the past, these services were provided for a relatively short time. For example, a person with mental illness might receive job coaching services for six weeks; the Office of Vocational Rehabilitation assumed the person would be an independent worker at the end of that time. Advocates pointed out that coaching services were needed for a longer time, given that most recipients of services for severe mental illness had been struggling with their disabilities for years. Some states are now providing job coaching for months and even years.

The last type of accommodation in Table 9.2 is *reassignment.* Some people may excel after moving to other jobs within the firm, positions with essential functions that differ from the job for which they were hired. This kind of accommodation is only possible in large companies which have many different positions for personnel to move through.

It is also interesting to discover what is not considered to be a reasonable accommodation. Perhaps most interesting among these is monitoring whether the person takes medication as prescribed. Medication monitoring is not considered to be a reasonable accommodation; employers do not have to check whether persons with psychiatric disability are regularly taking their meds because doing so does not remove a barrier unique to the work place.

Readers need to remember that most of these accommodations will have an impact on the company. Hence, accommodations are only likely to be applied if they do not cause undue hardship. This is where negotiation and collaboration needs to occur between worker and employer. Both parties need to be open to working on different ways to change the work environment so the person can be successful. This kind of problem solving is not accomplished in a one time, hour long meeting between boss and employee. It requires a commitment for repeated discussions and adjustments so the employee can best accomplish essential functions. Keep in mind, however, that this kind of effort—helping employees to work effectively—is not unique to persons with disabilities. Every worker, be they with or without disabilities, requires active and ongoing support from management. This is what personnel and human resource departments are for!

Disclose to obtain reasonable accommodations. Persons with psychiatric disability must *ask* for a reasonable accommodation to receive it. This can be done at any time in the course of the person's work with the company: when hired, during orientation, or ten years later. Although employees must notify their bosses of the need for accommodation, they need not worry about whether their request for accommodation includes all the appropriate legal terms.

"I'm having some problems at work because I'm depressed."

It is up to the employer to determine whether a request represents a need for reasonable accommodation.

"What can we do to the job to make it easier for you to accomplish the essential functions?"

The request for accommodation does not have to be in writing. In fact, a friend or family member can ask for reasonable accommodation on a person's behalf in certain circumstances; for example, Ferdinand was hospitalized for an unexpected relapse, and his wife called the employer to request unpaid leave.

Under the ADA, employers have the option of checking into the nature and extent of an employee's disability. This might include questions about one's psychiatric history and permission to speak to one's psychiatrist or other mental health professional. This permission is limited to discussing the nature of the disability and reasonable accommodations that would help the person be successful on the job. Bosses cannot go on a fishing expedition and ask unlimited questions about your private life. Moreover, employers have a legal responsibility to keep ALL information they discover about your disability confidential; it can be released to no one—in the office or to anyone else in the world— without the person's written permission.

On-the-Job Conduct and Direct Threat

Persons with psychiatric disabilities do not seem to have any more conduct problems than their co-workers. Nevertheless, circumstances may arise when an employer needs to discipline a worker with psychiatric disability. Some of these situations are covered by the ADA. Perhaps most interesting is the realization that employers may discipline workers for a mishap that results from their disability. For example, a person who shows up late for his assigned shift (because he has trouble waking due to his new medication) can be penalized. But isn't this contrary to reasonable accommodations? Aren't employees with disabilities supposed to receive special considerations at work?

The intent of the ADA is to be *prospective*. Reasonable accommodations are set up to handle *future* problems:

- How do I handle my schedule so I do not come late to work?

- Can I take notes in next week's meeting so I don't forget what was said?

- I have terrible dry mouth. Can I bring a drink to my work station?

They are not meant to be excuses for past problems. I was late for work today because I have manic-depression. Nope! This is not protected by the ADA. Hence, persons can be disciplined for problems related to mental illness if they have not sought some sort of accommodation for handling this problem.

One piece of on-the-job conduct is specifically discussed in the ADA: *direct threats*. Employers may refuse to hire a person with disability if they have reason to believe the person poses a direct threat to the physical well-being of others in the company. Obviously, concerns about direct threat are especially sensitive to persons with mental illness given the frequently cited stigma about dangerousness:

"The mentally ill are all homicidal maniacs!"

The ADA offers some protections against unjust applications of direct threat. Excluding persons from work based on a judgement of "direct threat" must represent an individual assessment of problems that suggest danger to others. A diagnosis of mental illness is not sufficient to assume persons with psychiatric disability are a direct threat nor is a history of past violence. An expert in mental illness (a psychiatrist or psychologist) needs to determine whether the person is likely to be harmful to peers if hired into the new job. Keep in mind that a person who is judged to be a direct threat now needs to be evaluated anew some months later should he or she reapply for a position.

What To Do if An ADA Violation Occurs

Employers might violate the ADA in four ways; these are briefly listed in Table 9.4. They might discriminate against persons with psychiatric disability by *refusing to hire them because of their disability*. Most employers are unlikely to blatantly refuse to hire someone because of his or her psychiatric history. They probably will not say, "I'm hiring someone else who isn't crazy." Instead, job applicants might suspect this kind of discrimination is occurring if the interviewer is asking many questions about mental health experience or if a prospective employer quickly cools after discovering a past history of psychiatric hospitalization.

A more subtle way to violate the ADA is through *limitation, segregation,* and *classification.*

> *"I didn't want to hire Mary Beth, but I had to because of the ADA. I'll just put her up on the second floor away from the rest of the sales pool so she doesn't bother anyone."*

Table 9.4
Four Ways Employers Might
Violate the ADA

- Not hire someone because of psychiatric disability.

- Limit or otherwise segregate new employees with disabilities.

- Not provide a reasonable accommodation.

- Penalize the person after asking for or obtaining a reasonable accommodation.

Employers are not permitted to treat persons with psychiatric disabilities as second-class citizens. Employers must provide the same range of opportunities and benefits as all others in that job classification. They cannot exclude insurance benefits, opportunities for promotion, or future incentives. Nor can they segregate persons with psychiatric disabilities away from others.

A third way to violate the ADA is *failure to provide reasonable accommodation.* As stated earlier, not all accommodations can be provided; some cause undue hardship to the employer. However, reasonable accommodations, by definition, are those which benefit the employee and do not overwhelm the financial resources of the company. Hence, failure to provide a reasonable accommodation can be construed as violating the ADA. Keep in mind however, that employers who offer another accommodation in place of the "reasonable one" identified by the person with psychiatric disability may be fulfilling their responsibilities in terms of the law.

A final violation of the ADA is *exacting retribution for reasonable accommodation*. Employers may not penalize persons with psychiatric disability for asking for or otherwise obtaining a reasonable accommodation or other protection under the ADA.

> *"Okay, I'll move you to a quieter location in the office. But you have to start two hours earlier each day."*

What should a reader do who has experienced work discrimination as defined by the ADA? Table 9.5 lists steps which the person should consider to rectify the situation. The best place to start is with employers themselves. As may become apparent from this discussion, issues regarding substantial limitations, essential functions, direct threats, and reasonable accommodations are complex. Perhaps a violation occurred because either the employer or person with psychiatric disability is unclear about the ADA. That is why earlier in this chapter we believed the best way for employers and persons with disabilities to make use of the ADA is through collaboration rather than court battles.

Table 9.5

Responses to Violations of the ADA

- Talk to the employer.
- Talk to a knowledgeable group for:
  - ➤ advice and support.
  - ➤ advocacy.
  - ➤ mediation.
  - ➤ litigation.

A simple question to the employer about why a specific accommodation was not provided, or whether a change in "time off" policy was a reaction to them, might quickly resolve any misunderstandings. We agree that this kind of assertiveness can often be difficult; the employer is in a position of much greater power on the job, making these kinds of frank discussions uncomfortable. Seeking out the guidance and support of a knowledgeable group might help. The Equal Employment Opportunity Commission (EEOC) is one group that provides useful advice. In addition, several of consumer/advocacy groups (listed in the *Learn More About It* section in the back of the book) can also be useful. In addition to being knowledgeable about the ADA, these consumer groups have walked in similar shoes and may be able to offer useful support. At this point, the goal of guidance and support is not to prepare for battle with the employer. Rather, it's to gain perspective on the difference in opinions that seems to be present between employer and new employee. In the process, the person with disabilities might learn ways to approach the employer in a mutually respectful way to resolve these differences.

Unfortunately, there are too many cases out there where employers are either knowingly discriminating against persons with mental illness or do not care about this discrimination when informed by others. In these situations, stronger responses are needed besides direct communication to the employer. The EEOC or other groups may be willing to advocate on your behalf. Advocacy from a Federal Agency can frequently motivate employers.

> *"I've been running this bakery for the past 20 years, and I've seen all kinds of rules and regulations. I didn't think this ADA stuff really mattered... until the Feds called. The office of the EEOC. I then sat down with Jeffrey (my employee with psychiatric disabilities) and we talked about reasonable accommodations."*

Sometimes getting the attention of an employer through an advocacy call may not be enough. Some groups offer mediation. They will sit down with employer and person with psychiatric disability to resolve the ADA questions between them. This may mean both sides come to a better understanding of accommodations that truly help the person with disability accomplish the essential functions of his or her job and do not cause undue hardship on the business. Once again, it is important to remember that mediation is preferred to some kind of court action; in this way, both parties are working together rather than fomenting angry feelings because one set of persons (employers or persons with psychiatric disability) is being pushed into actions which it prefers not to pursue.

Ultimately, some people will need the full weight of the court to keep their rights. The EEOC has administrative courts which can handle some violations. Alternatively, citizens can bring claims to civil courts for resolution. In either case, the best place to start with this kind of action is with an EEOC advisor. The EEOC is a government office so their services should be free. Information about the EEOC is provided in the *Learn More About It* section of this book.

The Fair Housing Act and Housing Discrimination

Although the ADA has some implications for housing discrimination (see Title II of the ADA, for example), the Fair Housing Act (better known as the FHA) is the body of laws most relevant to housing discrimination for persons with psychiatric disability. The original FHA, which was passed as part of the 1968 Civil Rights Act, prohibited housing discrimination because of race, color, national origin, religion, or sex. The FHA was amended in 1988 to state that housing discrimination is also forbidden because of family status or, relevant to the goals of this book, disability. Like the ADA, the FHA defines disability as a physical or mental disorder that substantially limits one or more major life activities. Mental disorders include chronic alcoholism or serious and persistent mental illness. The FHA applies to almost all housing stock in the United States except owner-occupied buildings with no more than four units, single-family housing sold or rented without the use of a broker, and housing operated by organizations and private clubs that limit occupancy to members.

The FHA provides broad prohibitions against unfair housing practices; a list of these prohibitions is summarized in Table 9.6. Landlords and their agents are not allowed to withhold rental property because a person has a psychiatric disability. They cannot ask questions about one's prior experiences with mental illness to make decisions about leasing property. Nor can they inquire about one's ability to pay rent because they have mental illness. The terms, conditions, and privileges that go along with renting the apartment have to be the same as all other renters in that building.

Landlords also have to permit reasonable accommodations to their facilities. Frequently, this has included architectural modifications for persons in wheel chairs (though the renter with disability usually has to pay for the modifications); these kinds of architectural accommodations are most relevant to persons with other physical disabilities. However, the amended FHA

Table 9.6
Selected Protections Offered by the Fair Housing Act in Terms of Psychiatric Disability

Because of psychiatric disability, landlords or their agents cannot:
1. refuse to rent or sell housing;
2. refuse to negotiate for housing;
3. make housing unavailable;
4. deny a dwelling;
5. set different terms, conditions, or privileges for sale or rental of a dwelling;
6. provide different housing services or facilities;
7. falsely deny that housing is available for inspection, sale, or rental;
8. for profit, persuade owners to sell or rent (blockbusting); or
9. deny anyone access to or membership in a facility or service (such as a multiple listing service) related to the sale or rental of housing.

also states that landlords have to make reasonable accommodations to policies and procedures governing their property. Unlike the ADA and employment, reasonable accommodations for the housing needs of persons with psychiatric disabilities are still uncharted waters. However, we could foresee several changes in building rules to accommodate persons with psychiatric disability:

- allow family members or service providers to co-sign a lease;

- allow family member or other third party to pay rent;

- allow providers unlimited access to property to provide services including emergency interventions; or

Because of psychiatric disability, mortgage lenders and their agents cannot:
  1. refuse to make a mortgage loan;
  2. refuse to provide information regarding loans;
  3. impose different terms or conditions on a loan, such as different interest rates, points, or fees;
  4. discriminate in appraising property;
  5. refuse to purchase a loan; or
  6. set different terms or conditions for purchasing a loan.

Landlords or their agents cannot:
  1. refuse to let a person make reasonable modifications to dwelling or common use areas, at the per-

- enhance noise reduction rules to reduce ambient stress.

What should a person do if they believe their rights are being violated according to the FHA? The same set of options that were listed in Table 9.5 for the ADA apply here, except the federal agency from which to seek assistance is the Office of Fair Housing and Equal Opportunity (FHEO) in the Department of Housing and Urban Development (HUD). Once again, the place to begin is to inform the landlord about your perceptions. Assistance from a consumer group or the FHEO may help (see the *Learn More About It* section at the back of the book for contact information.) If the landlord is not responsive to information, obtain advocacy or mediation services through FHEO or consumer groups. In more severe circumstances, FHEO can obtain legal help through the Department of Justice.

> son's expense, for the person with disabilities to use the dwelling; or
> 2. refuse to make reasonable accommodations in rules, policies, practices, or services for the person with disability to use the housing.
>
> **Finally, it is illegal for anyone to:**
> 1. threaten, coerce, intimidate or interfere with anyone exercising a fair housing right or assisting others who exercise that right; or
> 2. advertise or make any statement that indicates a limitation or preference based on disabilities.

NIMBY

Perhaps the cry all of us are afraid to hear when pursuing housing for persons with mental illness is NIMBY: Not In My Back Yard!

> *"I don't want those people moving into my neighborhood. They're dangerous. And they're all pigs; they'll mess up the community. Our property values will fall through the floor. Who would want to move into a neighborhood with a group home for mental patients?"*

The FHA expressly prohibits the kind of discrimination that NIMBY entails.

Landlords cannot keep out group homes for persons with psychiatric disabilities in areas zoned for this kind of housing. Lenders cannot refuse to support these kinds of projects if all other monetary issues are satisfactorily addressed. City governments cannot set up ordinances that prohibit housing for persons with psychiatric disabilities. Finally, no one—landlord, business person, or government official—can threaten housing advocates with penalties and retribution because of their housing efforts on behalf of persons with mental illness.

Political Action and Legislative Change

We reviewed only two of the major pieces of legislation related to the rights of persons with mental illness; there are many, many others. Elected officials in Washington are repeatedly considering bills relevant to the opportunities of persons with psychiatric disabilities. In the past year alone, Congress considered major legislation: that improves social security supports for persons with mental illness who are returning to work; that provides persons with mental illness more control over treatment, especially within inpatient settings; and that increases spending on research issues related to mental illness. Nor is this kind of agenda limited to the Federal Government. State and local governments are continuously making laws that impact people with mental illness. Perhaps most salient among this legislation are appropriation bills which direct how mental health and other human service agencies spend monies for services.

Ours is a representative government. We elect officials and send them to the Capitol to reflect our interests. These officials are responsive to the opinions of their constituents, especially when citizens organize to get their message out. Hence, another way to influence stigma and discrimination is to change the minds of politicians so they enact policies that are favorable to empowerment and recovery. In this section, we review ways to facilitate this kind of advocacy for a mental health agenda. Most of these suggestions reflect the wisdom of Advocacy Unlimited, Inc., a nationally known political advocacy group for persons with mental illness, located in Connecticut.

Effective Strategies for Lobbying Face-to-Face

When we approach a legislator or congressperson for support, we call it lobbying. Using a word like "lobbying" somehow makes the activity sound special, as if only a handful of specially trained "Lobbyists" can do this sort of thing. In reality, lobbying is no different than any other effort where a person is trying to convince another of a specific approach to a problem.

- *"I want my boss to start work 30 minutes later so those of us who take the 201 bus won't have to run to make it on time."*

- *"I want our pastor to move bible class to a night that does not conflict with my 12-step meetings."*

- *"I want my legislator to support the new bill that provides more funding for housing for persons with mental illness."*

These are all lobbying activities. We all have learned skills that help to convince people, as well as approaches which undermine our efforts. Table 9.7 summarizes many of the Do's and Don'ts of these kinds of activities.

Be brief, focused, and prepared. Most government officials are busy and will only have a limited amount of time to discuss a specific issue with you, so it is essential that you are punctual. They will appreciate a presentation that is short and to the point. Sometimes, you may have several issues which you wish to discuss with the legislator. In situations like this, it is best to

Table 9.7
The Do's and Don'ts of Effective Lobbying

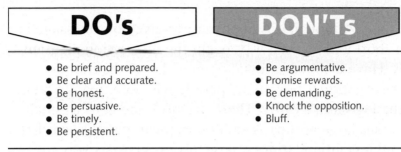

DO's	DON'Ts
• Be brief and prepared.	• Be argumentative.
• Be clear and accurate.	• Promise rewards.
• Be honest.	• Be demanding.
• Be persuasive.	• Knock the opposition.
• Be timely.	• Bluff.
• Be persistent.	

Adapted from materials developed by Advocacy Unlimited, Inc.

remember the old adage — "Pick your battles!" — and focus on the one or two things of most concern to you now. Overwhelming the legislator with several concerns is likely to dilute your message.

Interactions with government officials can be further focused by writing down the name of specific legislation which you support or wish to have voted down. You may have broad concerns about an issue related to mental health:

> *"Persons with mental illness should not be forced into treatment."*

You will have more success, however, when you focus the legislator's attention on a single bill that addresses these concerns. If laws related to these concerns have already been proposed in the legislature, mention the reference number and formal title which has been attached to it.

> *"Today, I'm here to talk to you about House Bill 136, Outpatient Commitment for Mental Illness."*

A brief set of written bullet points that can be reviewed with the legislator can also be helpful in your presentation.

Although it is important to give your message in a short and focused way, begin the interaction pleasantly. Have a conversational opener that starts friendly. Also, consider how many people will accompany you to the legislator's office. There are pros and cons to small versus large groups. A small group can be more cordial and less intimidating. A large group suggests you are speaking for a vast number of people. If you are going in a group, be clear who is going to facilitate the discussion with the official. Who will start off and break the ice? Which member of the group will discuss what point on the bullet sheet? Research suggests that persons with mental illness telling their own stories have the most influence on officials. Hence, groups made up of well-prepared consumers are likely to be more effective than presentations by professionals speaking for their clients.

Listen as well as talk. Communication is a 2-way street. Your senators and representatives may have useful information for you, too. Moreover, government officials are likely to work on your behalf if they believe you are respecting their view. Do not argue with the politician! Sure, it is likely that you may disagree with him or her. But remember, your goal is to convince the person of specific policies and gain their support. Arguing or bullying won't gain support.

Be persistent. Lobbying a legislator is only the first step in gaining support. Opinions are made over the long haul, not as the result of a one-time meeting. Look for openings to come back with more information. If a question arises for which you are unsure of the answer, follow up later with a reply. Remember, there are other ways to lobby a legislator in addition to face-to-face meetings; by mail or through the phone are good examples. All of these approaches can be used to gain the person's support on an issue.

Lobbying through the mail or by phone. Most of the rules listed above also apply to writing letters and calling: be brief, focused, and respectful. When writing, use your own thoughts and words. Sometimes, people join letter writing campaigns sponsored by a group; (e.g., participating in a stigma-busting effort promoted by NAMI.). The group may provide a standard set of statements to guide your letter writing. Legislators, however, prefer this standard message in your own words. That way, they are sure you are a real person with a personal opinion.

Make sure your letter is legible, signed, and has a return address. Citizens are likely to have greatest impact on representatives and senators from their district; that is, citizens who could conceivably vote for them in the future. You are letting the government official know that you are his or her constituent by putting down your address. Moreover, the legislator is likely to reply to you and will only do so if you provide a return address. Follow up your original letter with subsequent notes.

Lobbying by phone can be effective if a vote on a key issue is pending. Typically, you will reach an aide when you call. A simple statement asking for the legislator's vote on a specific bill will suffice. Usually, aides are keeping a running tally on phone calls; the sheer number of for and against votes called in by constituents. Numbers for federally-elected officials are provided in Table 9.8. Call the Capitol in your state for the phone numbers for state representatives and senators.

Table 9.8
Telephone Numbers for Elected Officials in Congress

Senate Republicans	1 800 842-1421	
Senate Democrats	1 800 842-1420	
House Republicans	1 800 842-1432	(leadership)
	1 800 842-8270	(rank and file)
House Democrats	1 800 842-1902	(leadership)
	1 800 842-8267	(rank and file)

Getting Started on Fighting Discrimination

We have reviewed only a handful of the laws and political activities that are relevant to the opportunities of persons with psychiatric disabilities. Those of you who are moved to learn and do more as a result of reading this chapter should check out the resources at the end of our book (*Learn More About It*). Consumer and advocacy groups have been struggling to gain the rights of their constituency (persons with mental illness) for decades. If you are moved to the cause as they are, consider joining a group with similar interests. If there is none in your area, reach out to an interesting group elsewhere and inquire about establishing a local chapter. You will attract like-minded people to your efforts quickly.

Chapter 10

The Fundamental Problem of Competing Philosophies

> "The mind of the bigot is like the pupil of the eye; the more light you pour on it the more it will contract."
>
> Oliver Wendell Holmes, Jr.

S ally Smith was admitted to the inpatient psychiatric unit at University Hospital in acute distress, hearing voices, and reporting paranoid delusions. After a comprehensive diagnostic work-up, the treatment team prescribed a medication regimen to control her symptoms. The patient was referred to a psychosocial rehabilitation program upon discharge to learn independent living skills that would help her cope with stress. She was also referred to a case manager who provided ongoing community support.

Sally Smith has been attending the Consumer Empowerment Project in her neigh-

403

borhood so that she can gain some control over her life. Sally admits that she obtained symptom relief with the help of medication and rehabilitation provided by her treatment team. Unfortunately, she also experienced a keen sense of loss of control because she depended on counselors and case managers too much. Sally sought an intervention program, operated by consumers, where she could regain her integrity, be of service to others, and learn to accept the disorder.

We want to close this book by considering a philosophical problem that probably adds to the staying power of stigma and discrimination. Namely, there are two paradigms[1] that govern the way in which severe and persistent psychiatric disorders are understood: the problems of mental illness are due to *Disease* or the problems result from *Discrimination*. These paradigms are evident in the two examples of Sally Smith. The Disease philosophy views severe mental illness as an external agent (like a bacterium) that must be identified and overcome. This is accomplished largely through medication and talk therapies conducted by experts. The Discrimination paradigm acknowledges the intrusive nature of the illness. However, worse impact of severe psychiatric disorder is caused by the stigmatizing reactions of one's community. The resulting stigma is equally as handicapping as the biological problems that caused the illness.

---

[1] *Paradigm* is a philosophical term which means the framework through which something like mental illness is understood.

The same person, and his or her struggle with severe psychiatric disorders, is described very differently depending on the philosophical perspective. Consider Sally Smith; is she best served in the hospital or should she pursue empowerment goals at the local consumer-operated program? There are no right or wrong responses to questions like these. In fact, an either-or mentality is not needed to answer questions like these; understanding her problems as a disease and in reaction to discrimination are both possible. But, we need to realize that Disease and Discrimination philosophies approach these questions differently, and yield distinct answers in the process. Moreover, the impact these approaches have for helping persons live with and over-come their disabilities is varied.

- If mental illness is a chronic debilitating disease, then shouldn't persons with men-tal illness admit their limited prospects and seek out professional support?

- If it is a disability that is the butt of stig-ma, then shouldn't persons with mental ill-ness be granted the full range of rights and privileges afforded most citizens?

In this chapter, we define the Disease and Discrimination philosophies. We then describe specific answers which proponents of these paradigms might address to key questions about mental illness: what is the nature of the person's problem? who should be in charge of treatment? where should it be conducted? We chose to approach this task differently from earlier chapters in our book. Although we base many of our views in the words of persons with mental illness, much of this chapter still reads like a philosophy book. We apologize if sometimes the ideas, like any good philosophy text, are a bit abstract. Nevertheless, we decided to add this chapter on philosophical differences in understanding mental illness—Disease versus Discrimination—because we believe these differences infect discussions on mental illness.

> *Dr. Jones:* Sally basically has a disease just like diabetes and, just like any other illness, needs to obey her doctor so she gets well.

> *Consumer Advocate*: You don't get it, Dr. Jones. Sally has learned to live with her mental illness just like the person with diabetes. Her problems now stem from discrimination.

Dr. Jones and the Consumer Advocate will never have a full exchange of ideas until they realize they are viewing Sally's problems from different angles.

Let us repeat the assertion we made above: namely, there is no right or wrong philosophy towards understanding mental illness. The problems of psychiatric disability are not caused by a disease to the exclusion of discrimination. Nor are the problems of mental illness attributed to discrimination alone and not also to disease. The challenge for us—reader and author—is to develop a personal compromise in terms of these two perspectives. First, this requires us to understand how the two philosophies compete.

The Disease Philosophy

The disease paradigm evolved, for the most part, out of the field of psychiatry with its standards clearly defined in volumes like *The Diagnostic and Statistical Manual of Mental Disorders, Fourth Edition* (known as the DSM-IV, it is considered the bible of American psychiatry). The DSM-IV views the process of diagnosis as fundamentally one of classification; describing disorders in terms of meaningful clusters of symptoms and dysfunctions. Examples of definitions from the DSM-IV on relevant disorders are summarized in Table 10.1. Severe mental illnesses are defined in terms of the symptoms that distinguish these disorders from other, less troublesome syndromes.

The goal of Disease researchers, then, is to make narrower discrimination of symptom clusters. For example, researchers who study schizophrenia have recently been interested in positive and negative symptom clusters that more closely define the disorder. Positive symptoms are the apparent manifestations of the disorder and include hallucinations and delusions, as well as bizarre talk and action. Negative symptoms reflect the absence of appropriate ways of functioning: disinterest in people, diminished spontaneous activity, flattened affect, and motor retardation. Finer distinction in symptom clusters is important because they may suggest differences in the causes of a disorder (also known as etiology).

Disease researchers are currently focusing on biological and environmental factors that account for the etiology of severe and persistent disorders. Etiological models examine both the original and current causes of symptoms. For example, one model of

Table 10.1

Some Clusters of Symptoms that Correspond with Severe Mental Illnesses Listed in the DSM-IV

Schizophrenia

A. Two or more of the following characteristic symptoms:
> delusions
> hallucinations
> disorganized speech
> grossly disorganized behavior
> negative symptoms like affective flattening, alogia, or avolition.

B. Significant social or occupational disabilities since the onset of the disorder.

C. Continuous signs of the disturbance for more than six months.

Schizoaffective Disorder

A. An uninterrupted period of schizophrenia during which time there was a Major Depressive or Manic Episode.

B. Presence of delusions or hallucinations for at least two weeks in the absence of prominent mood symptoms.

C. Symptoms for mood episode are present for substantial portions of total duration of illness.

Delusional Disorder

A. Presence of nonbizarre delusions (such as being followed, poisoned, loved at a distance, or deceived by lover) for at least one month.

B. Criterion A for Schizophrenia has not been met.

C. Apart from impact from delusions, functioning is not obviously impaired or behavior bizarre.

D. Not attributable to mood disorder.

Manic Episode

A. A distinct period of abnormally elevated or irritable mood.

B. Three of the following symptoms during the period of mood disturbance:
> inflated self-esteem or grandiosity
> decreased need for sleep
> more talkative than usual or pressured speech
> flight of ideas
> distractibility
> increase in goal directed activity
> excessive involvement in pleasurable activities.

C. The mood disturbance causes marked impairment in social or occupational functions.

schizophrenia describes *original causes in terms of genetics or early birth events that generate subtle cognitive and emotional vulnerabilities. These vulnerabilities may appear in childhood as mild cognitive problems; for example, difficulty paying attention. These vulnerabilities eventually interact with current environmental stressors so that the person with severe mental illness experiences either the onset of the disorder in young adulthood (the first apparent signs of the disease) or relapses later on.*

Description of the causes of symptom clusters points to specific interventions that may remedy these causes. Interventions have been clustered in a manner similar to causes; biological and environmental methods. Medications and medical treatments (like electroconvulsive therapy or ECT) address the effects of biological causes producing various symptoms. Generally, research is good on the effects of these treatments when appropriately prescribed. Moreover, rehabilitation strategies enhance the person's skills and resources so that he or she is better prepared to address environmental stressors. The effects of medication and rehabilitative therapies are maintained in the community through the efforts of assertive case managers.

The Discrimination Philosophy

Discrimination, as a view distinct from Disease, is understood via an economic and political analysis. The fundamental assumption of this paradigm is that persons with severe mental illness are an under-privileged minority suffering Discrimination by the majority. Like ethnic groups and persons with other physical disabilities, people with severe mental illness endure stigma that leads to significant social and economic injustice. Stigma in ethnic groups derives from skin color. Stigma experienced by persons with physical disabilities arises from their wheelchairs and other prostheses. Stigma in persons with severe mental illness stems from their distinct (or what the majority might call "abnormal") behaviors in the community. Esso Leete, a well-known advocate, described this stigma eloquently:

> "Sadly, in addition to handicaps imposed by our illnesses, the mentally ill must constantly deal with barriers erected by society as well. Of these, there is none more devastating, discrediting, and disabling to an individual recovering from mental illness than stigma. We are denied jobs, unwanted in our communities. We are seen as unattractive, lazy, stupid, unpredictable, and dangerous."

As a result, persons with severe mental illness have limited opportunities in employment, housing, and recreation.

Proponents of the Discrimination paradigm believe that the range of economic disadvantages is directly due to the stigma and discrimination commensurate with severe mental illness. This view differs significantly from problems as defined by Disease; namely, problems due to mental illness are the result of physiology and psychology. In fact, proponents of the Discrimination paradigm would quarrel with the description of psychiatric disability in terms of "normal" social functioning and goals. They believe that discriminating the goals and skills of persons with severe mental illness from the norm is further evidence of biased and prejudicial beliefs by the majority.

According to the Discrimination paradigm, the path to personal growth for persons with severe mental illness is first and foremost acceptance of one's difference from the majority. Persons with severe mental illness need to admit that the unremitting symptoms of the disorder are part of who they are. Just as African Americans should not try to hide their skin color, persons with severe mental illness should not be compelled to hide the behavioral aspects of their disorder. This task is achieved, in part, by client-centered psychotherapies where therapeutic values like unconditional positive regard and warmth provide an atmosphere for the person to discover him or herself.

More importantly, however, these goals are achieved through socio-political movements like advocacy and empowerment. Earlier in this book, we described empowerment as a process of enhancing personal and political power so that individuals can take action that improves their life situation. Persons with mental illness expect society to recognize their rights to economic opportunity and to make political and cultural changes so that these rights are guaranteed.

Some Differences Between the Two Philosophies

Disease and Discrimination paradigms overlap in many areas including a priority for individualized treatment and a goal of independence through active intervention. Many of the differences between Disease and Discrimination are different points on the same continuum rather than a black and white distinction. Nevertheless, Disease and Discrimination models yield several significantly different perspectives about persons with severe mental illness and their treatment, some of which are described in Table 10.2.

Table 10.2

Significant Differences in the Philosophies that Describe Persons with Mental Illness

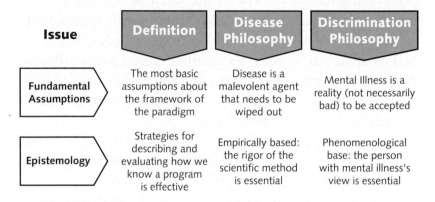

Issue	Definition	Disease Philosophy	Discrimination Philosophy
Fundamental Assumptions	The most basic assumptions about the framework of the paradigm	Disease is a malevolent agent that needs to be wiped out	Mental Illness is a reality (not necessarily bad) to be accepted
Epistemology	Strategies for describing and evaluating how we know a program is effective	Empirically based: the rigor of the scientific method is essential	Phenomenological base: the person with mental illness's view is essential

Differences in Fundamental Assumptions and Epistemology

At its most fundamental level, the Disease paradigm implies a normative or ethical view towards understanding and acting on human behavior. There are ways of acting that are appropriate and there are ways that are inappropriate; the right and wrong of individual behavior is frequently defined by societal norms or established codes of behavior. In America:

● Sitting quietly on a bus is normal.
   Screaming at invisible voices is not.

- Walking to work clothed is right. Being on the street naked is crazy.

- Seeing leprechauns in dreams is sane. Seeing little men when awake is not.

No longer do most Westerners attribute odd behavior to demon possession. The Disease model has redefined these "wrong" behaviors as symptoms. The goal of psychiatry is to identify causes of these symptoms and develop strategies that eradicate them.

The normative and ethical fervor of the Disease model is most apparent when compared to the assumptions of Discrimination which are fundamentally existential. According to this view, psychiatric disabilities are only *one* of many components of the whole person. Discrimination advocates do not recognize the moral imperative that is the basis of Disease. The Discrimination view believes that disabilities are no better nor worse than other parts of the person. Therefore, eradicating the disability diminishes the wholeness of the person.

> *"True, I hear voices sometimes and I have difficulties in some social settings with a lot of strangers. But, I also wear bifocals and can't hear in one ear. These all add up to who I am. I can't pretend they don't exist."*

The disabled individual's task is to acknowledge and accept this part of him or herself. Fighting the disability does nothing more than alienate people from some part of themselves. In the process, the person's struggle is only exacerbated. This view recalls a fundamental principle of humanistic approaches to growth and development. Mental health and personal growth requires that the individual live in a congruent manner with him or herself, accepting who they are.

Clearly, proponents of Disease and Discrimination paradigms clash at the most basic level. The aggressive Disease practitioner is attempting to identify and eradicate the biological causes of the disease. In the process, practitioners tell persons with mental illness to reject their symptoms and seek an alternative way of acting. Discrimination proponents would not only find this view unhelpful, but would argue that it worsens the person's experience with mental illness. Denying part of who one is will only serve to further alienate one's self from his or her essential character. Instead, persons should acknowledge the pains and difficulties commensurate with their discrimination. Perhaps they might struggle to find ways to cope with various symptoms (e.g., strategies to keep from being overwhelmed with fear when in the grip of a paranoid delusion). However, at the most basic level, they need to recognize unremitting paranoia as part of their existence and learn to live with it.

Epistemological differences. Epistemology is the study of how we know the world.

- How do we know a person hears voices?
- How do we know a certain medication helps persons with voices?

- How do we know whether supported employment really gets people back to good jobs?

- And how do we know getting back to good jobs is really a part of a quality life?

Philosophers define two ways of knowing: through our senses (what we see or hear) or via logical inspiration (does it seem to "add up?"). Proponents of the Disease model view themselves principally as scientists. Therefore, the various manifestations and causes of disease are best known via the laws of science. This is the basic format for using our senses to check out whether something works, an epistemology called *empiricism*. In this vein, objective observation of persons with mental illness and their problems is the first rule of psychiatry. Reliable and valid observation is only assured when scientist-practitioners act as aloof students of human behavior.

Advocates of the Discrimination model support a more *phenomenological* approach to knowing. Phenomenology is the philosophical perspective that believes the personal psychology of each individual is fundamentally private; outsiders cannot directly see or hear what people feel, think, or desire. If you're not sure of this assertion, try this experiment next time you are having dinner with a friend or family member. Before saying anything, guess what they are thinking. Some readers might be able to guess what the other person was thinking, but few people are going to be 100% accurate. In a like manner, no scientists, no matter how talented, can look into the minds of their research subjects. Because this fundamental psychology is private, the only way we can truly know what is on someone's mind is to ask them.

The phenomenological perspective is evident throughout our book. Repeatedly we illustrate facts about stigma with the words of a person with mental illness, how the experience seemed to them. For example, we opened Chapter 2 with a discussion of self-stigma.

> "Being immersed in a society that perpetuates disrespectful images of mental illness, many persons with psychiatric disabilities believe these images.
>
> > *'Everybody can't be wrong. Persons with mental illness must be morally weak.'*
>
> And once accepting this about mental illness, persons turn the belief on themselves.
>
> > *'If persons with mental illness are morally weak, and I have a mental illness, then I must be bad.'"*

What people say is an especially powerful way to get at their private experiences.

> According to the phenomenological perspective, persons with mental illness are thought to have special insight which is essential for a complete understanding of their disorder.
>
> > *"I've heard voices for ten years. You'll never know what it's like unless you've had*

*the same experiences. I guess in some ways
that makes me an expert on voices."*

Much of the insight of the person with mental illness is
also private, such that excluding their insight would omit
a large and essential body of information. No one can
know the shame of seclusion and restraints unless they
have been locked up. No one can know the frustration
of side effects unless they have had dry mouth and
shaky limbs. No one can know the sense of hopelessness
unless they have had mental health professionals say
they'll never work again. Because of their experience,
persons with mental illness share a kindred sense of the
strengths and limitations with others who have similar
disabilities. All this would be lost if the phenomenological perspective were ignored.

Psychology and psychiatry have struggled with
the split between scientific and the phenomenological
for almost the length of its history. Some theorists
believe that the two ways of knowing need not be dia-
metrically opposed. Recent research conducted by John
Strauss and Larry Davidson has shown this. They understand that persons with severe mental illness are privy
to experiences that are not manifest behaviorally; examiners are unaware of a person's auditory hallucinations
unless that person reports them. Therefore, self-report
strategies are used to elicit this information.

Few scientists, however, acknowledge that persons with mental illness have any special understanding
or insight into their private experiences. Rather, the
methodological and statistical wizardry of science is all
that is needed to make theoretical sense of private
experience. Empirical research also suggests that an

individual's ability to report private information may be limited by his or her insight into the disorder. Many persons with mental illness are unaware of the extent of their disorder and/or the limitations it imposes on them. Therefore, Disease proponents argue that the nature of severe mental illness in itself may hamper participation in more phenomenologically-focused investigation.

To avail this unique perspective, some Discrimination researchers have joined with persons with mental illness as co-investigators. Alternatively, persons with mental illness who have backgrounds in research have formed groups like the Consumer/ Survivor Research and Policy Work Group to study mental illness. Discrimination researchers also believe that the Disease perspective misdirects the focus of investigation. They describe a "blame the victim" perspective that dominates Disease-based research. Persons with mental illness lack skills, lack work histories, lack motivation, lack family ties, etc. It is these person-centered deficiencies that account for the disorder. Discrimination researchers counter that the focus on individual limitations misses the cultural, economic, and environmental forces that lead to the difficulties associated with mental illness. By now, the reader should be familiar with the stigma and discrimination that originate from society and compound the trials of severe mental illness. Perhaps, as a result, persons with mental illness will make better investigators of the external issues that influence mental illness.

Some Practical Differences Between Paradigms

Like most discussions of philosophy, the past few pages might seem up in the clouds and have nothing to do with the real world experiences of mental illness and stigma. There are, however, practical differences to viewing the problems of mental illness as Disease or Discrimination. These are summarized in Table 10.3. For example, the differences between Disease and Discrimination lead to differences in the community of proponents who adhered to each. Differences may also be seen in beliefs about: the roles of persons with severe mental illness and service providers, the appropriate place for treatment, the nature of these treatments, and the responsibility for care. Let's take a closer look at the ways in which these differences affect one's life.

Differences in philosophical culture. A philosophical culture refers to the group of people who agree with the premises of a specific paradigm. Proponents of the Disease philosophy, for the most part, have professional backgrounds. They tend to be psychiatrists, psychologists, social workers, nurses, and the like. Proponents of the Disease paradigm may also include family members and people with mental illness who are looking for a pharmacological or rehabilitation strategy that will fix the disorder. In terms of studying mental illness, this group tends to be empirically-minded.

Some groups educate their professionals in the Discrimination perspective. Graduate programs in rehabilitation psychology, for example, train students on ways to free those with psychiatric disabilities from

Table 10.3
Some Practical Differences in Philosophies that Describe Persons with Mental Illness

Issue	Definition	Disease Philosophy	Discrimination Philosophy
Philosophical Community	Characteristics of individuals who align with the philosophy	Most professionals, family members	Consumers, survivors, ex-patients, family members
Nature of Care	Appropriate interventions to improve the experiences of persons with mental illness	Assertive and prescribed based on the body of knowledge that defines psychiatry	Nonintrusive and supportive
Roles	Definition of the roles of the care provider and the person with mental illness	Providers are expert decision makers; persons with mental illness rely on professional expertise	Persons with mental illness are expert consumers; providers serve the demands of the consumer
Responsibility for Care	Responsibility of the caregiver and person with mental illness in terms of obtaining and providing treatment	The care provider has primary responsibility	The person with mental illness has sole responsibility
Venues for Care	Appropriate settings for treatment	The clinic	The clubhouse or the consumer's home
Prognosis	Expectations about likely outcome with and without treatment	Guarded and frequently pessimistic	Prognosis is not relevant, recovery occurs with acceptance

their under-privileged status. The Discrimination camp, however, is more of a grassroots community that is dominated by persons with mental illness and their families. They have formed consumer empowerment groups to help persons with mental illness advocate for their vision of care.

The cultures defined by each paradigm are outwardly visible via formal organizations, learned journals, and research funding bodies. Adherents of the Disease paradigm are likely to belong to professional organizations like the American Psychiatric Association or the American Psychological Association where membership bestows professional identities and resources that support these identities. Organizations that reflect the Discrimination paradigm are more often run by consumers or families and reflect an advocacy agenda. Examples vary from Consumer Empowerment Projects sponsored by many state departments of mental health to more extreme ex-inmate programs like the Mental Patients' Liberation Front in Boston or the Network Against Psychiatric Assault in San Francisco. One pitfall is that members of each type of group—consumer-based and professional—rarely attend the opposite group. As a result, each group loses the input of a diverse perspective.

Scholarly work produced by either paradigm is often given public voice in journals and periodicals. Disease-oriented investigators might consider quarterlies like the *American Journal of Psychiatry, Journal of Abnormal Psychology*, and *Psychiatry Research*. Manuscripts are reviewed for these journals depending on the rigor of their scientific design. Discrimination investigators might consider journals like *Psychiatric Rehabilitation Journal* and *Psychiatric Rehabilitation Skills*. While these journals consider scientific merit when reviewing manuscripts, they also actively encourage submissions by persons with mental illness and require professionals to carefully word articles so not to exacerbate stigma. In addition, many advocacy groups publish newsletters; see the *Learn More About It* section of this book for a sample list of these newsletters. While these newsletters might publish reviews of recent research, they also tend to be oriented to policy and advocacy. Much greater space is given to discussion of legal and political matters. Moreover, these newsletters prize "first person" perspectives. Editors of these periodicals believe that sharing the experiences of persons with their mental illness or with stigma is important in its own right.

The influence of divergent cultures is especially apparent when individuals from one perspective are seeking support or resources from the other community. For example, a Disease investigator interested in the impact of stigma on the course of mental illness may receive little support from persons concerned about the Discrimination paradigm. This can be an especially disconcerting experience to the well-intentioned researcher who is only trying to better understand stigma to resolve the problem.

There are some excellent examples of organizations and journals that seem to traverse both paradigms. *Schizophrenia Bulletin*, published by the National Institute of Mental Health, has excellent reviews of the empirical literature and original research. In addition, the journal solicits consumer and family participation through its "First Person Accounts." The National Alliance for the Mentally Ill (NAMI) is an organization of family members, consumers, and professionals that closely follows biological and behavioral research on severe psychiatric disorders promoting pharmacological and rehabilitative treatments that will remediate the disorders. In addition, NAMI members are some of the strongest advocates for empowering consumers. These two examples suggest that differences between cultures created by the two paradigms are not insurmountable.

Differences in the nature of care. Two different perspectives on what causes the problems of mental illness will likely lead to two different views on how to provide treatment. Proponents of the Disease model view persons with mental illness as patients and treatment providers as experts. Although most adherents to the Disease model are concerned with the person's experience of his or her disorder, they view the professional's understanding of the illness as primary. The nature of treatment under the Disease paradigm might then be characterized as assertive. Like treating cancer, Disease professionals diagnose and treat illness in a straightforward manner. Medications provide relief from many symptoms. Rehabilitative treatments developed by Disease proponents include various behavioral programs which are frequently applied to targeted behaviors of participants. The role of persons with mental illness is largely secondary to the professional's role because of the latter's expertise in prescribing medication and rehabilitation safely and effectively. Collaboration with the person with mental illness is most important in terms of facilitating compliance to the treatment regimen.

Proponents of Discrimination believe that persons with mental illness are consumers of care. As consumers, persons with mental illness have the ultimate responsibility for decision making: what medicines they will take, how long they will stay in the hospital, and when they will return to work. Consumers may survey professionals regarding the variety of provided services and select those that meet their needs.

"What has always been wrong with the mental health system is they have done things to me. Now because of more enlightened approaches, they will do things for me."

In this light, caregivers serve the consumer's perspective of the disorder. Therefore, caregivers must assess the needs of consumers and develop programs that meet those needs. According to the Discrimination perspective, generic programs must not be developed for populations of consumers. Rather, treatment programs must be suitably flexible to meet the individual needs of the participants.

Sometimes, the best way to meet consumer needs is for consumers to operate the program themselves. Some proponents of the Discrimination paradigm describe effective intervention programs that are operated by consumers; many of these were reviewed in Chapter 6. Others believe that only consumers can understand the difficulties of mental illness, so only consumers should operate these programs. Professional education is actually viewed as a negative in hiring staff for these programs. Perhaps the strongest reactionaries to the Disease paradigm believe that medication and behavior therapy have no role in the rehabilitation of the person with mental illness.

The greatest tension in providing care occurs when the professional (adhering to the Disease Paradigm) disagrees with the consumer (adhering to the Discrimination Paradigm) about a specific course of treatment. In community settings, professional and consumer might "agree to disagree" so that the consumer would look elsewhere for care. However, this ideal is often not realized because many economically disadvantaged consumers do not have a variety of options to consider when seeking treatment in other settings. That economic disadvantage affects choices about care is exactly what the proponents of the Discrimination paradigm rail against. Persons with mental illness have a right to an array of service providers from whom they might select an appropriate match, just like persons confined to a wheelchair have a right to ramps into public buildings.

The tension caused by differences in views about treatment is even greater in inpatient settings that seem to be dominated by the Disease paradigm. Most states in the union have laws that permit involuntary hospitalization when psychiatrists believe the person with mental illness is dangerous to self or others because of his or her mental illness. Many states also permit forced administration of antipsychotic medication, or seclusion, or restraints when deemed to be necessary by the psychiatrist. Although both sets of laws require due process and court involvement (reflecting the Discrimination view about equal rights), the actual use of these restrictions tends to reflect the Disease perspective and its concern for control and safety.

Proponents of a Discrimination perspective like Daniel Fisher believe there is a fundamental error in characterizing involuntary commitment and forced medication as treatment. They do not dismiss the need for involuntary interventions for dangerous individuals. Discrimination proponents believe, however, that these forms of intervention are needed for *all* dangerous people, mentally ill or not, and should therefore be administered by police and other public safety experts in accordance with normal concerns regarding civil liberties. In this way, the collaborative nature of treatment remains sacrosanct.

Venues of care. Services to assist persons in reaching their life goals will differ depending on where they are carried out. Philosophies can differ in terms of these venues. Interventions consistent with the Disease paradigm are typically conducted in clinics. Setup of the clinic is concerned with the efficient provision of services to a large number of persons with mental illness. Given the limited funding provided to the public care of persons with mental illness, efficiency is essential to serve the most persons best. Cost effectiveness should not be dismissed as the cold-hearted considerations of accountants. Considerations of cost effectiveness help policy planners decide how to stretch the limited dollar to best serve the largest group.

The venue of treatment for Discrimination proponents, and its considerations in terms of operation, is very different. Some have described a clubhouse model in which persons with mental illness run the entire enterprise. As reviewed in Chapter 6, good examples of this are the Fountain House in New York City and Thresholds in Chicago. The clubhouse evolved out of dissatisfaction with the lack of control experienced in typical institutional settings. Alternatively, Fairweather designed his lodge program in which residents with mental illness gain support and learn to cope from the peers with whom they reside. The power and control that these settings offer persons seem to clearly outweigh the decrement in treatment prowess that occurs because professionals do not have central roles.

Differences in prognosis. Proponents of the Disease philosophy tend to view the prognosis (or future outcome) of severe mental illnesses (such as schizophrenia) poorly. Poor prognosis stems from a notion that schizophrenia is a progressively dementing disorder. This view is still evident in DSM-IV, albeit in muted form; the current DSM definition of schizophrenia includes a marked reduction in social or occupational functioning after the onset of the disorder. As reviewed elsewhere in this book, recent findings from long-term follow-up studies of persons with schizophrenia suggested a somewhat brighter outlook. A progressively downhill course is not necessarily characteristic of the disorder. Nevertheless, the majority of persons with schizophrenia show residual social dysfunctions that require continued care. Therefore, the prognosis of persons with severe mental illness continues to be poor from the Disease perspective.

Contrast this view to the markedly different perspective of those who endorse a Discrimination model; they have been known to talk about *recovery from the disorder rather than a progressively downhill course. Proponents of this view have published testimonials by persons with mental illness who are no longer bothered by the symptoms of their disorder and who have achieved most of their interpersonal goals. Therefore, prognosis for those holding a Discrimination view is fundamentally hopeful and optimistic.*

Differences in prognosis recapitulate fundamental differences between paradigms. Note the two parts of the definition of recovery.

(1) "No longer bothered by symptoms;" persons with mental illness who have learned

to accept their symptoms are no longer
bothered by them.

(2) "Achieved most of their interpersonal
goals"; persons who set up goals that represent a true reflection of their possibilities and limitations will be able to attain
them.

The existential nature of the Discrimination view is likely to lead to a more positive prognosis.

Unanswered Differences and a Rapprochement of Philosophies

Recognition of differences between Disease and
Discrimination leads to unanswered questions that need
to be addressed in order for quality of care to improve.
For example, clinical researchers might be interested in
a question like, What are the best indicators of successful outcome: symptom-free community living or a sense
of self-determination and empowerment? Various conceptual arguments and research protocols could tackle
this query. Unfortunately, the different ways to resolve
this question lead to a second puzzle. What is the best
process for testing alternative perspectives? And perhaps even more basic, who is to infer meaning from the
evidence generated by these tests? Scientists are
methodologically well equipped to understand complex
patterns of evidence. However, persons with mental illness are more vested in implications of research efforts.

Intellectual quagmires like these are the stuff of
researchers and other thinkers. But we who are concerned about stopping stigma and discrimination need

to be aware that models for understanding mental illness differ even among reasonable people. Moreover, these differences can lead to varied perspectives that might be perceived as stigmatizing by members of the other perspective. While in the abstract, these differences in philosophy are a problem, they are especially poignant when the person with mental illness is caught between individuals representing either paradigm. Note the contrasting experiences of Sally Smith in the vignettes that began this chapter. The first step in resolving this predicament is educating all concerned about the divergence of perspectives. This sharing of information is the only way to keep persons with mental illness from being harmed by opposing views, no matter how noble they might be.

Chapter 11

Franklin Goodman Revisited

"The formula for Utopia on earth remains always the same; to make a necessity of virtue."
Clifton Fadiman

What will the world look like after we've stomped out stigma and replaced discrimination with opportunity? We end our book by speculating how Franklin Goodman's story might have turned out if he lived in more enlightened times.

Franklin Goodman

The blue and red commuter lurched forward from its platform at Northwestern Station, jostling Franklin Goodman in his seat. The train then clanked and groaned as it zig-zagged through a labyrinth of shinny steel track. Franklin was on his way from Chicago to Elmhurst, Illinois, a distance of about 25 miles. It was 8:40 in the morning, a Tuesday morning, and Franklin had a 10:00 interview with the Office of the Registrar at Elmhurst College. The train would get him to the Chicago suburb by 9:15 a.m., and it would be a short jaunt from there to the college. It was a sunny May day; he would get to his appointment in plenty of time.

Six months earlier, as a first-semester sophomore, Franklin had taken a medical leave from Elmhurst College when he became ill with schizophrenia. He remembered vividly the onset of his illness, and how dejected he had been that mental illness had, of all people, singled him out. He knew several other students at Elmhurst College who had mental illness, or who had a family member with a mental illness. This was some comfort to him, since all but one of them had reentered the college and taken up their studies after getting their illnesses in balance. This was Franklin's intention. His felt his struggle with schizophrenia was won.

A year and a half earlier, on the day Franklin entered Elmhurst College, he was struck by the grace of the campus and by the friendly bustle of life. Most everyone he passed on the college's sidewalks and footpaths smiled or nodded. He and the other men in his freshman dormitory quickly formed friendships. Like him, most came from middle class and upper middle class backgrounds, most were athletic, and all were solid students. Bill, Franklin's roommate, was from Rockville, Maryland. He was a short, blond, medium-built man; his angular jaw and darting eyes belied a quick intelligence and blithe disposition. Bill could describe the most mundane circumstances with exceptional comic timing, and in a bumbling fashion, which laced his conversation with laughter and charm.

That afternoon Bill and Franklin made their way through registration and to the bookstore. The lines were long, and Bill kept Franklin amused with his droll analysis of the day's events. Franklin, his arms full of books, turned sharply and bumped into a girl with long blond hair, causing her lose her balance and drop a drink on the floor. Franklin apologized profusely, picked up the crushed cup and, offering to buy her another, exchanged glances with the shapely bluejean-clad freshman. He knew straight away this was a girl he wanted to get to know.

The next morning Franklin and Bill went to the mandatory health and safety lecture at the gym. They learned about fire alarms, fire extinguishers, fire escapes, AIDS and venereal disease, signs of mental illness, sex and birth control, and substance abuse. It was old hat to the both of them, they had been schooled since grade school in AIDS, drug abuse, and mental illness. Neither wanted to be a drug user and neither wanted to get a mental illness, but both knew what to do should either occur, especially mental illness. They had long been taught how to recognize symptoms of mental illness so that treatments could be quickly administered.

Franklin's first year at Elmhurst was happy and successful. He remained good friends with Bill. The long-haired girl, who Franklin had nearly knocked down at the book store, became his friend and companion. Her name was Elizabeth; she went by Liz. She was from the Hyde Park neighborhood of Chicago; her father was the director of security at The University of Chicago. Franklin and Liz dated often. They spent long hours talking with each other; each knew the other's personality as well as two different people might. Friends of theirs, as well as acquaintances, saw them as a couple likely to make a serious commitment after graduation.

The summer between his first year and second year at Elmhurst College, Franklin worked in a hardware store that was owned by a friend of his father. He didn't like the job especially well, but the money was good and he'd spend most weekends with Liz, going to concerts and restaurants, taking drives in the country in Liz's car, camping and hiking at Devil's Lake in Wisconsin, and strolling through the collegiate architecture at The University of Chicago.

It was in the first week of August, two weeks before Franklin and Liz were due back at Elmhurst, that Liz first noticed Franklin's referential thinking. Franklin had been talking about his skill at selling snow blowers and his ambition to be more than a salesman for the rest of his life. He told Liz that he could tell what his customers were thinking. He said he thought he had ESP. When the price of the sale would come up on the cash register, that was usually a sign of the customer's satisfaction. If the numbers were all even, the customer was very happy. If they were mixed even and odd, the customers were just satisfied. If the numbers were all odd, customers were dissatisfied.

"That's referential," said Liz, as the two drove from Chicago to Indianapolis one afternoon to attend a rock concert.

"You think so?" said Franklin, who became pensive, carefully recalling his thoughts.

"Sounds like it to me. Have you had any paranoia? Voices? Mood swings?" said Liz, taking her eyes off the road for a moment to gaze in Franklin's eyes.

"You better go to the health service when we get back."

The next day Franklin presented himself to the health service at Elmhurst College and after a brief consultation, they referred him to a local specialist. The psychiatrist interviewed Franklin, prescribed a mild dosage of an antipsychotic, then referred Franklin to group therapy and to observation by the school's mental health clinic. They urged Franklin to report regularly to the clinic so they could record the pattern of his delusions and moods, and if they appeared to intensify, Franklin would start stronger medications.

As the semester carried on, Liz and Franklin were saddened that Franklin's delusions became more severe. He began hearing voices which usually preceded paranoid delusions. Franklin didn't hesitate telling Liz and his therapist about his delusions; he trusted their judgment. Besides, he wanted this matter cleared up, and keeping his thoughts to himself was a step in the wrong direction. When Franklin told Liz the devil was speaking to him, she knew at once that he was developing a major mental illness. Franklin speedily checked himself into the mental health clinic at school. Their recommendation was to go to the hospital to get his medications adjusted, then, if necessary, take the rest of the semester off of school and return the next semester as a first semester sophomore.

Franklin chose to go into the hospital. This, he thought, would be the fastest way to address his illness and get back to school. He needed not fear the expense. His insurance policy through Elmhurst College paid 90% of his hospitalization, 80% of his doctor bills, and fully 100% of his medications.

On a crisp November day, Franklin presented himself to the psychiatric unit at Elmhurst General Hospital carrying a suitcase. The day before, a preadmission counselor from the hospital had come to Franklin's dormitory at Elmhurst College to speak with him. He counseled Franklin about the unit's policies which he might see as degrading, but were absolutely necessary for the safety of other patients. Franklin could not bring razors, items that could be broken into chards, or other sharp objects. He should leave his medications at home. Otherwise, Franklin should prepare for some enjoyment. He should bring several changes of clothing, a workout outfit and a bathing suit for the unit pool. He should bring literature which he found inspirational and entertaining, and some of his favorite clothes for semi-formal group nights. He was encouraged to bring a cellular phone. Public phones were also available on the ward.

The counselor told Franklin that there was a lot of social interaction on the unit, but there were entertainment centers in each room for those who preferred their privacy. His family and girlfriend were invited to visit most any time. They could even spend the night. If he and Liz wished privacy in the evening, that could be arranged, so long as he took his medications before retiring.

At intake, Franklin was a little nervous, anticipating the week to ten days that he expected to be hospitalized. The intake nurse calmed his nerves.

"I remember when I first went through intake I was scared to death." she said.

"You mean the first patient you checked in?"

"No, as a client," she smiled and pumped the blood pressure cuff around Franklin's arm. "I have manic-depression. I'd say 80% of the staff here are former clients, including some of the doctors."

As the preadmissions counselor had predicted, Franklin enjoyed his stay in the hospital. Liz and several of his friends, including Bill, arrived in the evenings to participate in the activities and games. There was music, athletics, movies, a dance. Franklin was started on a stronger dose of an antipsychotic and a mood stabilizer, then he was observed. At the end of the hospitalization, he was deemed fit enough to try and return to school.

Franklin did just that, and two days after his release from the hospital he was back in class. But as the weeks rolled by, his illness was causing him more problems than expected: his concentration was suffering, he felt listless, and, though not as badly, he was still hearing voices. Liz and his friends and teachers were constantly concerned about how he was feeling, but Franklin could not give positive reports. Early in December he called Liz, then his parents, and told them that he had decided to take the rest of the fall semester off. Everyone was disappointed but they knew that mental illness was a tough illness to overcome. Franklin's parents offered to take him home for a semester, where he would not be too far away from Liz and his friends.

Franklin returned home, downhearted. This would be a temporary setback said his parents, and they stepped up his meetings with his psychiatrist to twice a week. His father's insurance covered as many sessions a year as Franklin needed. Soon it was decided to try Franklin on another, more expensive antipsychotic.

"Go ahead," said Franklin's father, "It's covered."

"This means weekly blood tests," grimaced Franklin.

"It's covered," said his father, giving Franklin a hug. "You're just going to have to get used to getting stuck by a lot of needles."

Franklin's train screeched to a slow halt at Elmhurst train station. With a small jump he descended to the platform and began walking to the Office of the Registrar where he would reapply from a semester's absence. He had actually taken a semester and a half off. The registrar would extend his medical absence to include both semesters so there was no blemish on his record.

"Hey Franklin!" said a voice from down the sidewalk. It was a friend from his freshman dormitory on inline skates. "Welcome back!" The friend skated up to Franklin.

"I heard you got sick," he said.

"Yea, schizophrenia," said Franklin.

"Oh, bummer. You okay now?"

"Yea, real good," said Franklin with a big smile.

"Dude, you're okay!" With that the skating friend high-fived Franklin and skated away.

A similar conversation repeated itself three or four times before Franklin reached the registrar's office. Beaming, he walked up the steps and pulled open the door. At the registrar's office, Franklin identified himself to a clerk who got his record.

"You ready to come back?" said the clerk with a smile.

"As ready as I'll ever be," smiled Franklin.

"Welcome back. You deserve a pat on the back."

Franklin met Liz for lunch at a cafe in Elmhurst away from campus. She wanted to know how the morning had gone.

"Great," said Franklin. "People are so nice to welcome me back."

"You deserve some credit," said Liz. "Mental illness isn't an easy thing to overcome."

"Well, I'm back."

"When are we getting down to serious business," said Liz, her lips revealing a clever grin.

"I'm serious if you're serious," said Franklin.

"Just don't start calling me Mrs. Goodman yet!"

Learn More About It

by Amy Green

Organizations

Agencies and Anti-Stigma Groups

Chicago Consortium for Stigma Research
www.StigmaResearch.org

> 7230 Arbor Drive
> Tinley Park, IL 60477
> Fax: 708-444-4475
> Phone: 708-614-2490

CCSR is dedicated towards understanding the phenomenon of stigma, developing and testing models that explain why it occurs, and evaluating strategies that help to diminish its effects.

World Federation for Mental Health
www.wfmh.org

> Membership Information:
> Ms. D. Maguire, WFMH
> 1021 Prince Street
> Alexandria, VA 22314-2971

Fax: 703-519-7648
Phone: 703-838-7543

An international organization whose missions include improving the quality of mental health services, reducing stigma and protecting human rights of persons with mental illness, as well as encouraging campaigns for public education. Their website features a quarterly newsletter, information on conferences, and "World Mental Health Day."

Otto Wahl's Homepage and Guide for Stigmabusters
www.iso.gmu.edu/~owahl/INDEX.HTM

Dept. of Psychology
George Mason University
Fairfax, VA 22030

Dr. Wahl provides numerous resources on mental illness and stigma, including links to organizations that fight stigma, recommended readings, and recent research.

National Stigma Clearinghouse
community2.webtv.net/stigmanet/HOMEPAGE

245 Eighth Avenue
Suite 213
New York, NY 10011
Phone: 212-255-4411

Provides free materials and information on combating stigma.

National Mental Health Association (NMHA)
www.nmha.org/newsroom/stigma/index.cfm

> 1021 Prince Street
> Alexandria, VA 22314-2971
> Phone: 703-684-7722   Fax: 703-684-5968

The legacy of Clifford Beers, the goals of the NMHA are to spread tolerance and awareness, improve mental health services, prevent mental illness, and promote mental health. Register with their website and receive legislative alerts and news releases via e-mail. Their site also provides discussion boards, information on affiliates, and an events calendar.

Empowerment and Advocacy Groups

The Consortium for Citizens with Disabilities
www.c-c-d.org

> 1730 K Street NW, Suite 1212
> Washington, DC 20006
> Phone: 202-785-3388   Fax: 202-467-4179

This is a Coalition of approximately 100 national disability organizations who work together to advocate for national public policy to ensure the self-determination, empowerment, independence, integration, and inclusion of both adults and children with disabilities in all aspects of society.

CONTAC (Consumer Organization Technical Assistance Center)
www.contac.org

> 1036 Quarrier Street, Suite 208
> Charleston, WV 25301

> Phone: 888-825-8324 or 304-346-9992
> Fax: 304-345-7303

A resource center for consumers/survivors/ex-patients and consumer-run organizations across the United States promoting self-help, recovery, and empowerment.

The Disability Rights Activist
www.disrights.org

Provides information for anyone interested in the rights of persons with disabilities to help advocate and work for such rights. The website gives information on news, issues, conferences, and organizations, in addition to publications and newsletters.

National Alliance for the Mentally Ill (NAMI)
www.nami.org

> Colonial Place Three
> 2107 Wilson Blvd.
> Suite 300
> Arlington, VA 22201-3042
> Phone: 800-950-6264   TDD: 703-516-7227
> Fax: 703-524-9094

An organization founded by parents of people with mental illness, NAMI now boasts substantial participation by family members and consumers alike. The NAMI network stretches across the U.S., with the Washington D.C. office being particularly skilled in following and influencing national political initiatives.

Judge David L. Bazelon Center for Mental Health Law
www.bazelon.org

> 1101 15th Street, NW
> Suite 1212
> Washington, DC 20005
> Phone: 202-467-5730

A non-profit legal organization that advocates for the civil rights and human dignity of persons with mental disabilities. Provides many links to state advocacy resources.

National Empowerment Center
www.power2u.org

> 599 Canal Street
> Lawrence, MA 01840
> Phone: 800-769-3728

The empowerment center provides a variety of services, such as referrals, networking, conference, lectures, workshops, and consultations. Their mission is "to carry a message of recovery, empowerment, hope, and healing to people who have been diagnosed with mental illness." They also publish the NEC Newsletter about advocacy, recovery, and self-help.

National Mental Health Consumer Self-Help Clearinghouse
www.mhselfhelp.org

> 1211 Chestnut Street, Suite 1207
> Philadelphia, PA 19107

> Phone: 1-800-553-4539 or 1-215-751-1810
> Fax: 1-215-636-6312

This is a consumer run national technical assistance center funded by the Center for Mental Health Services. Their focus is on helping consumers plan, provide, and evaluate mental health and community support services.

Treatment Advocacy Center
www.psychlaws.org

A non-profit organization "dedicated to eliminating legal and clinical barriers to timely and humane treatment for Americans with severe brain disorders who are not receiving appropriate medical care."

Federal Agencies and Programs

Rehabilitation Services Administration
www.ed.gov/offices/OSERS/RSA

Knowledge Exchange Network (KEN)
www.mentalhealth.org

> P. O. Box 42490
> Washington, DC 20015
> Phone: 800-789-2647

Sponsored by the Center for Mental Health Services, part of SAMHSA (Substance Abuse and Mental Health Services Administration). A "one-stop national clearinghouse for free information about mental health, including publications, references and referrals to local and national resources and organizations."

National Center for the Dissemination of Disability Research

www.ncddr.org

> 211 E. Seventh Street
> Room 400
> Austin, TX 78701-3281
> Phone: 800-266-1832   or   512-476-6861
> Fax: 512-476-2286

National Institute of Mental Health

www.nimh.nih.gov

> Public Inquiries
> 6001 Executive Blvd.,
> Room 8184, MSC 9663
> Bethesda, MD 20892-9663
> Phone: 301-443-4513
> Fax: 301-443-4279

Professional Organizations

American Psychiatric Association

www.psych.org/main.html

> 1400 K Street, NW
> Washington, DC 20005
> Phone: 202-682-6000   Fax: 202-682-6850

American Psychological Association

www.apa.org

> 750 First Street NE
> Washington, DC 20002-4242
> Phone: 800-374-2721   Fax: 202-336-5500

International Association of Psychosocial Rehabilitation Services

www.iapsrs.org

> 10025 Governor Warfield Parkway
> Suite 301
> Columbia, MD 21044
> Phone: 410-730-7190   TTY: 410-730-1723
> Fax: 410-730-5965

Self-help and Mutual Aid Organizations

GROW

> Illinois Branch Center
> 2403 W. Springfield
> Champaign, IL 61821
> Phone: 217-352-6989   or   618-632-7366

Emotions Anonymous

www.emotionsanonymous.org

> P. O. Box 4245
> St. Paul, MN 55104-0245
> Phone: 651-647-9712   Fax: 651-647-1593

National Depressive and Manic-Depressive Association (NDMDA)

www.ndmda.org

> 730 N. Franklin Street
> Suite 501
> Chicago, IL 60610-3526
> Phone: 800-826-3632   or   312-642-0049
> Fax: 312-642-7243

Recovery, Inc.

www.recovery-inc.com

> 802 N. Dearborn
> Chicago, IL 60610
> Phone: 312-337-5661
> Fax: 312-337-5756

Further Reading

Otto Wahl. (1995). *Media Madness: Public Images of Mental Illness*. New Brunswick, NJ: Rutgers University Press.

David D. Burns. (1999). *Feeling Good: The New Mood Therapy*. New York: Avon Books.

Mowbray, Moxley, Jasper, & Howell. *Consumers as Providers in Psychiatric Rehabilitation.*

Department of Health and Human Services. (1999). *Mental Health: A Report of the Surgeon General.* Available: www.osophs.dhhs.gov/library/mentalhealth/index.html or at 1-877-9-MHEALTH.

Speakers Roundtable. (1995). Speaking Secrets of the masters: The Personal Techniques used by 22 of the World's Top Professional Speakers. Harrisburg, PA: Executive Books.

Other Sources of Interest

Americans with Disabilities Act (ADA) Resources

Americans with Disabilities Act Handbook
ada.handbook.homepage.com

The Americans with Disabilities Act (ADA) Handbook published by the Equal Employment Opportunity Commission (EEOC), and the U.S. Department of Justice (DOJ) can be purchased online through a secure server at the Government Printing Office.

Americans With Disabilities Act Information
www.usdoj.gov/crt/ada

The US Dept. of Justice's resource page for the ADA. Voluminous, and not limited to computer and Internet issues, but at least it should be fairly authoritative, if you're willing to wade through the material.

The Americans with Disabilities Act (ADA)
www.robson.org/capfaq/ada.txt

Government publication - full text

General Mental Health Information

PsychNet-UK
www.psychnet-uk.com

A website for persons wanting in-depth information on mental health and psychology.

Internet Mental Health
www.mentalhealth.com

This site provides information on a wide variety of mental health topics, including medications, research funding, and various disorders.

The American Psychological Association
www.apa.org

Information for students, the public, and psychologists.

Mental Health Net
http://mentalhelp.net

An award winning website that provides information on mental health, psychology, and psychiatry on-line.

Independent Living Resources

Independent Living USA
www.ilusa.com/links/ilcenters.htm

Provides contact information for Independent Living Centers nationwide, as well as in several foreign countries.

Psychiatric Survivors Resources

Support Coalition International
www.mindfreedom.org

> 454 Willamette, Suite 216
> P. O. Box 11284

> Eugene, OR 97440-3484
> Phone: 877-MAD-PRIDE

An organization dedicated to "winning human rights in the mental health system," the group considers itself part of the psychiatric survivors liberation movement. They also have a newsletter called *Dendron News*, which they describe as "breaking the silence about human rights and alternatives to psychiatry."

MadNation
www.madnation.org

> 4386 W. Pine Blvd.
> One East
> St. Louis, MO 63108
> Phone: 314-652-0424
> Fax: 661-791-7058

An international community of mental health consumers/survivors/ex-patients on-line, MadNation describes itself as "people working together for social justice and human rights in mental health." You can join for free and subscribe to their daily Mad-Zine or just browse through collections of essays, news, and views related to the mental health system.

Index